HUNGER SIGNS IN CROPS

A SYMPOSIUM

Prepared by

GEORGE M. BAHRT

BAILEY E. BROWN

ARTHUR F. CAMP

H. D. CHAPMAN

H. P. COOPER

O. W. DAVIDSON

ERNEST E. De TURK

GEORGE N. HOFFER

HENRY A. JONES

JAMES E. McMURTREY, Jr.

EDWIN R. PARKER

ROBERT M. SALTER

GEORGE D. SCARSETH

JOSHUA J. SKINNER

Edited by GOVE HAMBIDGE

Published by

THE AMERICAN SOCIETY OF AGRONOMY

AND

THE NATIONAL FERTILIZER ASSOCIATION

WASHINGTON, D. C.

Typography, Layout, and Printing by
JUDD & DETWEILER
WASHINGTON, D. C.

Color Plates and Halftones by
STANDARD ENGRAVING CO.
WASHINGTON, D. C.

Foreword: What the Book is About

WHEN we human beings lack certain essential nutritive elements, we get serious nutritional diseases—rickets from a lack of calcium, phosphorus, and vitamin D; nutritional anemia from a lack of iron; beriberi from a lack of thiamin; pellagra from a lack, probably, of nicotinic acid; scurvy from a lack of ascorbic acid; and so on through a considerable list. The symptoms of these diseases are pretty clearly recognized by physicians.

Even when there is no acute disease, an essential nutritive element may be sufficiently lacking to give us a borderline case—some minor but perhaps troublesome ailment that keeps us from being really healthy. Frequently these borderline ailments too can be diagnosed by the shrewd eye of the physician, sometimes supplemented by laboratory tests.

Much of this knowledge is new, and it is of untold value. It means that many human ills—even many untimely deaths—can now be considered absolutely needless; much of our common inability to meet the demands of life with full nervous and physical vigor can be eliminated.

Best of all, we do not have to depend on the physician to achieve these things for us. As the modern knowledge of nutrition spreads, anyone who will take the trouble to understand and use it has the control of life and health, insofar as they are affected by food, within his own hands.

At the same time, farmers are now better able to feed their livestock for maximum health and productiveness because knowledge of human and animal nutrition have advanced together.

What has all this to do with the subject of fertilizers and crop plants?

There is a close connection in more ways than one. Plants too are living things. They take in food and convert it into body tissues and energy; they can be healthy and vigorous or they can be ill and die; they have their acute diseases and their minor ailments; and they require certain nutritive elements just as surely as do we human beings. Many of these elements, in fact, are the same ones we require. Without them, the plant too suffers from hidden hunger. It needs a balanced diet as much as we do.

[i]

You cannot tell a plant to stick out its tongue and say "Ah," but there are other ways of examining it for symptoms of ill health. It may show unmistakable signs of hidden hunger—nutritional deficiency—if we can only recognize them.

The purpose of this book is to help us to recognize the signs of nutritional deficiency in crop plants. It was written by scientists who have made a close study of this subject, each in his own particular field, for many years.

As in the case of human nutrition, the best thing about this knowledge is that it is not all in the hands of the experts; it can be used by the layman. The farmer who will take the trouble to study the symptoms of malnutrition in plants is in a position, in many cases, to correct the difficulties himself.

Much of this knowledge also is new. A few years ago, for instance, what farmers called "firing" of corn was attributed to drought. Now it is known that though firing of corn is made worse by lack of moisture, it is fundamentally due to nutritional deficiencies—shortage of essential elements in the food supply of the plant.

And just as one nutritional element after another was found to be vitally necessary for human health, so one element after another was found to be essential for the health of plants. There is a real parallel between the discoveries in these two fields.

After it was found that lack of one or another plantfood could cause definite nutritional diseases in plants, the next step was to make a close study of the symptoms. A number of scientists have been doing this in the United States and other parts of the world for many different kinds of plants and many plantfoods. They have used field studies, plot studies, pot studies, and nutrient-solution studies.

The work requires great patience and a close knowledge of what the plant is like in normal health. The scientist notes down every visible effect or symptom in a plant deprived of this or that element, being careful not to be fooled by something that is not a symptom. Then he tries to put the complicated lot of symptoms into some order and describe them with the utmost accuracy so they will be understandable and useful in diagnosis.

That is what has been done in this book for a considerable number of important crops.

Some of the chapters include a key for quickly identifying a deficiency by its symptoms. (These keys are arranged in the form sometimes used for plant identification, with all coordinate headings marked by the same letter, rather than in ordinary outline form.) There is also a wealth of illustrations in color and in black and white. With the accompanying legends, they are intended to tell as complete a story as possible by themselves.

The book is not to be considered as the final word by any means. Active work is still going on in this field, and much remains to be done. The reader will note, for instance, that there is not as complete or as definite information about all deficiencies in some crops as in others—sometimes because of inherent difficulties, sometimes because less research work has been done in the latter cases.

Thus, the farmer will need to use caution in diagnosing deficiency symptoms, and where there are uncertainties he will want to get expert help from scientific workers. He should be especially careful about confusing deficiency symptoms with conditions due to disease, organisms, insects, or other causes.

In a few cases, injuries caused by excesses of certain elements are mentioned in the text or illustrated in figures, but no attempt has been made to cover this subject systematically.

Now a brief account of how the book came to be written.

Early in 1936, The American Society of Agronomy felt that enough is known about the symptoms of malnutrition in plants—though there is much yet to be discovered—to prepare a monograph on the subject, and that such a monograph would fill a growing need. The Committee on Fertilizers, headed by R. M. Salter, appointed a subcommittee to look into the possibilities, with J. E. McMurtrey, Jr., as chairman. As a first step, this group got the assistance of the Plantfood Research Committee of The National Fertilizer Association in rounding up all available colored photographs of malnutrition symptoms, and these were exhibited at the 1936 meeting of the Society of Agronomy.

Early in 1937, plans were outlined for the book, Hunger Signs in Crops, and the authors were selected. A major problem from a practical standpoint was to keep the price from being prohibitive; it would be very high for a small edition of a book with as many colored illustrations as were needed in this case to give maximum usefulness. However, the authors, as members of The American Society of Agronomy, contributed their work without compensation; Charles J. Brand and H. R. Smalley contributed much time and effort that would ordinarily have been part of overhead expenses; and The National Fertilizer Association, through its Soil

Improvement Committee, agreed to be responsible for the sale of enough copies, in addition to the ordinary demand, to make a fairly large printing possible and thus materially reduce the cost per copy. (While these acknowledgments are being made, credit should also be given to Marion J. Drown for a great deal of detailed editorial work on the chapters, and to Mary A. Bradley for indexing.)

So wide a range of material on malnutrition symptoms in plants has not before been brought together in a single volume, and it should be useful alike to farmers, students and teachers of agriculture, technical workers, and everyone concerned with the proper management of soils and crops. Care has been taken to keep the book as nontechnical as possible so as to give it wider usefulness. Even the usual lengthy bibliographies have been cut down to a few references. Fertilizer analyses, however, appear throughout the book in the technical form. This is so familiar to farmers and others concerned with agriculture that it hardly needs explanation. In such an analysis (4-10-6, for example) the first figure stands for the percentage of nitrogen (N) in the total mixture, the second for the percentage of available phosphoric acid (P_2O_5), and the third for the percentage of available potash (K_2O).

The editor would be remiss if he did not emphasize one other reason why he thinks the book is important aside from the main point, which, of course, is its immediate practical value. It marks one more step in the study of nutrition from the soil on up through man. What the soil does not have, plants will not get, and animals and men will lack also. The welfare of man is intimately bound up with the welfare of soils and plants because all our food comes in the first instance from plants; even our meat, milk, eggs, and fish are simply plant substances rebuilt into other forms.

There is a vastly significant story here which we can see as yet only in dim outline. Much more will be heard about it as time goes on, and everything that will help to fill in the many gaps in the story is a contribution to human welfare.

GOVE HAMBIDGE.

Washington, D. C.
    March 1941.

CONTENTS

(Page numbers are given for the topics in each chapter.)

Page

CHAPTER I

George D. Scarseth, Robert M. Salter

The plant nutrients, 1: Water, 2; oxygen, 3; carbon, 4; nitrogen, 5; potassium, 5; phosphorus, 6; sulfur, 7; magnesium, 8; calcium, 8; iron, 9; manganese, boron, zinc, and copper, 9. Soil acidity, 10. Why read the hunger signs? 12.

CHAPTER II

J. E. McMurtrey, Jr.

The background of diagnosis, 16. Nitrogen deficiency, 18. Phosphorus deficiency, 19. Potassium deficiency, 21. Magnesium deficiency, 23. Calcium deficiency, 26. Boron deficiency, 30. Manganese deficiency, 31. Sulfur deficiency, 32. Iron deficiency, 32. Copper deficiency, 33. Zinc deficiency, 35. Recognizing compound deficiencies, 36. A comparison of symptoms, 36. Key to plant-nutrient deficiency symptoms of tobacco, 40. Selected references, 41.

CHAPTER III

George N. Hoffer

Differences in plants as indicators of plantfood deficiencies, 57. Value of chemical tissue tests, 57. Production of typical symptoms in controlled nutrient cultures, 58. Deficiency symptoms in corn, 59: Nitrogen, 59; phosphorus, 61; potassium, 64; magnesium, 69; calcium, 70; boron, 72; zinc, 73. Deficiency symptoms in small grains (wheat, oats, barley, rye), 74: Nitrogen, 76; phosphorus, 77; potassium, 78; magnesium, 79; boron, 80; manganese, 80. Chemical tissue tests, 81: Tests for corn, 81; tests for small grains, 83. Methods for preparing reagents for the chemical tissue tests, 84. Literature cited, 85.

LIST OF ILLUSTRATIONS

Chapter III (Corn and Small Grains)—*Continued*

CHAPTER V (Cotton)

CHAPTER VI (Vegetable Crops)

[xi]

CHAPTER VIII (Legumes)—*Continued*

COLOR PLATES

CHAPTER IX (Citrus)

FIGURES

COLOR PLATES

CHAPTER I

Why Do Plants Starve?

By George D. Scarseth and Robert M. Salter [1]

NO ONE worries about a healthy plant. It is when a plant fails to grow vigorously that the farmer becomes concerned. A plant will slow down in its normal rate of development or will show other signs of trouble whenever any one of the many factors that contribute to its well-being gets out of balance. The Indian learned that burying a fish under a corn hill produced better plants, and that corn grew better where a brush pile had been burned. The Indian did not realize that he fertilized the soil with nitrogen and phosphate from the fish and with potash from the wood ashes. Other necessary elements also were provided by the fish and the ashes. What they were did not matter so long as there was enough fish and ashes and not much corn was needed.

When more corn was demanded and production had to become commercial, more facts than the Indian had were necessary. Crop production became a matter of economics. To produce efficiently and economically we have had to learn more about the science of growing plants.

THE PLANT NUTRIENTS

Since corn is a widely known plant, let us use it to obtain a picture of what materials such a plant requires for its growth. It will be helpful as background for a better understanding of the articles in this book to have a clear conception of what it takes to produce 100 bushels of corn on an acre of ground.

The plants producing 100 bushels of corn on 1 acre would have about:

> 4,000 pounds of stover
> 800 pounds of cobs
> 5,600 pounds of shelled corn
> 5,200 pounds of roots

—a total of about 15,600 pounds of air-dry matter. Excluding all water, this amounts to about 13,700 pounds of moisture-free dry matter. In table 1 are listed the raw materials needed to produce such a crop.

[1] George D. Scarseth is Soil Chemist, Purdue University, and Robert M. Salter is Director, North Carolina Agricultural Experiment Station.

[1]

TABLE 1.—RAW MATERIALS USED BY PLANTS AND AN APPROXIMATION OF THE
AMOUNTS USED BY ALL THE CORN PLANTS ON 1 ACRE, PRODUCING AT THE RATE
OF 100 BUSHELS TO THE ACRE

Substance [1]	Symbol	Pounds per acre	Approximate equivalent
Water	H_2O	4,300,000 to 5,500,000	19 to 24 inches of rain
Oxygen	O_2	6,800	Air is 20 percent oxygen
Carbon	C	5,200 carbon or 19,000 carbon dioxide	Amount of carbon contained in 4 tons of coal
Nitrogen	N	160	8 100-pound bags of a 20-percent nitrogen fertilizer
Potassium	K	125	3 100-pound bags of muriate of potash
Phosphorus	P	40	4 100-pound bags of 20-percent super-phosphate
Sulfur	S	75	78 pounds of yellow sulfur
Magnesium	Mg	50	170 pounds of Epsom salt
Calcium	Ca	50	80 pounds of limestone
Iron	Fe	2	2 pounds of nails
Manganese	Mn	0.3	1 pound of potassium permanganate
Boron	B	0.06	¼-pound box of common borax
Chlorine	Cl	Trace	Enough in the rainfall
Iodine	I	Trace	1-ounce bottle of tincture of iodine
Zinc	Zn	Trace	The shell of one dry-cell battery
Copper	Cu	Trace	25 feet of No. 9 copper wire

[1] The analyses for nitrogen, potassium, phosphorus, magnesium, and calcium were made on corn grown at Lafayette, Ind., in 1938, 1939, and 1940. The other figures are from various sources. The composition of corn plants would vary on soils of different levels of fertility, and that of other types of crops would vary from that of corn in minor details.

It is evident from this table that plants require the vital nutrients in widely differing amounts. Each substance also has its own peculiarities. Some, for example, may be present in the soil in plentiful quantities yet be unavailable to plants because they are tied up in chemical compounds the plants cannot use. In order to have a better understanding of what these nutrients do for plants and why plants may starve for lack of them, let us review a few facts about each.

WATER

From the roots that reach into the soil to the tip of the most remote leaf, a plant is one continuous water pipe. The solid structures of plants are made up of cells that consist of delicately organized gel-like substances (colloids) that have a great attraction for water. This attraction pulls water into the plant with such a strong suction that almost 99 percent of certain parts of the cells may be water—water that has been extracted from soil containing perhaps only 15 or 20 percent.

The water system in the plant acts as a channel through which the plant nutrients pass from the roots to the proper compartments, to be built into such foods as sugars and amino acids (the building materials of protein), which in turn are transformed into cellulose and other compounds that make up the solid structures of the plant. Any byproducts or excess can be carried out of the plant by the water to be excreted back into the soil. In fact, roots give off carbon dioxide, which, with the water in which it is dissolved, is a weak acid that aids in dissolving minerals from the soil.

The normal functioning of a plant cell depends on an adequate intake of water so that turgor (normal tension or rigidity) can be maintained and the tissue-building process can proceed. Since water is continually passing through a plant and out—as water vapor—through the stomata, or breathing pores, of the leaves, turgor depends on maintaining a delicate balance between intake and outgo. The cell sap contains various salts that exercise a "pull" on water, so that it will pass from a zone of low salt concentration in the soil to one of high salt concentration inside the plant cells—a process called osmosis. An excessively high salt concentration in the soil near the roots, resulting from too localized an application of fertilizer, may upset this process and cause the plant to lose water instead of absorbing it. The turgor of the cells then decreases and the plant wilts.

Any slight decrease in turgor upsets the machinery inside the leaf, and some symptoms that resemble malnutrition may show up. Thus the appearance of the plant may suggest starvation for nitrogen, potassium, or some other element. In fact, there may actually be starvation, for droughts that cause plants to suffer for water may also affect the availability of nutrients and their accessibility to the roots. Roots depend on soil moisture to make the nutrient elements movable.

OXYGEN

Fortunately the earth is blessed with a liberal supply of oxygen, which is as vital to plants as it is to man. It is seldom realized that approximately 50 percent of the composition of the dry matter in a plant is oxygen. It enters into combination with all the elements listed to form oxides and complex organic compounds. When a plant is functioning in full vigor and health there is a shifting and balancing of the oxygen between the elements that are being rearranged into plant-tissue parts. This shifting of the oxygen is called oxidation when it involves adding oxygen and reduction when it involves reducing the amount of oxygen.

In certain reduced forms, some elements become poisonous to the plant. Two such poisons that are very common are the nitrites and sulfites. In the oxidized forms—that is, with oxygen added—these become nitrates and sulfates, which are nontoxic. Reduction is as necessary as oxidation in healthy plants, however, because some compounds such as the nitrites are reduced still further to be used in building proteins.

Any upset in the balance of oxidation and reduction processes resulting from an unbalance in the nutrients taken into the plant will show up as an unhealthy symptom. Potassium may be mentioned as an important element affecting the oxidizing and reducing processes. When insufficient potassium is present in a plant such as corn, iron is made insoluble by excessive oxidation and accumulates in the nodes.

Carbon

Carbon appears in many forms—as the pure crystalline diamond, as graphite in "lead" pencils and axle grease, as coal and soot, as the carbon dioxide that gives the sparkle and fizz to soda water. In plants, it is a brick in the cell walls of the tissue, a component of sugar, an atom in the flavor of the juices, a part of the structure of color, and even an element in the fragrance of the blossom. In fact, carbon is the keystone of all organic substances. Before there could be life, carbon had to be organized into many of its thousands of combinations with other elements.

Carbon is pulled out of the carbon dioxide of the atmosphere and built into these extraordinary structures by the energy of the sun acting on the green sacks of chlorophyll in the cells of the leaves. This is a master construction job not yet duplicated by man. Whenever a plant is unable to perform this construction job with carbon because of a shortage of some element necessary to the process— or because of an excess, from which an unbalance sometimes results—some symptom of abnormal functioning will appear.

It is not often appreciated that plants must use so much carbon for their growth as is indicated in table 1. The air contains only about 3 one-hundredths of 1 percent of carbon dioxide. Thus vast volumes of air must be worked over by plants in order to obtain enough carbon in the form of carbon dioxide. In fact, if the air were richer in this substance, plants could grow bigger than they now do. The plants of the coal age did grow bigger than modern plants, and some geologists have held the theory that the atmosphere was richer in CO_2 then than now.

NITROGEN

Modern farming practices are nitrogen depleting. When America passed from the Indian to the white man, the storehouse of nitrogen in the organic matter of the forest and prairie soils was opened for rapid emptying. In the warm climate of the South this did not take long; in the cooler North it has been a slower process. Crop production today depends largely either on restoring organic matter to the soil in order that, through decay, it may furnish a revolving supply of nitrogen for crops, or on supplying it in the form of fertilizers. Both procedures are necessary for practical reasons.

There are about 75 million pounds of nitrogen in the air above every acre of land and sea, but to most plants it is as useless in this gaseous form as sea water is to a thirsty man. Just as salty water must be distilled to make it suitable for drinking, the atmospheric nitrogen must be combined with oxygen, carbon, or hydrogen before it is of any use to growing plants. Some bacteria, such as those on legume roots, are able to perform this miracle. The chemist too can "fix" atmospheric nitrogen in fertilizer forms. Nature has not supplied nitrogen in abundance in forms available to plant life except through the slow process of storing it away in virgin soils high in organic matter.

Plant roots take up nitrogen in the form of ammonium and nitrate salts. Inside the cells these are converted into amino acids, of which there is a large number. The amino acids are recombined to form proteins. Any unbalance, whether from insufficiency or excess, in the supply of nutrients will upset this process. Since nitrogen, as the most important element in proteins, is used in such large quantities, a deficiency is very common in the case of plants grown on most upland soils.

POTASSIUM

If you stood leaning against the wall of a bank that had a million dollars in its vaults, and you had only one dime in your pocket, there would be a total of one million dollars and ten cents within the area occupied by the bank and you. Out of this great sum, however, only the single dime in your pocket would be available for your use. A soil may have a total of 40,000 pounds of potash stored within an area of 1 acre to a depth of 6 inches, but have only 100 to 600 pounds or less held in such a way that plants can get it.

No practical device is known that will unlock the vast storehouse of unavailable potassium in the soil for the use of plants. In view of the large amount needed, it is clear that the fertilization of the soil by adding available potash to it is one requirement plant growers must meet.

It seems strange that plants should need so much potassium when, so far as is now known, they do not build it into the structure of any of their parts. A plant will hold its potassium salts from being washed or leached out as long as it is living, but as soon as the plant is killed by cutting, the potassium, no longer held, will be washed out readily—as, for example, by rain on dried hay or corn shocks. Some potassium salts will also move from the plant back into the soil as the plant matures.

Not much is known about the function of potassium in plants. More is known about what happens to a plant when this element is deficient. From such information, theories are advanced that potassium enhances the plant's ability to resist disease, cold, and other adverse conditions, and that it functions in the processes whereby sugars are made from carbon dioxide and water. Perhaps it acts as a condenser or "squeezer" in focusing the energy of the sun to a point where these two compounds will combine.

Potassium starvation is so common in most of the important crops that all growers should know its symptoms.

PHOSPHORUS

The threads in plant cells that pull the materials of the cell's interior apart to form two new cells contain phosphorus. If the supply is scanty, the rate of cell division is slowed down and the plants remain stunted and spindling. The formation of sugar seems to be independent of the phosphorus supply, for a phosphorus-starved plant will continue to form sugar to such an extent that the amount actually becomes abnormally large. Some plants tend to turn reddish or purplish in color with the increase in sugar content, and this is one symptom of phosphorus starvation. The high sugar content may also be associated with a decrease in the formation of starch and cellulose from the sugar. The formation of cellulose is a part of cell-wall building and cell division; thus the theory holds fairly well that the formation of new cells requires an adequate amount of phosphorus.

Phosphates are also a part of certain of the amino acids that form phosphate-bearing proteins.

Since most soils have a marked capacity to turn inorganic soluble phosphates into insoluble and unavailable forms, the behavior of this element in relation to the acidity or alkalinity of the soil and its content of clay and of organic matter is of tremendous economic importance. This subject is too lengthy to discuss here; the reader may refer to textbooks on soils for details.

Because of the destruction of organic matter by farming practices, and the losses of phosphorus through removal by crops and by erosion, this is one of the elements that is very generally deficient in soils. A study of phosphorus-deficiency symptoms in crop plants is likely to reveal to the farmer that the situation is more acute than he realized.

Sulfur

This is a major plant nutrient that has not often been in the spotlight. Plants frequently contain more sulfur than phosphorus, calcium, or magnesium, yet we seem to be better acquainted with the latter elements. Pass a cabbage field when it is thawing out after a killing frost, and the smell of hydrogen sulfide coming from the decomposing plants will be a potent reminder that sulfur is very much a part of a healthy plant.

When yellow sulfur burns, the sulfur is converted to sulfur dioxide (SO_2), a gas that has a choking, stinging effect if inhaled and is useful as a refrigerant in automatic ice boxes. In the plant, sulfur is built into cystine, an amino acid that forms protein. In the soil, the sulfur is oxidized and combined with such basic ions as those of calcium, potassium, and ammonia to form sulfates.

One of these sulfates is calcium sulfate, or gypsum (also called land plaster or "plaster"). Legend has it that Benjamin Franklin spelled out the word "gypsum" on a hillside in Pennsylvania with calcium sulfate, and for a time it stood out in bold contrast because the plants it affected were stimulated in growth. Later it was reported that the word could still be seen, but because the plants were poorer where the gypsum had been added. Probably the increased plant growth had exhausted the soil until it was less fertile than if it had been untreated. It would have been interesting to have had these plants examined for nutritional-starvation symptoms.

Another common sulfate is ammonium sulfate, a byproduct of the steel industry. It is used as a fertilizer primarily because it contains

20.5 percent nitrogen in the ammonia form, but in fact it also contains 25 percent sulfur. The superphosphates made by the sulfuric acid process contain much sulfur in the form of calcium sulfate. Some potash is produced and used as a fertilizer in the form of potassium sulfate. Thus, sulfur has found its way back to the soil as if it were getting a free ride. The cost has usually been charged to the other plant nutrients that acted as carriers.

Rain also returns to the earth as much as 10 pounds or more of sulfur per acre annually. This has to be picked up as a gas by the atmospheric moisture from smoke produced by the burning of coal that contained some sulfur. In regions where little or no coal is burned, sulfur for plant use may be deficient.

Plants that have insufficient sulfur show characteristic symptoms that may resemble those of nitrogen starvation.

MAGNESIUM

Ordinarily most crops contain more calcium than magnesium. The difference will vary with the crop and the composition of the soil.

We owe the beauty of a green world of vegetation to magnesium. It is the key element in the molecule of chlorophyll—the green pigment in plants that traps the energy from the sun and makes plant life possible. This pigment starts the chain of events that begins with green plants and goes on up through animals and man.

Magnesium is credited with being a companion for phosphates; it combines with phosphates so that the latter can be moved to their proper places in the plant in the form of magnesium phosphate compounds. This bond of attraction still has some mystery about it and must wait for additional research to be better understood.

CALCIUM

The carbon dioxide in the soil solution makes it a potent solvent for calcium compounds; thus calcium is leached out of the soil as calcium bicarbonate. The soil acidity is increased by this process. Probably more calcium than sodium has been carried into the oceans. The sea is salty from the sodium salts, and it would be milky from calcium salts except for the fact that the calcium has been combined into the shells of marine animals to be redeposited as limestone. This is one of the interesting examples of how calcium is used by animals to build bony material. In plants it is built into the walls of the cells to form a protective "sieve" for the nutrients to seep through in passing into the cells. It also acts as a cement between the walls of the cells to hold them together.

As the cell processes go on to develop the complex substances in the plant, some organic acids are formed that would be harmful excessive byproducts were it not for the neutralizing effect of calcium. Oxalic acid, for example, is formed into calcium oxalate. The calcium in plants seems to exist in a fine balance with magnesium, potassium, and possibly boron. Any upset in this balance due to an excess or lack of any of them will result in an abnormal performance of plant functions. What may appear to be an excess of calcium in a plant may be a lack of one or more of these other elements, and the remedy may be to add the deficient element or elements instead of cutting down the apparent excess of calcium. Similarly, an apparent excess of potassium, magnesium, or boron may really be a deficiency of calcium.

IRON

Plants need very little iron, yet it is a most essential element. The top 6 inches of the soil may contain as much as 20 tons or more of iron per acre as iron oxide, Fe_2O_3, yet on occasional iron-rich soils plants may starve for lack of this element. In acid soils the iron is usually available to all plants, but in some neutral or alkaline soils it is so insoluble that some plants may have difficulty in absorbing enough. Again, where excessive amounts of soluble phosphates have been added to the soil, the iron may be made unavailable to plants by being precipitated as an insoluble iron phosphate. This may happen in acid as well as in alkaline soils. It is more likely to occur in sandy than in clay soils, because the latter have greater power to fix or "lock up" excessive soluble phosphates.

The chlorosis that develops in plants starved for iron is associated with failure to form chlorophyll, yet it has not been found that iron is built into this pigment. For the present we must accept the fact that iron is associated in some way with the making of chlorophyll.

MANGANESE, BORON, ZINC, AND COPPER

These elements have sometimes been called the minor elements because they are required by plants only in trace amounts. This does not mean that they are not as vital to the well-being of plants as the other elements discussed, for they are all the word "vital" implies. Fortunately, they occur in sufficient quantities in most soils, but one or another of them is of major importance in the case of some crops on some soils.

A lack of sufficient manganese or boron is most likely to be associated with calcareous or heavily limed soils. When either of these is lacking, the plant is just as handicapped in performing its normal function as when it is starving for any one of the major elements.

Manganese seems to act as a two-handed (double-valence) reception committee, of which zinc and copper are also members, to greet the other nutrient ions as they enter the plant cell and to direct them to their respective positions for carrying out their functions in the plant. Another way to describe this is to say that these minor elements act as catalysts.

Boron seems to be closely related to some function that calcium performs in the plant. Whenever the proportion of calcium to boron ions in the plant becomes unbalanced because of a lack of boron, the terminal parts of the plant fail to develop properly and the other characteristic boron-starvation symptoms become evident. If this calcium-boron balance becomes upset because of a shortage of calcium or an excess of boron, injury to the plant is likely to result. Thus both a deficiency and an excess of boron produce characteristic symptoms.

Zinc has been found to be effective in treating some physiological diseases, but not much is known about its action in plants. As yet it has been found necessary to use zinc only on certain soils of the Gulf Coast States and California. No upland soils that are low in organic matter have been found lacking in sufficient copper for plants. The need for copper appears to be associated with high organic-matter content, particularly in the case of peat soils that are alkaline and contain appreciable quantities of ferrous iron.

An important point about these trace elements is that in quantities larger than the plant needs they are likely to be toxic or poisonous to the plant, yet the actual quantity may still be small. Excessive as well as deficient amounts will produce certain characteristic symptoms.

SOIL ACIDITY

Soil acidity is mentioned here because it so greatly affects the behavior and availability of most of the plant nutrients. It is well to understand what soil acidity is and how it is measured.

The principal acid in soils is not hydrochloric, nitric, or any other of the common drug-store acids. Such acids are soluble and would easily wash out of the soil, resulting in decreased acidity. But soil acidity is known to increase with prolonged movement of rain water through the soil. This comes about because the main soil acids are themselves the colloidal particles of clay.

The clays do not wash out of the soils by leaching, but the ions of calcium, magnesium, potassium, and sodium that were fastened (adsorbed) to the surfaces of the clays when the soil was virgin or very fertile and full of these alkaline elements have become loosened and washed down and out of the soil. When the clay particles are saturated with a mixture of calcium, magnesium, potassium, and sodium ions, the soil has no acidity and is alkaline—or, as some say, "sweet." (The term "sweet" is incorrect and should not be used.) When these alkaline plant elements are leached out, the acid hydrogen element from the soil carbonic acid ($H_2O + CO_2 = H_2CO_3$, carbonic acid) becomes attached or adsorbed to the spots on the clays from which these alkaline elements had been removed, with the result that the clay becomes a hydrogen clay and the soil becomes acidic.

There are other soil acids, too, such as organic acids produced by decomposing vegetable matter, but it is the clay acid that is dominant in acid soils. Since clays in soils are the principal acids, a heavy soil with a great deal of clay would have more acidity to be neutralized by liming than a sandy soil with only a small amount of clay in it.

The strength (intensity) of acids is stated somewhat like the size or gage of wire, in which the smaller the gage number the heavier the wire. The gage of soil acidity is called the pH scale (fig. 1). Here too the smaller the number of the pH value the stronger the acid. Thus, a pH of 4.0 is about the extreme of acidity for any soil. A pH of 7.0 is neutral, and above pH 7.0 the soil is alkaline and may contain free lime.

The pH value indicates the intensity or strength of an acid and tells nothing about the amount. It is easier to understand this if it is compared to intensity and quantity in the case of heat. Heat is measured in degrees of temperature and in calories. The degrees of temperature indicate the intensity (strength) of heat only, and the calories indicate the amount of heat. Thus a chunk of rock at a temperature of 70° F. could be heated to 100° easily if the rock was only 1 cubic inch in size, because the heat capacity in calories would be small. But if the rock was very large, as big as a house, the heat (calories) needed to produce the same temperature change would be great, because of the much greater heat capacity of the bigger rock. Both the small and the large rocks at the same temperature would register the same heat intensity, yet the amount of heat in the larger rock would be greater than that in the smaller rock in proportion to their relative sizes. In a similar way, soils can have the same pH value and still differ greatly in lime requirements. A sandy loam with a clay content of 12 percent would not require much lime to change its acidity from pH 5.0 to 6.5, but a clay loam with a clay content of 24 percent would require about twice as much lime as the sandy loam to produce the same change in pH.

Few crop plants will grow below pH 3.5 or above pH 9.0. The most favorable pH range for most crop plants is 6.2-7.2.

WHY READ THE HUNGER SIGNS?

Information about the functions of the various nutrient elements in plants has been obtained by scientists largely through carefully conducted experiments in the field, greenhouses, and laboratories.

Most of the intensive studies on the fundamental nature of nutrition have been made in greenhouses, with soils in pot tests and with nutrient-solution cultures, in which the plants were grown directly in the solution or on sand or gravel to which the nutrient solution had

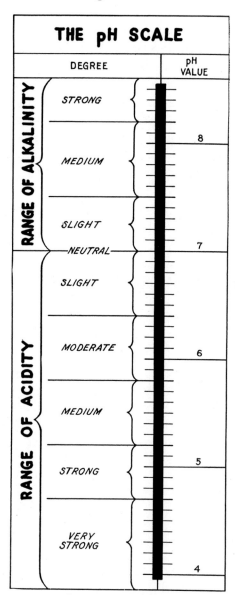

Courtesy of National Lime Association

Figure 1.—The pH scale, showing the ranges of acidity and alkalinity at which crop plants grow.

been added. Field experiments have been used chiefly for testing the practical and economic aspects of fertilizers.

Soil tests have been helpful in diagnosing nutritional deficiencies, and plant-tissue tests have been used in verifying starvation symptoms. The tissue tests are likely to find increased use in the future, for they permit plant growers to detect nutrient deficiencies, particularly in the case of the major elements, before the plants show any visible signs of trouble. No grower can afford, however, to disregard the hunger signs that plants show when starving for a nutrient element. The information obtained from the deficiency symptoms requires no laboratory or experiments and is free to anyone who wants to learn what the hunger signs say.

CHAPTER II

Plant-Nutrient Deficiency in Tobacco

By J. E. McMurtrey, Jr.[1]

W HEN the soil does not contain adequate quantities of the chemical elements necessary for the normal development of plants, it becomes a matter of great importance to supply these elements by means of manures or fertilizers. But first it is necessary to discover some simple, practical method for finding out what elements are lacking.

This can be done by careful observation of the growing plant, which should and does furnish the most direct evidence of its own nutritional condition.

It is possible, of course, to compare the growth of plants by measuring their dry weight, and in fact this is the method that has usually been followed in experimental work. It is not well adapted to the needs of the farmer, however, and in the case of tobacco it does not by any means tell the whole story. With tobacco, the total tonnage produced is not the only thing of importance. Much of the value of the crop depends on that complex and elusive factor, quality. Quality in turn depends on color, aroma, fire-holding capacity, texture, elasticity, body, ability to improve with aging, and other characteristics. Moreover, the qualities required are different for the several so-called types or classes of tobacco— cigar, flue-cured, burley, Maryland, dark air-cured, and dark fire-cured. Conditions during growth unquestionably influence the quality of the final product, though it is by no means possible as yet to tell exactly in what ways. There is no doubt, however, that the grower who wants a high-quality product should keep the plants growing normally and during growth watch for signs that something is wrong.

Careful experimental work during the past several years has resulted in a systematic method of recognizing or diagnosing a shortage of any one of several chemical elements by the symptoms produced in the tobacco plant.

[1] J. E. McMurtrey, Jr., is Senior Physiologist, Bureau of Plant Industry, United States Department of Agriculture.

The subject matter of this chapter is essentially that of United States Department of Agriculture Technical Bulletin 612, with additional color plates.

Credit is due Marcel L. F. Foubert, Frank M. Blake, and F. S. Knoblock of the Section of Illustrations, Division of Publications, U. S. Department of Agriculture, for photographs used in this chapter.

THE BACKGROUND OF DIAGNOSIS

According to modern views, the higher plants require the follow-ing chemical elements in order to make normal growth, and they require these elements in suitable quantities and forms: Carbon, hydrogen, oxygen, nitrogen, phosphorus, sulfur, potassium, cal-cium, magnesium, iron, manganese, copper, zinc, and boron. The importance of silicon, molybdenum, and aluminum in the growth of the tobacco plant under field conditions has not been fully de-termined, though these elements have been reported by some in-vestigators to be of importance in the growth of other plants.

The elements nitrogen, phosphorus, sulfur, potassium, calcium, magnesium, iron, manganese, copper, zinc, and boron are present in varying quantities in agricultural soils. Sometimes they may be present in abundance, but one or more of them may be tied up in chemical compounds that plants cannot readily use. This, of course, is equivalent to a shortage. Decreased growth results when the supply of any one of these elements is insufficient. Since this is true for all of them, it is necessary to watch for other signs besides decreased growth to discover which element is not present in large enough quantities.

These signs or symptoms of mineral hunger in plants may of course be modified to some extent by other factors affecting growth. Light, temperature, and the amount and distribution of the water supply all have an influence on growth, and they also affect the total quantity of the chemical elements required by the plant and the rate at which these elements must be supplied. Even under these varying conditions, however, the characteristic symptoms due to the deficiency of an element will be found to be essentially the same.

There are certain other complexities that might be noted at this point.

To say that a single element is deficient is ordinarily the same as saying that there is an excess of other elements in relation to that one. The result is an unbalanced nutritional condition in the plant. It may not always be possible to distinguish between the effects due to the deficiency and the effects due to the relative excess of the other elements. In some cases, too, there may be a large excess of some one element, and this may interfere with the solubility, absorption, or utilization of another element to such an extent that acute deficiency symptoms appear, even though there is an abundant supply of the second element. Similar effects may result from the acid-alkaline reaction of the soil (or any other medium in which the plant is grown). Again, symptoms of poisoning may be added to symptoms of mineral deficiency. Finally, there is the question of what happens when more than one element is deficient. This last, however, is not so complex as it might be, since the visible effects are usually those characteristic of the element that is most deficient.

A deficiency of an element may occur at any time during the life of a plant, and neither its size nor its age alters the effects. As a rule the most typical symptoms are those that show up first, and these are the ones that serve best to distinguish a shortage of one element from that of another. After the diagnosis has been made, the practical remedy is usually obvious and more or less easily applied. In most cases under field conditions it would consist simply in adding the missing element in suitable form to the soil.

Even though the missing element is supplied, however, deficiency symptoms may occur if the element is not supplied in the right amount for the prevailing conditions, or if the conditions are such that it is unavailable for use by the plants. These are points that must be kept in mind by the grower. The tobacco plant has a relatively high content of minerals, as evidenced by the amount of ash that remains after it is burned. Its growth is rapid, and adequate supplies of the necessary elements should be constantly present in the soil.

It should be noted that in practice complete absence of an essential element from the soil rarely if ever occurs. Also, the seeds contain small quantities of the essential elements, and the young seedlings are commonly grown on virgin soils liberally manured and fertilized. Thus it is possible for the young plants to build up small reserve supplies, particularly of the elements that move readily from one part of the plant to another. Finally, commercial fertilizers—and even ordinary "pure" chemicals—usually contain small quantities of various elements as impurities in addition to the elements they are supposed to contain. The plant, then, is always grown under conditions such that, though a given element may be more or less deficient, it is perhaps never entirely lacking.

The most essential requirement for recognizing deficiency symptoms is a thorough knowledge of the plant itself—its life history and habits, how it looks and how it acts at all stages of growth. It is also necessary to know how diseases and insect pests affect the plant, so their effects may not be confused with the symptoms of plantfood deficiency. The successful grower has this knowledge through long acquaintance with the plant under practical conditions. In fact, once he learns what the deficiency symptoms are, he may be able to recognize them much better than the specialized scientist, who is less familiar with the plant under all the conditions of practical culture.

Because of its large area, the tobacco leaf is an excellent subject on which to study the effects of any environmental factor on growth. Since the plant is produced for its leaf, studies of tobacco leaves during growth may eventually have an unusually important practical application. Most of the symptoms described in the following pages are found in the leaves. Other symptoms could be found, of course, by careful examination of the root or stem.

NITROGEN DEFICIENCY

Under field conditions, the most common deficiency is probably a shortage of nitrogen. As a matter of fact, the nitrogen supply for the tobacco crop must be controlled to produce leaf of a certain type. Some types of tobacco must even be grown under conditions of relative nitrogen starvation—flue-cured tobacco, for example, and to some extent burley and Maryland. Cigar leaf, on the other hand, can be produced successfully only when there is an abundant or luxury consumption of nitrogen by the plant.

Even when tobacco must be grown under conditions of relative nitrogen deficiency, however, the supply cannot be reduced to the proper point until the plant has reached a certain size and stage of maturity. This is apparently an important requirement if the tobacco is to ripen properly.

The plant may show signs of nitrogen deficiency at any period of growth, from the seedling stage to maturity.

The effect first becomes apparent as a decrease in the normal green color. At the same time, growth slows down or stops.

After the first change in the greenness of the plant, the lower leaves turn lemon yellow to orange yellow, the shade apparently depending on the intensity of the green before the nitrogen deficiency occurred. The darker shades of yellow occur on the plants that had the deeper shades of green.

This yellowing is followed by a drying up, or firing, of the yellowed leaves. The number of leaves the plant loses depends on its size and the acuteness of the shortage of nitrogen.

The remaining leaves on the plant tend to assume an erect position, forming an acute angle with the stalk.

The bud leaves tend to retain their normal condition. Apparently their needs are met by a transfer of nitrogen from the older leaves.

If the nitrogen shortage becomes acute at the flowering stage, flowering and fruiting are accomplished by a similar transfer of nitrogen from the older tissues, but the quantity of seed is reduced.

The effects of a deficiency of nitrogen are shown in plate 1, page 43. Here the light-green color of the plant is evident, as well as the yellowing of the lower leaves and the tendency of the unyellowed leaves to stand more upright than usual. (These same symptoms have been reported in plants grown in solution cultures when the supply of nutritive elements was accurately controlled.)

A nitrogen deficiency appears to reduce in some way the water content of the plant. This probably accounts for the fact that a nitrogen shortage and a water shortage sometimes show much the same symptoms. A nitrogen shortage, however, may occur when the plant is standing in water all the time, as in a solution culture.

The effects of a nitrogen shortage can be seen in the cured leaf. Its size is reduced, the amount of reduction depending on the stage at which the shortage occurred. The color is also affected, differently with different types and methods of curing. The flue-cured type of tobacco has the desired lemon-yellow color only when the nitrogen supply is reduced to the point of deficiency at the ripening stage. With the cigar type, nitrogen deficiency is decidedly injurious at any stage; it results in undesirable colors and other poor qualities not well understood. The nitrogen supply is also known to influence nicotine content to a great extent, low nitrogen generally producing a leaf with a low nicotine content.

PHOSPHORUS DEFICIENCY

Practically all tobacco soils except those derived from phosphatic limestones are initially deficient in phosphorus. Phosphorus deficiency, however, causes tobacco plants to exhibit growth effects less characteristic than those resulting from a shortage of any of the other essential elements.

The symptoms that serve to identify the condition are a certain type of slow growth and lack of maturity.

With this stunted growth, the plant assumes a rosette condition. The color is very dark green, as shown in plate 2, page 44.

The size and shape of the leaves are altered (fig. 1). The leaves tend to be narrow in proportion to length. Usually there appears to be no abnormality of the leaf other than in size, shape, and color, but in a few instances spots have been evident on the lower leaves of the plant, as shown in figure 2. These spots do not occur consistently on phosphorus-deficient plants either in the field or in solution cultures.

The leaves form an acute angle with the stalk, as seen in plate 2, page 44.

Figure 1.—A and C show the small, rather narrow leaves that result from phosphorus short-age. B is from a plant liberally supplied with phosphorus.

Under field conditions, firing of the lower leaves has not appeared to any considerable extent.

The bud leaves tend to retain their normal appearance, possibly because phosphorus is transferred to them from the older parts of the plant. Similarly, flowering and fruiting are successfully accomplished when the shortage becomes manifest at this stage of growth.

If tobacco is to have the desired quality when cured, it is essential that the leaf reach a certain stage of maturity before harvest. Leaves from plants suffering from phosphorus deficiency are immature and therefore have an undesirable quality. The cured leaf tends to be dark brown, dark greenish, or black.   The crop is also frequently delayed until late in the season, when the weather is unfavorable for curing, especially in the case of the air-cured types.

Figure 2.—Leaf spot such as this sometimes occurs as a result of phosphorus deficiency.

POTASSIUM DEFICIENCY

Tobacco requires a great deal of potassium; in fact, what would be a luxury consumption from the standpoint of yield alone seems to be necessary to produce leaf of high quality.   The plant shows striking symptoms when potassium is not present in adequate quantity, though under field conditions the reduction in growth is not so marked as in the case of a shortage of nitrogen or phosphorus.   Many tobacco soils do not supply sufficient amounts of potassium for normal growth, and probably the first deficiency effects reported for tobacco were those due to a deficiency of potassium. The deficiency symptoms tend to be aggravated by dry weather.

The lower leaves of the tobacco plant suffering from potassium hunger show a typical mottling, or a loss of green color (chlorosis) at their tips and margins, as shown in plate 3, page 45.

This is rapidly followed by the development of specks of dead tissue (necrosis), usually as small spots in the center of the mottled areas.

Later the areas of dead tissue may enlarge and run together to such an extent that most of the leaf tissues between the veins are involved. As the dead areas enlarge and involve more and more tissue, they dry to a brown color, so that the whole plant comes to have a brownish or rusty appearance. The parts of the leaf that remain green are darker and more bluish than normal.

The dead areas may fall out, producing a ragged appearance of the leaf, as shown in plate 4, A, page 46.

Even before the mottling and the appearance of dead spots, the leaves become cup-shaped from the under side. Probably this is because growth slows down at the edges but continues in the center, so that the margins seem to roll inward and downward. This crumpled effect becomes more marked as the living tissue continues to grow around the mottled and dead areas.

The mottling appears to progress rapidly from the lower to the upper leaves.[2] There may be some loss of the older leaves, but this is not characteristic as it is in the case of nitrogen deficiency.

In all cases observed, the bud leaves tend to retain their normal appearance, apparently because potassium is transferred to them from the older parts of the plant.

Symptoms of potassium hunger may be observed on young seedlings from the seedbed (fig. 3) as well as on the large plants in the field.

It has been consistently reported that under field conditions a liberal supply of potassium enables the plant to withstand or ward off attacks of leaf spot caused by bacteria. Perhaps under conditions of shortage the development of dead areas, already described, allows the organisms causing certain leaf-spot diseases to enter the tissue at these points. This would hasten the break-down of the tissue.

---

[2] In rapidly growing plants in the field, after the lower leaves are almost mature the upper leaves may show the mottling and spotting without the lower leaves showing any decided symptoms.

It is well recognized that in some manner potassium aids in maintaining the general vigor of the plant.   There appears to be a relationship between potassium and nitrogen in this connection. With cigar tobaccos, grown under high-nitrogen conditions, it is difficult to obtain the protective action of potassium found with Maryland and flue-cured types, where the nitrogen supply is purposely limited.

Figure 3.—This plant, from a seedbed, shows that even seedlings may be affected by potassium hunger.

In the cured leaf, potassium shortage is shown by reduced size and a ragged appearance, as illustrated in figure 4, B.   The cured leaves are off type in color, though they do not show the distinctive color patterns described for the growing leaves.   They also lack body, elasticity, aroma, and ability to condition when exposed to moist air, and they have a poor fire-holding capacity.

MAGNESIUM DEFICIENCY

Magnesium deficiency has been given the common name of "sand drown" since it is most prevalent in deep sandy soils and during seasons of excessive rainfall.   The deficiency symptoms rarely appear in the field until the plants have attained considerable size, more commonly after topping when the growth rate is rapid. Thus the leaves usually attain almost normal size and shape. Other symptoms of magnesium deficiency, however, are very striking.

Since magnesium is part of the chlorophyll molecule, the green pigment is affected when the magnesium supply is short. The loss of green color commonly progresses in a definite manner.

First the lowermost leaves of the plant lose their normal color

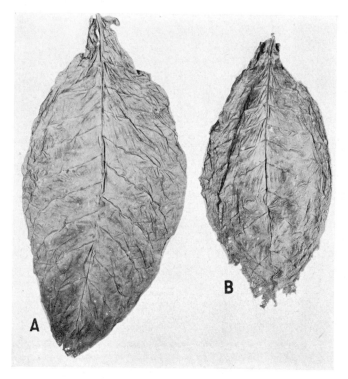

Figure 4.—Cured leaf, Maryland type, B showing reduced size and ragged appearance due to potassium hunger. A, cured leaf from a plant liberally supplied with potash.

at the tips and margins (plate 5, page 47) and between the veins. The color may vary from a pale green to almost white, depending on the acuteness of the shortage. The veins and the tissue close to them tend to retain the normal color long after the rest of the leaf has lost practically all its green pigment. Even in extreme cases, when the lower leaves become almost white, they rarely dry up or develop dead spots.

The loss of color characteristic of magnesium hunger proceeds uniformly, as a rule, from the base of the plant upward (plate 4, B, page 46).[3] On the individual leaf, it begins at the tip and margin

[3] Under experimental conditions, in solution cultures, some of the old lower leaves may not lose their green color when the plant is growing rapidly and magnesium is suddenly with-

and proceeds toward the base and center. The yellow as well as the green pigments appear to be affected. The entire area of the leaf and all the leaves of the plant may be involved in extreme cases, though the bud tends to remain normal.

The contrast between the pale and the normal tissue is sharp-

Figure 5.—Flue-cured tobacco leaves. B shows dark, irregular patches and other signs of poor color due to magnesium deficiency. A is from a normal plant.

est in plants with a dark-green color. It is not so striking when the plant is light green in color because of a low supply of nitrogen or sulfur.

It was pointed out above that symptoms of magnesium deficiency usually appear when the plant has attained considerable size. They have been observed, however, even in the seedling stage, as plate 6, A, page 48, shows. The extent of the dwarfing that results from a

drawn. Also, in solution cultures the appearance of dead spots even before loss of color has been reported. This spotting has also been observed in plants grown in soil cultures in the greenhouse when the soil was leached with an excessive amount of nutrient solutions lacking magnesium. It has not been observed to any extent in field cultures, but it might possibly occur with rapidly growing plants under excessive rainfall.

magnesium shortage seems to be simply a question of when the shortage operates and how acute it is. The yield is reduced to the extent that dwarfing occurs, but as already noted this may not be severe if the shortage becomes acute only at a late stage of growth.

The reduction in the quality of the cured leaf is more serious. It is indicated by dark and irregular colors, loss in weight, dry leaf

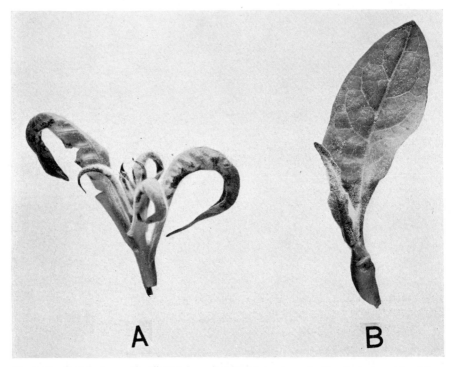

Figure 6.—Terminal growth affected by mineral deficiencies. A, The first stage of calcium shortage; note the hooking downward of the bud leaves; B, an early stage of boron deficiency—break-down of tissues at the base of the leaf.

tissues, and a lack of body and elasticity. These signs of lowered quality are more evident in the flue-cured (fig. 5) than in the air-cured types of leaf. It has been reported that magnesium is an important constituent in cigar tobacco and that when the magnesium content is low, the ash tends to be dark in color.

CALCIUM DEFICIENCY

Calcium has long been recognized as an essential plant nutrient, but it has been erroneously assumed that all agricultural soils contain enough of it for strictly nutritive purposes. It is commonly used, in the form of hydrated lime or calcium carbonate, not as a food for plants, but to bring about the best soil reaction for plant growth. The ions, or small electrified particles, of calcium may be said to antagonize the ions of objectionable substances, or to neutralize or render them harmless. It is quite probable, however, that in some cases favorable results are also due to the nutrient value of the calcium.

When the calcium supply is deficient, the tobacco plant shows distinctive abnormalities in growth. Just what form these abnor-

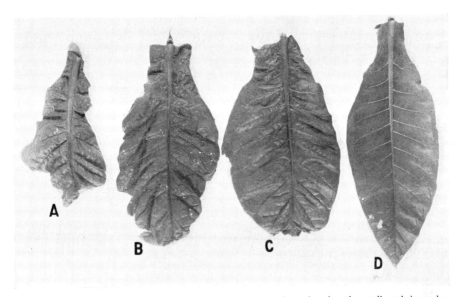

Figure 7.—A, B, and C are young leaves from a tobacco plant showing the scalloped, irregular edges due to calcium deficiency. D is from a normal plant.

malities take seems to depend to some extent on what other substances are present under a given set of conditions. This is in keeping with the function of the calcium ion as an antagonizer of other ions. Magnesium gives the most striking illustration of this relationship. Quantities of magnesium that produce normal growth in the presence of calcium seem to become poisonous in its absence. What happens in this case is typical, for all practical purposes, of calcium deficiency in general.

The first symptom of calcium deficiency is the development of a light-green color, followed by a peculiar hooking downward at the tips of the young leaves making up the terminal bud (fig. 6, A).

This is followed typically by the death of the young leaves, which break down first at the tips and margins. If complete break-down does not occur and growth takes place later, portions of the tips and margins of the affected leaves are missing, and this gives them a scalloped appearance (fig. 7). As the illustration shows, they are also distorted. The older leaves, however, may be normal in shape (plate 7, page 49).

The plant as a whole is abnormally dark green. In the later stages of extreme calcium shortage, the terminal bud dies. This is

Figure 8.—Tobacco plant after recovery from a calcium shortage in dry weather. Note that the young leaves at the top have grown normally.

equivalent to topping, and it results in a thickening of the older leaves. In some cases of acute shortage, dead spots may develop and loss of color may occur on the older leaves, though these effects have rarely been observed.

When lateral shoots or suckers begin to develop in the leaf axils after the death of the terminal bud, their terminal growth in turn goes through the same stages, and the buds die.

These effects were first reported on plants grown in solution cultures, and later they were found to be typical in the field.

The topmost leaves sometimes show no abnormality (fig. 8) when deficiency symptoms are evident on the middle leaves. This appears to occur in dry periods, when the roots may have penetrated to greater depths than usual, enabling the plant to draw on subsoil reserves of calcium.

A symptom that has been experimentally reproduced by adding excess manganese in the presence of calcium has sometimes been observed in the field. The young leaves lose color and then develop

Figure 9.—Effects of calcium shortage on flowering parts of tobacco. Note (B) the drying up of the corolla and the distortions of the calyx. A is from a normal plant.

dead spots. In the experimental work, the condition has been corrected by the application of limestone.

In the case of plants grown in the greenhouse, the floral parts show striking effects if the calcium shortage does not become acute until the flowering stage. In figure 9, A shows the floral parts from a normal plant and B those from a plant grown under conditions of calcium shortage. In plant B there has been a tendency to shed blossoms and buds, and the flowers that remain show a dieback of the corolla, with the pistil protruding. In most cases there are spots of dead tissue on the calyx lobes. This condition has been observed in the field during the past season (1940).

It is evident from these various symptoms that there is little or no transfer of calcium from the older tissues to the growing points, as there is in the case of the other elements previously described. This means that if normal growth is to occur there must be a continuous supply of calcium available to the plant.

The effects of calcium deficiency on growth are disastrous to the cured leaf. The malformation and thickening of the leaf, the death of the terminal bud, and the other physiological disturbances combine to produce a tobacco of extremely poor quality.

BORON DEFICIENCY

The effects of boron starvation on plant growth had been reported in experiments with solution cultures some time before they were recently recognized under field conditions.

An acute boron shortage first produces marked changes in the tip or growing point of the plant.

The young leaves of the terminal bud become light green in color—paler at the base than at the tip. They also show a somewhat drawn appearance. When these symptoms appear, the leaves have already ceased to grow.

Next the tissues at the base of the young leaves show signs of break-down (fig. 6, B). If growth should take place later, before all the tissues are broken down, these leaves would be distorted by the growth around the injured tissue. Usually they have a one-sided or twisted appearance. The stalk toward the top of the plant may also show a distorted or twisted type of growth.

The death of the terminal bud (plate 8, page 50) follows these stages. This automatically tops the plant, causing the leaves to thicken and increase in area. The upper leaves tend to roll in a half-circle downward from the tip toward the base. They are abnormally light in color, and become smooth, stiff, and brittle. When the midrib or secondary veins are broken, their vascular tissues show a dark discoloration.

Lateral buds (suckers) may develop in the axils of the leaves or at the base of the stalk, but they typically break down like the terminal bud.

When boron shortage does not become acute until the flowering stage, the flower buds are shed and no seed pods are set.

These symptoms would indicate that there is little or no transfer of boron from the older plant parts to the younger growing points. Therefore a continuous supply must be available for normal growth.

Only a very minute amount or trace of boron, however, is needed or even tolerated by the plant. Any considerable amount acts as a poison.

It has not been possible to make extensive observations of the effects of boron deficiency on the cured leaf. From the observations available, it is evident that marked effects are to be expected in view of the striking modifications in growth produced by boron shortage.

MANGANESE DEFICIENCY

When tobacco plants apparently manifesting a new disease were submitted to the Department of Agriculture by a grower, it was possible to identify the symptoms as those of manganese hunger because the same symptoms had been produced experimentally in sand and solution cultures. Later the identification was substantiated by field trials on the area from which the plants were taken.

Distinctive symptoms of manganese shortage, however, have been reported in only a few cases in the field. Perhaps they are rare because this deficiency is usually associated with a neutral or alkaline soil reaction. Such a soil reaction favors the black root-rot disease (*Thielaviopsis basicola* (Berk. and Br.) Ferraris), which limits growth and would tend to hide the effects of a shortage of manganese.

The first visible symptom of manganese hunger is a loss of color in the young leaves. This loss of color follows out the minutest branches of the veins, or vascular system. Between the veins the tissue is light green to almost white (plate 6, B, 3, page 48), while the veins themselves remain darker. The leaf has a checkered appearance because of the contrast between the green veins and the tissues that have lost their color.

The loss of color is followed by the development of spots of dead tissue, which may drop out, giving the leaf a ragged appearance. Usually this spotting is not confined to the tip and margins, as in the case of potassium deficiency, but involves parts scattered over the entire leaf.

The plant as a whole may be considerably dwarfed (plate 9, A, 2, page 51), and in general appearance it is light green.

The cured leaves from plants affected by manganese shortage are of decidedly poor quality. The most apparent effects are the dead spots and the lack of desirable color (plate 9, B, page 51). The leaf also lacks body, elasticity, and aroma.

SULFUR DEFICIENCY

Tobacco plants suffering from sulfur deficiency have not often been found under field conditions—chiefly, perhaps, because most commercial fertilizers contain an ample amount of sulfur, many of their common ingredients being high in this element. In addition, the rainfall in the tobacco-growing regions usually brings down considerable quantities of sulfur. In fact, sulfur deficiency becomes evident in dry periods, when the shortage is produced intentionally.

The first evident symptom is the light-green color of the plant as a whole, though there is a tendency for the young leaves to be lighter than the older ones. (In solution cultures the light-green color is largely confined to the younger leaves.)

The plants do not lose their lower leaves by firing, as they do in the case of nitrogen shortage. This fact serves to distinguish the two deficiencies.

In Georgia and South Carolina, some blistering of the leaves has been associated with sulfur deficiency in the case of flue-cured tobacco.

There may be some reduction in growth and frequently there is a characteristic crimping downward of the leaves at the tips. (Plate 10, page 52.)

As a rule, the effects of sulfur deficiency have been apparent under field conditions only in the early stages of growth. They are evident only during dry periods, and recovery has been observed to take place rapidly and completely when rain occurred. Apparently the rain supplies the needed sulfur.

The cured leaf of plants suffering from sulfur shortage shows color effects that are sometimes desirable and sometimes undesirable. In the case of flue-cured leaf, a sulfur deficiency may be advantageous, provided yields are not seriously reduced; it produces more desirable colors than an overabundance of sulfur. In Maryland leaf, on the other hand, an abundant sulfur supply produces the more desirable colors.

IRON DEFICIENCY

As yet, iron deficiency has not been observed in tobacco under field conditions. It has been reported as occurring in plants other than tobacco, however, and it is worth while to describe the symptoms produced experimentally in tobacco grown in sand or solution cultures. In the case of plants other than tobacco, the deficiency is associated with neutral or alkaline soils. This might account for the failure to find it in field-grown tobacco, since the situation would be complicated by the root-rot organism mentioned in the case of manganese deficiency.

A leaf of a tobacco plant grown experimentally under conditions of iron shortage is shown in plate 6, B, 1, page 48. It will be observed that the leaf is suffering from chlorosis or loss of green color. This is typical of other plants affected by iron deficiency, and in fact for a long time it was the only recognized type of chlorosis occurring in plants.

As shown in plate 11, page 53, the loss of color first becomes evident in the young or upper leaves of the tobacco plant. The leaves making up the terminal bud lose color between the veins and become light green or white. In extreme cases the veins also lose their color and the whole terminal bud may turn almost white. Usually, however, the principal veins tend to retain their color, as do the lower leaves of the plant.

The affected leaves characteristically show no breaks or areas of dead tissue, though sometimes they dry up. Apparently this occurs under conditions of bright sunlight and dry air.

The fact that the growing point is immediately affected indicates that iron is not transferred from the older parts of the plant and that a continuous supply must be available if growth is to be normal.

COPPER DEFICIENCY

As in the case of iron, symptoms of copper shortage have not yet been observed in tobacco under field conditions, though they have been observed in other plants. Since they have been associated with soils high in organic matter, like those on which tobacco is sometimes grown, it seems worth while to describe the effects of copper hunger on tobacco plants grown experimentally in the greenhouse.

As figure 10, B, shows, the upper leaves are unable to retain their turgor or rigidity, so that they wilt badly. Such plants are permanently wilted; they do not recover at night or during cloudy periods like plants that have wilted on a hot day.

There is a reduction in growth in proportion to the extent of the copper shortage and the stage of growth at which it operates.

When a copper deficiency becomes evident during the flowering stage, the seed stalk does not stand erect and the amount of seed is reduced.

Copper is one of the elements that is needed by plants only in very small amounts. In nutrient solutions, the amount needed to correct a deficiency was found to be from one-sixteenth to one-eighth part per million—equivalent to half an ounce of copper in some 30 to 60 thousand gallons of water. Amounts in excess of these small quantities produced a decided stunting of the plants.

Figure 10.—Effect of copper deficiency on growth of tobacco. A, Normal plant grown in nutrient solution with copper added; B, plant grown without copper—note the extreme and permanent wilting of the upper leaves.

Under field conditions, the amount to be applied would depend on the fixing power of the soil for this element. The chemical situation would seem to make it inadvisable to include copper compounds in standard fertilizer mixtures at least until there is evidence that copper is deficient in a wide variety of soils, since the phosphates would combine with copper to form cupric phosphate, which is relatively unavailable for use by plants because it does not easily dissolve. In case of deficiency, it may prove best to apply the copper as a spray directly on the plants.

ZINC DEFICIENCY

Zinc is another element that has not been known to cause deficiency symptoms in field-grown tobacco. However, there is a disease of tobacco, occurring in wet periods, which is characterized by a leaf spot commonly attributed to bacteria. It causes a breakdown of the leaf, and frequently a large part of the crop is severely damaged. The symptoms correspond in many respects to those produced experimentally by a shortage of zinc. It is not possible to say with certainty as yet whether zinc deficiency is a factor in this disease.

Striking effects are produced in the tobacco plant, as shown in plate 12, page 54, when zinc is withheld in sand or solution cultures.

Typically, the lower leaves first show a slight loss of color at the tips and margins. This is followed by the development of areas of dead and broken-down tissue. Usually a small area is involved at first, and in some cases this area is surrounded by a halo such as has been reported for leaf spots produced by bacterial inoculation.

In most cases the dead areas, which at first have a water-soaked appearance, spread rapidly. Frequently an almost total collapse or death of the leaf tissue follows in a very short time. The breakdown may come so quickly that the early stage, characterized by loss of color, may not be evident. Sometimes, too, the lowermost leaves of the plant are not the only ones involved.

The small veins are not involved at first, but frequently they also soon break down.

As a rule, the dead leaf tissue finally dries to a brown color.

There is some shortening of the internodes—the spaces between the leaves on the stem—and the green leaves appear to be thickened.

It will be noted that in some ways these symptoms resemble those described for potassium hunger. There are distinct differences, however. In the case of potassium shortage, the first breaks or lesions in the tissue are more sharply confined to the leaf tips and margins; the small veins do not ordinarily break down at all; and the break-down proceeds much more slowly.

As in the case of copper, it does not appear advisable at present to include zinc in fertilizer mixtures. Zinc would combine with soluble phosphates to form zinc phosphate, which cannot readily be dissolved, particularly in alkaline soils. The use of small amounts of zinc is sometimes desirable, but spraying seems to be the most practical method of application. In any considerable amount, zinc is poisonous to most plants.

RECOGNIZING COMPOUND DEFICIENCIES

In practical plant culture, where the causes of an abnormal condition cannot be determined from the nature of the treatment given the soil as they can be in experimental work, it is necessary to make an accurate diagnosis from the symptoms alone. For this reason, various combinations of mineral deficiencies were tried out under field conditions to see what the symptoms would be under these circumstances. Not all the possible combinations have been tested, but so far, with a single exception, there has been little or no blending of symptoms; the visible effects have always been those of one deficiency which appeared to dominate the rest.

This should simplify the problem of diagnosis and treatment. If there should be more than one deficiency, the dominant one can be recognized and corrected, then the next that appears, and so on.

When potassium, calcium, and magnesium were withheld, the symptoms were essentially those of potassium deficiency, though the reduction in growth was more extreme. When the potassium shortage was corrected, the plants still showed a marked reduction in growth, but the other symptoms were those of magnesium shortage alone, without any signs of calcium deficiency.

On untreated plots without any added fertilizer, the plants usually show the symptoms of nitrogen deficiency. In some cases, however, the dominant symptoms have been those of potassium deficiency alone, or phosphorus deficiency alone, or even sulfur deficiency alone.

The one case of blended symptoms so far observed occurred with a combined shortage of magnesium and sulfur, experimentally produced. Here, the sulfur shortage gave the plants a light-green color, and as already pointed out, this tended to mask the striking color pattern ordinarily produced by magnesium hunger.

A COMPARISON OF SYMPTOMS

So far, the symptoms produced by these mineral deficiencies have been described one by one. It has already been said that the symptom common to all of them, though it may be more marked in some cases than in others, is reduced growth. This is clearly shown in figure 11, in which a normal tobacco plant is placed beside six abnormal plants, each affected by a different deficiency.

The symptoms other than reduced growth will now be compared to bring out the differences between them.

The first thing that strikes the observer making such a comparison is that the symptoms of mineral shortage can be classified into two broad groups.

Figure 11.—Tobacco plants suffering from various mineral deficiencies—B, nitrogen; C, phosphorus; D, potassium; E, boron; F, calcium; G, magnesium. Reduction of growth has occurred in all cases. A is a normal plant.

In one group, it is primarily the older leaves of the plant that are affected. This is the case with deficiencies of nitrogen, phosphorus, potassium, zinc, and magnesium. Apparently, when there is a deficiency of one of these elements in the soil, the element can be readily transferred from the older parts of the plant to the young growing parts, so that the new growth does not show deficiency signs.

In the other group, it is primarily the new growth and young leaves that are affected. This occurs with deficiencies of calcium, boron, sulfur, iron, copper, and manganese. The elements apparently cannot be moved readily from one part of the plant to another.

The needs of the growing parts are therefore not supplied when there is a deficiency in the soil, and these parts sicken and die.

The first thing to look for in diagnosing a deficiency, then, is the part of the plant that is affected. This will tell in which major group the deficiency belongs.

In the first group—symptoms primarily in the older parts of the plant—the effects can be subdivided into (1) those that are more or less general, and (2) those that are local.

General effects on the plant as a whole or on the older leaves are produced by nitrogen and phosphorus deficiencies. These two, then, make up subdivision (1). In both cases there is considerable dwarfing, and the leaves tend to assume an erect position, forming a rather acute angle with the stalk. In the case of nitrogen deficiency, the plant is abnormally light green, and more or less firing is evident on the lower leaves. In the case of phosphorus deficiency, the plant is abnormally dark green, there is little or no firing, and the leaves are unusually narrow in proportion to length.

Local effects on the older leaves are produced by magnesium, zinc, and potassium deficiencies. These three make up subdivision (2). The local effects are loss of green color (chlorosis) and sometimes the development of areas of dead tissue (necrosis).

In the case of potassium deficiency, the chlorotic areas are yellowish and produce a mottled effect. They surround small dead spots or specks at the tips and margins of the leaves and between the veins. As the dead areas develop and dry up, they give the leaves a rusty appearance. Other parts of the plant are bluish green. An early symptom of potassium deficiency is a crimping under or cupping downward of the lower leaves at the tips and margins, and this becomes more pronounced as the deficiency becomes more acute.

In the case of magnesium deficiency, the pale areas are light green to almost white and occur between the principal veins, not primarily at the tips and margins. There is little or no spotting with dead tissue or cupping under of the tips and margins of leaves.

In the case of zinc deficiency, dead spots develop all over the leaf, not specifically at the tips and margins. Frequently they involve secondary and sometimes primary veins. The dead areas break down much more rapidly than in potassium deficiency.

So much for the first broad group.

The group characterized by effects on the young leaves or terminal growth can be classified in three subdivisions: (1) Chlorosis, or loss of color, in the young leaves without death of the terminal bud, which indicates a deficiency of iron, sulfur, or manganese; (2) death of the terminal bud preceded by loss of green color in the bud leaves, which indicates a deficiency of calcium or boron; (3) permanent wilting of the upper leaves, which indicates a deficiency of copper.

In subdivision (1)—chlorosis of the young leaves without dieback of the terminal bud—the veins tend to retain their green color if iron is the deficient element. The loss of color usually takes place only between the principal veins, although they too may be affected in extreme cases, when the entire leaf becomes white or yellow. Usually there are no dead spots.

If sulfur is the deficient element, the veins as well as the rest of the leaf tend to be light green—in fact, they may be even lighter than the rest of the leaf. There is not as great a loss of color as in the case of iron or manganese deficiencies, so that the leaves do not become white or yellow. There are no dead spots.

If manganese is the deficient element, the entire vein system of the leaf—even to the minutest branches—retains its green color in sharp contrast to the pale tissue between the veins. This gives the leaf a checkered appearance. Later, these leaves develop small dead spots scattered over the surface.

In subdivision (2)—death of the terminal bud—the young bud leaves first lose their green color and hook downward for about one-third of their length if calcium is the deficient element. Then the tips and margins of these leaves die, so that if growth occurs later they look scalloped and distorted. The plant is dark green.

If boron is the deficient element, the young bud leaves first lose their color at the base, which has a drawn appearance. The tip may remain green for some time. Usually the affected tissue rapidly breaks down, and if growth occurs later, before the leaf is too far gone, it has a distorted or twisted appearance. The color of the upper leaves of the plant is an unhealthy light green, and they roll downward in a semicircle from the tip toward the base. The principal veins and the midrib of affected leaves are extremely brittle, breaking readily when folded, and the tissue of the veins is discolored brown or black.

In subdivision (3), there is no typical chlorosis, and dieback of the terminal bud has not been observed. The dominant symptom of copper shortage is permanent wilting of the upper leaves.

The key which follows has been worked out for quickly identifying an unknown plantfood deficiency in tobacco.

KEY TO PLANT-NUTRIENT DEFICIENCY SYMPTOMS OF TOBACCO

A. Causal parasites or viruses present (not included in present discussions).
Parasitic and virus diseases

A. Causal parasites or viruses absent. More or less localized effects and decreased growth.   Commonly classed with nonparasitic diseases

B. Effects localized on older or lower leaves or more or less general on whole plant.   ELEMENT DEFICIENT

    C. General on whole plant; also, yellowing and drying up or "firing" of lower leaves. Plant light or dark green.

      D. Plant light green. Lower leaves yellow, drying to a light-brown color. Stalk short and slender if element is limiting in later growth stages . .   **Nitrogen**

      D. Plant dark green. Lower leaves may yellow and dry to a greenish-brown to black color; stalk short and slender if element is limiting in later growth stages . . . .   **Phosphorus**

    C. Local, occurring as mottling or chlorosis with or without spots of dead tissue on lower leaves; little or no drying up of lower leaves.

      D. Lower leaves chlorotic and typically show no dead spots. Tips and margins turned or cupped upward. Stalks slender . . . .   **Magnesium**

      D. Lower leaves mottled or chlorotic with small or large spots of dead tissue.

        E. Small spots of dead tissue between the veins at leaf tips and margins, which are tucked or cupped under. Stalks slender . . . .   **Potassium**

        E. Spots rapidly enlarge, involving in most cases the secondary and sometimes the primary veins. Leaves thick. Stalks with short internodes . . . .   **Zinc**

B. Effects localized on newer or bud leaves of plant.

    C. Terminal bud dies. Death is preceded by peculiar distortions at the tips or bases of young leaves making up the bud.

      D. Young leaves making up terminal bud first typically hooked, then die back at tips and margins so that later growth of such leaves produces a cut-out appearance at tips and margins. Stalk finally dies back at terminal bud . . . .   **Calcium**

      D. Young leaves making up terminal bud first light green at base; then break-down may take place at base of young leaf; if later growth follows, leaf shows twisted growth. Stalk finally dies back at terminal bud . . . .   **Boron**

    C. Terminal bud remains alive; wilting or chlorosis of newer or bud leaves, with or without spots of dead tissue; veins light or dark green.

      D. Young leaves permanently wilted, no spotting or marked chlorosis. Stalks immediately below seed head unable to stand erect when shortage is acute at flowering stage . . . .   **Copper**

      D. Young leaves not wilted, chlorotic with or without spots of dead tissue scattered over leaf.

        E. Young leaves chlorotic with spots of dead tissue scattered over leaf. Smallest veins tend to remain green, producing a checkered effect on leaf . . . .   **Manganese**

        E. Young leaves chlorotic without dead spots. Chlorosis does or does not involve veins so as to make them dark or light green in color.

          F. Young leaves with veins of a light-green color or of same shade as tissue between veins . . . .   **Sulfur**

          F. Young leaves chlorotic, principal veins typically green. Stalk short and slender . . . .   **Iron**

SELECTED REFERENCES

(1) ANDERSON, P. J., SWANBACK, T. R., and STREET, O. E.
    1932. POTASH REQUIREMENTS OF THE TOBACCO CROP. Conn. State Agr. Expt. Sta. Bul.
    334, pp. [137]–217, illus.

(2) GARNER, W. W., BACON, C. W., BOWLING, J. D., and BROWN, D. E.
    1934. THE NITROGEN NUTRITION OF TOBACCO. U. S. Dept. Agr. Tech. Bul. 414, 78
    pp., illus.

(3) —— McMURTREY, J. E., JR., BACON, C. W., and MOSS, E. G.
    1923. SAND DROWN, A CHLOROSIS OF TOBACCO DUE TO MAGNESIUM DEFICIENCY, AND THE
    RELATION OF SULPHATES AND CHLORIDS OF POTASSIUM TO THE DISEASE. Jour.
    Agr. Res. 23:27–40, illus.

(4) —— McMURTREY, J. E., JR., BOWLING, J. D., JR., and MOSS, E. G.
    1930. MAGNESIUM AND CALCIUM REQUIREMENTS OF THE TOBACCO CROP. Jour. Agr. Res.
    40:145–168, illus.

(5) —— McMURTREY, J. E., JR., and MOSS, E. G.
    1922. SAND DROWN, A CHLOROSIS OF TOBACCO AND OTHER PLANTS RESULTING FROM
    MAGNESIUM DEFICIENCY. Science 56:341–342.

(6) GRIS, E.
    1844. NOUVILLES EXPÉRIENCES SUR L'ACTION DES COMPOSÉS FERRUGINEUX SOLUBLES,
    APPLIQUÉS À LA VÉGÉTATION, ET SPÉCIALMENT AU TRAITEMENT DE LA CHLOROSE
    ET DE LA DÉBILITÉ DES PLANTES. Compt. Rend. Acad. Sci. [Paris] 19:1118-1119.

(7) KUIJPER, J.
    1930. BOORZUUR TEGEN DE TOPZIEKTE VAN DE TABAK. Deli-Proefsta. Medan Vlugschr.
    50, 7 pp.

(8) McMURTREY, J. E., JR.
    1929. THE EFFECT OF BORON DEFICIENCY ON THE GROWTH OF TOBACCO PLANTS IN AERATED
    AND UNAERATED SOLUTIONS. Jour. Agr. Res. 38:371–380, illus.

(9) ——
    1933. DISTINCTIVE EFFECTS OF THE DEFICIENCY OF CERTAIN ESSENTIAL ELEMENTS ON
    THE GROWTH OF TOBACCO PLANTS IN SOLUTION CULTURES. U. S. Dept. Agr.
    Tech. Bul. 340, 43 pp., illus.

(10) ——
    1935. BORON DEFICIENCY IN TOBACCO UNDER FIELD CONDITIONS. Jour. Amer. Soc.
    Agron. 27:271–273, illus.

(11) ——
    1937. CROSS TRANSFER OF MINERAL NUTRIENTS IN THE TOBACCO PLANT. Jour. Agr. Res.
    55:475–482, illus.

(12) ——
    1938. DISTINCTIVE PLANT SYMPTOMS CAUSED BY DEFICIENCY OF ANY ONE OF THE CHEM-
    ICAL ELEMENTS ESSENTIAL FOR NORMAL DEVELOPMENT. Bot. Rev. 4:183–203,
    illus.

(13) ——
    1938. SYMPTOMS ON FIELD-GROWN TOBACCO CHARACTERISTIC OF THE DEFICIENT SUPPLY
    OF EACH OF SEVERAL ESSENTIAL CHEMICAL ELEMENTS. U. S. Dept. Agr. Tech.
    Bul. 612, 31 pp., illus.

(14) —— LUNN, W. M., and BROWN, D. E.
    1934. FERTILIZER TESTS WITH TOBACCO, WITH SPECIAL REFERENCE TO EFFECTS OF DIF-
    FERENT RATES AND SOURCES OF NITROGEN AND POTASH. Md. Agr. Expt. Sta.
    Bul. 358, pp. 255–290, illus.

(15) —— ROBINSON, W. O.
    1938. NEGLECTED SOIL CONSTITUENTS THAT AFFECT PLANT AND ANIMAL DEVELOPMENT.
    U. S. Dept. Agr. Yearbook 1938:807-829, illus.

(16) Moss, E. G., McMurtrey, J. E., Jr., Lunn, W. M., and Carr, J. M.
    1927. FERTILIZER TESTS WITH FLUE-CURED TOBACCO. U. S. Dept. Agr. Tech. Bul. 12, 59 pp., illus.

(17) Wilfarth, H., and Wimmer, G.
    1902. DIE WIRKUNG DES KALIUMS AUF DAS PFLANZENLEBEN NACH VEGETATIONS-VERSUCHEN MIT KARTOFFELN, TABAK, BUCHWEIZEN, SENF, ZICHORIEN UND HAFER. Arb. Deut. Landw. Gesell. 68, 106 pp., illus.

Plate 1.—A tobacco plant grown under conditions of nitrogen shortage. Note the light-green color and the firing of the lower leaves.

Plate 2.—Symptoms of phosphorus deficiency in tobacco. Note the abnormally dark-green color and erect position of the leaves.

Plate 3.—A tobacco plant suffering from potassium hunger. Note the loss of color at tips and margins of leaves and the spots of dead tissue associated with cupping under of leaves.

Plate 4.—A, Potassium hunger in tobacco. Left, leaf from base of plant already has a ragged appearance. Center, leaf from higher up is less affected. Right, leaf from still nearer the top has just begun to be affected.

Plate 4.—B, Magnesium deficiency in tobacco. Four leaves, from the base of the plant upward (left to right), showing stages in loss of color. The lower leaves are the first to be affected.

Plate 5.—Magnesium deficiency (sand drown) in tobacco. Note the loss of color in the lower leaves, especially at tips and margins.

Plate 6.—A, Tobacco seedlings from plant bed. Plant 2, from untreated portion of seedbed, shows magnesium-deficiency symptoms. Plant 1 is normal 2 weeks after the soil was treated with 4 pounds of Epsom salts per 100 square yards. Compare the color and root development of the two plants.

Plate 6.—B, Tobacco leaves suffering from two mineral deficiencies: 1, Iron; note the loss of color except along the principal veins; 3, manganese; note the checkered appearance and associated dead spots. 2 is a leaf from a normal plant.

[48]

Plate 7.—Tobacco plant suffering from calcium shortage. The young leaves are distorted, while the older, lower leaves look normal.

Plate 8.—Boron shortage in tobacco. Note distorted upper leaves and dead terminal bud.

1   2

Plate 9.—A, Dwarfing, light-green color, and dead tissues due to manganese deficiency are shown in 2; 1 is a normal tobacco plant.

1   2

Plate 9.—B, Hands of cured tobacco, Maryland type. 1, from normal plants; 2, from plants suffering from manganese shortage—note the lack of desirable color and the spots.

A

B

Plate 10.—A is a normal tobacco plant. B shows the reduced growth and crimping downward of leaves at tips characteristic of sulfur shortage.

Plate 11.—Iron chlorosis in tobacco. A is a normal plant. B was grown in a sand culture to which no iron was added; note loss of color in the upper leaves.

Plate 12.—Tobacco plants grown in sand culture, with zinc (A) and without zinc (B). Note the loss of color and the spotting of leaf tissues in B.

CHAPTER III

Deficiency Symptoms of Corn
and Small Grains

By George N. Hoffer [1]

SOMEONE has said, "If starved plants could only squeal like hungry pigs, we would pay more attention to their fertilizer needs."

Fields of healthy, vigorous corn and of wheat or other small grains indicate high soil fertility. In some cases, it is true, higher yields may be obtained from new strains of hybrid corn or from improved varieties of small grains than from older strains or varieties grown at similar levels of soil fertility. The range of adaptation of these improved varieties to variations in the amounts of available plant nutrients may be very wide. Yet it is not indefinitely so. Sooner or later all varieties are affected by limitations in the amounts of the plant nutrients that are available in the soil.

All crops require at least 10 or more different plantfood elements, and when the available supply of any one of these becomes exhausted, growth is seriously impeded. The symptoms of a deficiency may be regarded as the "language" the plants use to indicate the nature of the distress affecting them (fig. 1). In some ways these symptoms afford a better understanding of the nutrition relationships between soil and plant than can be obtained from detailed chemical analyses of the soil. Whenever possible, dominant symptoms of plant-nutrient deficiencies in corn and small grains should be translated into plans for corrective practices in the soil-management program.

Yet it is difficult at times to interpret the symptoms of plantfood deficiencies in the field because so many environmental factors constantly affect the plants. Prolonged periods of adverse growing weather may harm corn plants, and severe winters may adversely affect winter grains. Insect and fungus diseases may make inroads on the crops and cause difficulties in the interpretation of deficiency symptoms. Diseases, insects, and unfavorable weather are all likely to be most harmful to plants already weakened by malnutrition, complicating the symptoms in the field. For these reasons it is

[1] George N. Hoffer, formerly Professor of Plant Physiology, Purdue University Agricultural Experiment Station, is now Manager of the Midwest Office, American Potash Institute, Inc.

necessary to study typical deficiency symptoms in plants grown under controlled nutrient conditions in the greenhouse and in the experimental plots of agricultural experiment stations.

The most common symptoms in corn and small grains at the present time are those caused by deficiencies in the supplies of nitrogen, phosphorus, potassium, and magnesium. Deficiencies of calcium and boron have not been reported in the field. Deficiencies of zinc and manganese occur in relatively small local areas.

Figure 1.—Learning the "language" of hungry corn plants is first aid in correcting your soil-fertility problems.

Nitrogen-starvation symptoms are shown by corn plants in practically all parts of the country. Nitrogen is commonly deficient in the sandy soils of the South. Phosphorus, as well as nitrogen, is deficient in most acid soils. Practically all muck and high-lime soils, and most sandy soils, are deficient in potash, which is needed generally in the soils in the Southern States as well as in many soils in the Midwest that have been limed, treated with phosphate, and planted to legumes. Besides these obvious examples, there are many soils of good original fertility which, through erosion, leaching, crop removal, and mismanagement, are now coming to need replenishment of their plantfoods.

On many farms the benefits from liming acid soils to obtain better responses to applied phosphates and to favor nitrification and the growth of legumes have been proved repeatedly. The value of manure is unquestioned. The introduction of legumes into the rotation is important. Even though these crops require plantfood materials in large quantities, they serve as a connecting link between the vast reserves of free nitrogen in the air and the fixed nitrogen demanded by other crops in the rotation; and they accomplish this best when properly inoculated and well fertilized. Plowed under, they enhance the tilth of the soil and supply an abundance of organic matter with a high mineral content for subsequent crops in the rotation.

DIFFERENCES IN PLANTS AS INDICATORS OF PLANTFOOD DEFICIENCIES

Some crop plants are better indicators of plant-nutrient deficiencies than others. The broad leaves of the tobacco plant are especially reliable indicators of the state of health of the plant. The symptoms of plant-nutrient deficiencies in tobacco are definite and readily recognized. Corn plants with their wide expanse of leaves appear to be more sensitive to changes in the supplies of available plant nutrients than are the small-grain plants with their smaller and narrower leaves. Thus corn plants in rotation with other crops serve as an excellent indicator of the fertility of the fields in which they are growing.

Though small grains in the rotation also may show signs of deficient soil fertility, their symptoms are, as a rule, less striking and more difficult to interpret than those of corn. Late frosts in the spring, prolonged wet periods, and insect invasions often have damaging effects on the small-grain plants and make it difficult to diagnose the disturbance as definitely due to malnutrition. For these reasons the symptoms shown by corn plants will be discussed at length while those of the small grains will receive only general attention.

VALUE OF CHEMICAL TISSUE TESTS

It has been found by experience that the use of simple qualitative chemical tests for the presence of nitrates, inorganic phosphates, and potassium salts in the tissues of corn and small-grain plants aids greatly in the field diagnosis of the symptoms induced by deficiencies of these plantfood materials. When well nourished and in good health, corn and small-grain plants carry reserves of these salts in their tissues during the active growing season, and the presence of such reserves is indicated by the tests. When plants are starved for any of these nutrients, the tissue tests are negative and confirm the symptoms indicating deficiency.

These chemical tests are invaluable for use in the field when other complicating factors due to climate, disease, or insects are involved. The tests can be used at any time during the growing season. Their use will be discussed in connection with the diagnosis of deficiency symptoms. The tests themselves and the preparation of the chemical reagents will be described at the end of the chapter, page 81.

The best background for the diagnosis of deficiencies of the major nutrients is good field experience and the ability gained from it to evaluate all of the factors influencing the growth of corn plants. When this experience is supplemented with the information gained by making comparative chemical tissue tests on the highest yielding strains of corn plants and those growing under deficient nutrient conditions, a firmer basis is established for planning changes in the soil-management and fertilizer programs.

No attempt has been made to prepare a key for the classification of the symptoms of plant-nutrient deficiencies in corn and small grains based on external symptoms only, because of the difficulties of interpreting them without the supplementary use of the tissue tests. Sometime later it may become possible to reduce them to a key, when further research contributes new chemical tests for other plant nutrients for use in the field.

PRODUCTION OF TYPICAL SYMPTOMS IN CONTROLLED NUTRIENT CULTURES

Thornton and his associates in the Department of Agronomy, Purdue University Agricultural Experiment Station, while conducting a greenhouse experiment in which a Crosby silt-loam soil of low fertility was used, made a comparative study of the symptoms occurring in many common plants induced by deficiencies of nitrogen, phosphorus, and potassium. Photographs of the results of these studies with corn, wheat, oats, barley, and rye are used to illustrate the symptoms found in the young plants.

The symptoms shown by corn plants are so striking that it is believed important to use them in determining plantfood needs not only for the corn crop but also for the other crops in the same rotation. It has been found that when the corn crop suffers from a lack of essential plant nutrients, all of the other crops in the rotation will also respond to applications of the deficient nutrients.

DEFICIENCY SYMPTOMS IN CORN

Plate 1, A, page 87, shows typical symptoms of nitrogen, phosphorus, and potassium deficiencies in young corn plants grown under controlled conditions in the greenhouse. The healthy plants in the last pot to the right were fertilized with a complete fertilizer, and serve as a check for comparison. Nitrogen was omitted in the first pot, but phosphate and potash were supplied. In the second pot no phosphate was applied, and in the third, no potash. Comparison of each of these pots with the plants that received complete fertilizer shows the relative importance of nitrogen, phosphate, and potash in this particular soil. In other soils, of course, the relative importance of these major plant nutrients might be quite different. The general symptoms of deficiencies, however, would be the same.

NITROGEN

Nitrogen enters into the composition of many organic compounds in the plant. As an essential element in protein, it is needed for the growth and development of all of the living tissues. The total amount of nitrogen in corn and small-grain plants is greater than that of most of the other elements. But free atmospheric nitrogen cannot be used by the plants here discussed. It must be supplied chiefly in the form of nitrates, or as ammonia-nitrogen, and it should be available throughout the growing season.

The importance of nitrogen for the growth of young corn plants is well demonstrated by comparing the plants not supplied with nitrates (PK) and the plants supplied with complete fertilizer (NPK) in plate 1, A. The nitrogen-starved plants were supplied with the same quantities of phosphates and potash as were those in the NPK pot. In the PK pot the typical symptoms of nitrogen starvation were produced. The plants were stunted and spindling. The leaves became greenish yellow to orange yellow in color, the tip ends gradually dying. Severe nitrogen starvation is indicated by these leaf symptoms.

When nitrogen deficiencies occur later in the growth of corn plants in the field, similar leaf symptoms develop, as shown in plate 1, B. The yellowing of the tissues occurs first in the older leaves and follows the midrib from the leaf tip. Later the tip begins to dry and the whole leaf may become involved, showing an effect frequently referred to as "firing." This symptom is often found in sandy soils in dry weather; even in muck soils during a prolonged hot, dry period the plants may become definitely starved for nitrogen. Nitrogen-starved plants up to the stage of growth shown in plate 1, B, may be benefited by application of nitrogen fertilizers.

When corn plants are suffering from a lack of water, the tissues wither and dry out without the leaves necessarily becoming yellow. Yellowish-green to yellow leaves almost invariably indicate nitrogen hunger. In certain cases, however, they may be due to phosphorus starvation.

When the foliage symptoms of corn plants indicate a possible deficiency of nitrogen, a quick confirmation can be obtained by testing the plant tissues for the presence of nitrates, as described at the end of this chapter, page 81. If the tissues from plants with yellowish-green or yellow leaves contain nitrates, obviously there can be no deficiency of available nitrogen in the soil and the symptoms must be caused by some factor other than nitrogen starvation. Yellowish corn leaves are sometimes found to contain an abundance of nitrates under certain conditions of phosphorus starvation. Apparently the nitrates in these plants cannot be assimilated without adequate phosphates in the tissues. This relation has been described by DeTurk (7),[2] and is illustrated in plate 2, C, page 88, under phosphorus-deficiency symptoms.

By using the chemical tissue test for nitrates many interesting relations between the corn plants and their environment are discovered. Some of these relations are as follows: (1) Many weeds growing adjacent to corn plants frequently will accumulate nitrates while the corn plants will starve for nitrogen. Comparative tests on corn, pigweed, smartweed, and other associated plants supply ample reasons for controlling weeds in corn fields other than to conserve moisture. The competition of weeds for plant nutrients often becomes serious in cornfields. (2) When corn is planted too thickly in hills, comparative tests on plants from these hills with those from hills containing one or two plants only, usually show that the overcrowded plants are starved for nitrogen. (3) If the soil is acid, comparative tests on corn plants from limed and unlimed areas will show the effects of liming on nitrification.

When young corn plants show symptoms definitely diagnosed as due to nitrogen starvation, use nitrogen fertilizers for side dressing the plants if they can be applied before the last cultivation. Use

[2] Italic numbers in parentheses refer to Literature Cited, p. 85.

a quickly available nitrogen carrier so as to apply 40 to 50 pounds of nitrogen per acre along the row. Subsequent nitrate tissue tests will indicate when the proper amounts of nitrogen fertilizers have been used to correct the deficiency.

Nitrogen-starved corn plants show better than any other crop in the rotation that the organic matter in the soil is too low and that the failure to turn under legumes, or the absence of legumes in the rotation, may be responsible for the lack of sufficient organic matter and fixed nitrogen to meet the needs of the nonleguminous crops in the rotation. In fertile soils nitrogen is obtained in abundance from the decomposing organic matter.

Phosphorus

It is definitely known that all plant cells contain phosphorus compounds and that they are necessary for the cell division which results in the growth of the plants. Phosphorus is concentrated in the growing tissues in the tips of roots and shoots. It is found also in the developing kernels of grain, and when corn plants approaching maturity become starved for phosphorus, the developing seeds will accumulate this nutrient at the expense of all the mature tissues. Phosphorus is necessary, therefore, for the reproduction of these plants.

It is difficult to describe definite symptoms indicating phosphorus deficiency in corn. A retarded rate of growth and slow maturity of the plant are the chief symptoms, especially when other nutrients, such as nitrogen and potassium, are shown to be available in sufficient quantities. This effect of phosphorus starvation in delaying maturity is particularly noticeable during the pollination stage. When the silks emerge slowly, defective types of ears are produced. Such ears are imperfectly pollinated and show rows of unfertilized seed rudiments. Figure 2 shows defective ears from plants starved for phosphorus during the later stages of growth. Note the irregularly formed rows of kernels.

In plate 1, A, the young corn plants not supplied with phosphorus (NK) are spindling and dark green, and the leaves and stems have a tendency to become purplish. The purplish color in plate 3, page 89, is due, according to DeTurk (7), to the effect of accumulated sugars on the formation of the purple pigment, anthocyanin. The accumulation of sugars is due to phosphorus deficiency, but the color itself is also dependent on the presence of the genetic factor for purple-pigment production in the particular strain of corn affected. DeTurk has kindly supplied the two colored prints shown in plate 4, page 90. The plants were grown in controlled nutrient-solution cultures. Note that none of the plants of strain CC5 in plate 4, A, show any purpling of the leaves, even when they received only 5 parts of phosphorus per million of total solution. In plate 4, B, the plants of inbred Hy, also with 5 parts per million, are strongly purple. These differences in response are found to be

Figure 2.—Ears produced on slowly growing, phosphorus-hungry plants are often imperfectly pollinated because of the delayed emergence of the silks. Dropped rows of kernels result.

common in other strains of corn and show that the purple coloring is limited to strains with the proper genetic constitution for its formation.

Unfavorable growing conditions such as a prolonged period of cool weather in the spring may cause a similar purpling in young plants. In this case it may be more or less temporary, but it has been reported frequently during cool weather in the northern parts of the Corn Belt.

DeTurk (7) has reported that under conditions of severe phosphorus starvation the leaves of young corn plants may display symptoms very similar to those induced by nitrogen deficiencies, as shown in plate 2, C. Chemical tests of these tissues showed that they contained an abundance of nitrates. Phosphorus is necessary for the assimilation of the nitrates, and the plant tissues actually starve for nitrogen even though they contain the nitrate salts.   The interrelation of these two plant nutrients is readily observed when tissue tests for both nitrates and phosphates are made on the plants. Thus a high nitrate and a negative phosphate test reflect a deficiency of available phosphorus even though the foliage symptoms indicate nitrogen hunger. Tissue tests often relieve the confusion from interpreting symptoms solely on the basis of foliage characteristics.

Because of such uncertainties, symptoms of phosphorus hunger in corn plants should be confirmed by chemical tests on the plant tissues for the presence or absence of reserve quantities of inorganic phosphates.   Corn plants utilize these phosphates rapidly, and in vigorously growing plants small reserves only may be found.   The avidity with which young corn and small-grain plants draw upon the supply of phosphates in the soil for their early growth and establishment of their root systems makes it imperative that an abundant supply be available.   It explains the almost unfailing early response of these crops to phosphatic fertilizers properly applied.   Conversely, an early retardation in the growth of the plants almost always reflects a phosphorus deficiency.

Since inorganic phosphates are combined very rapidly into organic compounds in corn plants, and these are utilized to build up new plant parts and finally the mature grain, a reserve supply of inorganic phosphates in the plants is necessary throughout the growing season.   Whether a reserve is present at any particular time can be detected readily by relatively simple chemical tests (27) in the cornfield, as described on page 81.

The tissue tests can be made on plants at any stage of growth and much practical information on the relative availability of phosphates in different soils can be gained from them.   They serve to check on the effectiveness of applied phosphatic fertilizers.   Very often the amounts of phosphates supplied are insufficient for the best growth and maturing of the corn crop.

The relative effectiveness of using phosphates in the row compared with broadcasting and plowing under can also be shown by testing the plants during the growing season.   In such studies the chief differences in the appearance of the plants may be in their size.   Small plants may appear healthy otherwise, but the more rapid, sturdier growth of other plants in the same field may be explained by the larger quantities of inorganic phosphates found in their tissues.

On soils alkaline in reaction, however, poor growth may be due not to lack of phosphorus but to a deficiency of one or more of the so-called minor or trace elements; manganese and boron are sometimes needed to balance the plantfood supply and enable the plants to grow normally. In acid soils the phosphates may be fixed in combinations with iron and aluminum. Chemical tests on the tissues tell at once whether phosphates have been absorbed.

POTASSIUM

Investigations show that potassium is intimately related to the production of sugars, starches, cellulose, and proteins in plants, yet, so far as is known, it does not enter permanently into the composition of any of these organic compounds. It is needed in all processes of growth of the plant cells and also influences their rate of respiration. Potassium helps to protect plants from excessive losses of water during periods of drought, and it lessens the injuries due to low temperatures. Potassium salts move readily from one part of the plant to another, and because of this mobility the symptoms of potassium hunger appear first in the oldest leaves. The younger parts of the plant draw the potassium away from these older parts (*16*).

Potassium salts are needed in abundance for the normal growth and development of the corn plant from the time the seed germinates until the plant is matured and the next generation is provided for in the new set of seeds. Healthy, vigorous corn plants always contain large amounts of potassium salts in their tissues, whether in the seedling stage or in plants approaching maturity.

Eckstein, Bruno, and Turrentine (*8*) have described the symptoms of potash deficiencies of all commercially important crops.

The supply of available potash in the soil may become acutely deficient at any stage of growth of the corn plant. The signs of hunger may appear in the seedlings or young plants, or they may not become apparent until the plants are approaching maturity. The symptoms will be described as they appear at different stages of growth of the plants.

In Young Plants

The first symptom of potassium deficiency is a diminution in the rate of growth of the seedlings and young plants. Soon definite leaf characteristics develop that point to potassium starvation. The young leaves are yellowish green to yellow in color, or sometimes only streaked with yellow. The edges and tips become dry and appear scorched or fired. These early symptoms are shown in plate 5, A, page 91.

When the deficiency of available potash is less acute, though growth is retarded, the leaf symptoms may not appear until the plants are further developed. In plate 1, A, the plants growing in the pot without potash (except what was originally in the soil) are just beginning to show the marginal scorch symptom. The plants are severely stunted in contrast with those in the pot with complete fertilizer.

When the foliage symptoms of potassium starvation are recognized early in the growth of corn plants, it is possible and profitable to apply muriate of potash in the row or hill and correct the deficiency. The application should be made prior to the last cultivation, and it is suggested that 150 to 200 pounds of muriate of potash per acre be used. In 15 experiments in Iowa in 1935 on high-lime soils, an average increase of 12.8 bushels was obtained by side dressing the young corn plants with muriate of potash at the rate of 200 pounds per acre. In southern Illinois, during the same season, an average increase of 8.2 bushels was obtained in three tests on acid, poorly drained soils (12). Each year since then profitable responses have been obtained by similar treatments (18).

In Older Plants

As the plants increase in size, the need for potassium increases, and if the supply becomes inadequate, foliage symptoms similar to those found in younger plants appear. The leaves are streaked with yellow or yellowish green, and the edges are dry and scorched. This marginal scorch (plate 6, C, page 92) is the outstanding leaf symptom. In severe cases the leaves become badly damaged and the growth of the plants is dwarfed because the tissues between the nodes do not develop fully. In the plant in plate 7, page 93, all of the leaves show the marginal firing. The plant is weak. Only small areas of the leaves remain green and in condition to manufacture carbohydrate foods for the developing ears. If these plants produce ears, they are usually chaffy nubbins of low feed value. The tip ends of the ears are unfilled; the kernels that do form are poorly matured and starchy, and they easily become infected with ear-rot organisms, which often affects germination detrimentally. Ears from potassium-starved plants are shown in figure 3.

Figure 4 shows the characteristic differences between nitrogen- and potassium-starved corn plants. Nitrogen-starved plants grow spindling and the leaves are yellowish green to yellowish orange in color. The oldest leaves become dry and appear fired as shown in plates 1, B, and 6, B. The potassium-starved plants are dwarfed in size, the leaves appear to be too long for the stalks, and they are affected by the typical marginal scorch. Such plants become weak and lodge badly because of a defective root system.

Figure 3.—A, Ears on plants receiving complete fertilizer. B, Potassium-starved ears from plants receiving nitrogen and phosphorus only are of low feed quality.

Hoffer (15) has shown that iron compounds accumulate in the tissues of the joints of corn plants when the supply of available soil potash is deficient. The iron accumulations are seen when the plants are split open lengthwise and an acidulated solution of potassium thiocyanate (see page 84) is applied to the

Figure 4.—Nitrogen-hungry plants grow spindling and tall. Potassium-starved plants have relatively short internodes and are dwarfed. The leaves appear too long for the height of the plant.

exposed joint tissues. The amount of iron accumulated at the points shown in figure 5 is determined by the amount of potassium salts in the plant sap. When potassium is entirely lacking, the purplish-red color is intense. These iron accumulations disrupt the translocation of foods from the leaves to the roots, and the latter are starved and weakened. They then become predisposed to injuries by many of the fungi or molds inhabiting soils in which corn has been grown for some time. When the roots become sufficiently rotted the weakened plants may lodge so badly that they lie flat on the ground. Lodging of corn plants, as shown in figure 6, is an important symptom indicating a deficiency of available potash in the soil. Heavy accumulations of iron compounds in the joint tissues confirm the symptom.

Healthy, vigorous plants always contain potassium salts in the leaves and stalk tissues in quantities that can be detected by simple chemical tests adapted for use in the field (p. 82). A negative test indicates a definite deficiency even before the appearance of the foliage symptoms. Many investigators have found that the content of potassium in the sap of the corn plant reflects the relative availability of this element in the soil. Tests are often needed to distinguish potassium-deficiency symptoms from those induced by bacterial wilt (Stewart's disease) and the leaf disease caused by *Helminthosporium* species. If potassium is present in diseased plants showing symptoms resembling potassium starvation, it eliminates a deficiency of potassium as a contributing factor.

The recognition of symptoms of potassium starvation late in the development of the plant is important even though nothing can be done to benefit the current crop. The symptoms are useful in formulating plans for the management of these fields in the future.

It is true that potassium becomes available slowly in many soils, but researches by Bray (3), in Illinois, show that there is no way of increasing the rate of liberation of potassium in depleted soils enough to meet the requirements of the corn crop satisfactorily. It has been proved also that when the corn crop suffers from a lack of enough available potassium for normal growth and production, all of the other crops in the same rotation will also respond to potash fertilization. In many fields where limestone and phosphate have been used for growing legumes in the rotation with corn, potash deficiencies are appearing because of the large quantities of potassium removed in the increased hay and grain yields.

Figure 5.—When chemical tests are used to confirm nutrient-deficiency symptoms in the field, they are made on corn-plant tissues as indicated. Tests for potassium are made on the tissues in the base of the leaves; iron accumulations in the joint tissues indicate potassium starvation also. Tests for nitrates are made on the internodal tissues throughout the plant. Tests for phosphorus are made on stalk tissues just below the tassels.

Magnesium

Magnesium is a component of the chlorophyll molecule, the green pigment in all plants.   The salts of magnesium are mobile and distributed throughout the entire plant.   The younger parts of the plant may draw on the older parts for magnesium when the soil supply becomes low, and this relation helps to explain the type of symptoms that result.

Figure 6.—Plants in foreground are starved for potassium.   Weak stalks result when the available potassium in the soil becomes depleted by crop removals in a rotation following limestone and phosphorus fertilization.

The symptoms in corn are definite and easily recognized.   When the supply of magnesium becomes deficient, the chlorophyll in the oldest leaves reflects the trouble first.   Here a slight yellow streaking develops between the parallel veins in the leaves. With the continued migration of magnesium from the older leaves to the younger parts of the plant, there is a definite and sharply defined series of yellowish-green, light-yellow, or even white streaks extending the entire length of the leaves.   With an acute deficiency, these streaked tissues may dry up and die, and all of the leaves ultimately may show the streaking.   Plate 5, B, shows these symptoms as they appear in a mature plant.

Magnesium deficiency in corn has been reported from various parts of the Southern States and has also been found in Massachusetts (*17*).   In some cases the deficiency is believed to be intensified by the unbalanced plant-nutrient conditions resulting from the continued use of sodium salts in fertilizing other crops in the corn rotation (4).

Magnesium-deficiency symptoms may become prevalent in parts of the Corn Belt and should be watched for in the more acid, unlimed soils. Usually, however, nitrogen and phosphorus deficiencies occur in these acid soils, and until they are corrected the magnesium deficiency may not become dominant. The use of dolomitic limestones for other crops in the rotation has no doubt delayed the appearance of magnesium-deficiency symptoms in corn plants in many localities.

Calcium

Calcium is essential for the growth and development of corn plants. Some of it becomes permanently fixed in various tissues of the plants. The leaves contain the largest quantities, less is found in the stems and roots, and the least amounts are in the grain and cob. Numerous roles have been ascribed to calcium, although some are little understood. Calcium influences the translocation of foods manufactured in the plants and the physiological availability of other nutrient elements, and it acts as a neutralizing agent preventing the accumulation of toxic materials in plant tissues.

The corn crop grows mostly on soils that are only slightly acid or that have been limed for other crops in the rotation, and consequently it has suffered little if any from a deficiency of calcium. No definite symptoms of calcium deficiencies have been described in corn growing in the field.

DeTurk[3] has produced calcium-deficiency symptoms in corn plants growing in controlled nutrient cultures. Young plants show very distinct symptoms. The tips of the unfolding leaves gelatinize, and when dry they stick together. As the plant continues to grow, the tip ends of the leaves form the pattern shown in plate 2, B.

In these investigations DeTurk has shown also that some strains of corn can tolerate a deficiency of available calcium better than others. Figures 7 and 8 show the difference between an inbred strain of yellow dent corn and an open pollinated yellow variety. Fifty parts per million of calcium were necessary for the inbred strain to grow normally, while only 10 parts were needed by the open-pollinated variety. These physiological differences in response may explain the wide variations in adaptation that some strains of corn possess, particularly in open-pollinated varieties.

[3] Private correspondence with the author, 1940.

Courtesy of E. E. DeTurk, University of Illinois

Figure 7.—Calcium hunger. Yellow dent corn, inbred Tr, has a high calcium requirement. With 10 and 25 parts of calcium per million each plant shows the tip ends of the leaves gummed together. With 50 parts of calcium per million the plants appear normal.

Courtesy of E. E. DeTurk, University of Illinois

Figure 8.—Calcium hunger. The open-pollinated strain of Reid Yellow Dent corn used in this experiment has a low calcium requirement. Plants grow well with 10 and 25 parts of calcium per million. Compare these plants with those in figure 7.

BORON

Boron salts are readily fixed in plants, and they are relatively immobile in comparison with salts of potassium, magnesium, and phosphorus. A continuous supply during the growth of the plants is necessary. Boron is required in small amounts by most plants and has a place in the fertilization of fruit, truck, and field crops that is becoming increasingly important. The demands of the corn crop and of cereals in general seem to be lower than those of such crops as the legumes, tomatoes, and sugar beets in the same rotation with them. No reports on boron-deficiency symptoms of corn occurring in the field have been noted to date, although there is no reason to believe that they may not be found after laboratory studies and soil and tissue tests provide the means for recognizing them.

Pettinger, Henderson, and Wingard (*22*) attribute a type of sterility in corn to boron starvation. Sand cultures were used in their experiments.

Eltinge (*9*) describes the effect of boron deficiency on the corn plant as causing a thickening and brittleness of the roots. The leaves of the young plants do not unroll and the leaf tissues break down.

Ferguson and Wright (*11*), working with sand cultures, found that a deficiency of boron caused no external symptoms on Golden Bantam sweet-corn plants, but the ears showed a marked corky brown band extending along the outer edge of the cobs at the base of the kernels. Cobs of plants supplied with boron had a clean, healthy, greenish-white color.

J. W. Shive, of the New Jersey Agricultural Experiment Station, has kindly submitted a photograph of corn leaves (fig. 9) taken from boron-starved plants grown in pot-culture tests conducted by him. A normal leaf (A) is compared with the boron-deficient leaf (B), showing wide white stripes between the veins. These stripes are formed by the coalescence of small, white, elongated spots between the veins. The younger leaves on these plants are dwarfed, and when the older leaves are stripped back the tissues of these younger leaves are seen to be white and the growing tips dead. When the amount of boron exceeded the normal requirement of the corn plant, toxicity resulted and the symptoms produced were very similar to those induced by potash starvation. The edges of the leaves (fig. 9, D) became brown and appeared scorched.

ZINC

"White bud" of corn plants is a type of chlorosis frequently found in fields in constant cultivation in central, north, and northwest Florida. Zinc sulfate applied to corn in these acid mineral soils will correct the chlorosis and give increased yields of corn. Barnette, Camp, Warner, and Gall (2) describe the symptoms shown by seedlings as follows:

Figure 9.—Corn leaves. A, Normal leaf. B, Boron-starved plant; youngest leaves and tip of shoot dying. C, Older leaves develop yellowish-white stripes. D, Boron toxicity causes an edge "scorch," very similar in appearance to a symptom of potassium starvation.

Courtesy of J. W. Shive, New Jersey Agricultural Experiment Station

In affected soil areas symptoms of white bud begin to appear within a week or two after the emergence of the corn seedlings. The full development of the chlorophyll in the older leaves of the seedlings scarcely takes place before light yellow streaks appear between the veins. Small white spots of inactive or dead tissue develop rapidly in the leaves, while some small white areas that never have chlorophyll are present. The unfolding buds have leaves that are white to light yellow in color. This latter characteristic has given rise to the use of the term "white bud" by farmers.

Plate 2, A, shows a zinc-starved corn plant. The lower leaves have died and the upper leaves show yellow striping between the veins, while the inner, youngest leaves are practically white. The internodes of the plant are definitely shortened and the growth is stunted.

No reports of zinc deficiencies in the Corn Belt States have been noted to date.

DEFICIENCY SYMPTOMS IN SMALL GRAINS (WHEAT, OATS,
BARLEY, RYE)

The common symptoms induced by deficiencies of nitrogen, phosphorus, and potassium in wheat, oats, barley, and rye are in many respects similar for all these crops. The symptoms displayed by young plants only will be described for two reasons: (1) Unless the symptoms are recognized before the plants are 6 or 8 inches in height, no remedial practices can be used that will benefit the crop; and (2) the symptoms shown by older plants in the process of

Courtesy of Purdue University Agricultural Experiment Station

Figure 10.—Wheat in Crosby silt loam of low fertility. Pot 20 (NPK), which received complete fertilizer, serves as check; plants healthy and vigorous. Pot 17 (PK), nitrogen starvation; plants stunted, greenish yellow, with weak purplish stems. Pot 18 (NK), phosphorus starvation; plants dark green, leaves purplish-tinged. Pot 19 (NP), potassium deficiency; dark-green, weak plants, with oldest leaves yellowish brown and tip ends deadened.

heading out or later are often so complicated by diseases and other factors that it is difficult to attribute them definitely to malnutrition.

Figures 10, 11, 12, and 13 show wheat, oat, barley, and rye plants, respectively, growing in pot cultures which received the same treatments given the corn plants in plate 1, A. In each case the plants that were given complete fertilizer (NPK) serve as a check for comparison with those in the other pots in which one plant nutrient was omitted.

In the field, because of the density of growth of the small grains, deficiency symptoms are reflected by many plants in a mass. The most readily identified symptoms are those resulting in differences in the color and height of the plants, their stooling ability, and the strength of the stalks.   No attempt will be made to classify the causes of different types of shriveled grain.

The chief ultimate value of determining the causes of deficiency symptoms in the small grains is the information gained for correcting the soil-management program for all crops in the rotation with these small grains.   It is important that symptoms be diagnosed carefully before any remedial measures are considered.

Courtesy of Purdue University Agricultural Experiment Station

Figure 11.—Oats in Crosby silt loam of low fertility. Pot 16 (NPK) received complete fertilizer, serves as check; plants healthy and vigorous. Pot 13 (PK), nitrogen starvation; plants spindling, yellowish green, slightly purplish stems. Pot 14 (NK), phosphorus starvation; plants dark green, stems weak, slightly purplish-tinged. Pot 15 (NP), potassium deficiency; dark-green, weak plants, with oldest leaves brown and tip ends deadened.

At best the leaf symptoms displayed can be interpreted only with difficulty, because there are so many factors to complicate them. Valuable help is obtained in determining the nutrient needs of these crops by making comparative tissue tests for nitrates, inorganic phosphates, and potassium on healthy plants of high-yielding varieties and those showing defective growth in different fields, or even in the same field (p. 83).   The comparative tests will invariably give the clue to the nutrient deficiency.   It is particularly instructive to determine the causes of different kinds of lodging induced by deficient or unbalanced supplies of nutrients; to check on the relation of available phosphates to stooling; to study the nitrogen-potassium relations to the incidence of rusts, mildews, and other diseases.   Field chemical tests are also useful at times in interpreting a lack of response of these crops to fertilizers improperly applied.

NITROGEN

The plants in the PK pots in figures 10, 11, 12, and 13 are all starved for nitrogen. In the case of the spring-planted oats (fig. 11) and barley (fig. 12), the plants are erect and spindling, the leaves are yellowish green to yellow, and the stems are purplish green. In

Courtesy of Purdue University Agricultural Experiment Station

Figure 12.—Barley in Crosby silt loam of low fertility. Pot 4 (NPK) received complete fertilizer, serves as check; plants healthy and vigorous. Pot 1 (PK), nitrogen starvation; plants spindling, yellowish green. Pot 2 (NK), phosphorus starvation; plants dark green and leaves slightly tinged with purple along the edges. Pot 3 (NP), potassium deficiency; plants normal green, with decidedly weak stems; oldest leaves with tip ends yellow brown and "fired."

the case of wheat (fig. 10) and rye (fig. 13), the plants are stunted and yellowish green in color. Yellowish-green color is common to all of these nitrogen-starved crops. Plate 8, A, page 94, shows a nitrogen-starved leaf from an oat plant; it is yellow and the tissues are drying out from the tip toward the base. This leaf symptom is the same for wheat (plate 10, B, page 96) and for barley and rye.

Cool, wet weather during the early spring inhibits the formation of available nitrogen in the soil. Often plowing under corn and other crop residues results in starving the newly seeded oats or barley for nitrogen, because the bacteria active in the decomposition of the organic matter use what little nitrogen is available in the soil and none is left for the new plants until nitrification becomes active in warm weather. Plate 9, A, page 95, shows a field of oats seriously handicapped by nitrogen deficiency. The turned-under corn stubble contained no reserve nitrates to benefit the oat crop. When the previous corn crop was amply supplied with nitrates, a "corduroy" effect is noted in small-grain fields—the plant nutrients leach from the corn residues and fertilize the adjacent oat or barley plants.

Another common demonstration of nitrogen deficiency occurs when small grains are seeded in fields that were in pasture the

Courtesy of Purdue University Agricultural Experiment Station

Figure 13.—Rye in Crosby silt loam of low fertility. Pot 12 (NPK) received complete fertilizer, serves as check; plants healthy and vigorous. Pot 9 (PK), nitrogen-starved plants are very weak, stunted, and greenish yellow, stems with slight purple tint. Pot 10 (NK), phosphorus-starved plants are dark-green and stunted. Pot 11 (NP), potassium-deficient plants are normal green, weak-stemmed, oldest leaves tipped with yellowish brown.

preceding season. Dark-green patches of vigorously growing plants are found on spots that had been fertilized by droppings. These "Juno spots" demonstrate a general lack of fertility in the rest of the field and show the value of manure for fertilization.

Although the symptoms of nitrogen deficiency are rather specific in young small-grain plants, there are times when it may be desirable to confirm them by the use of chemical tissue tests prior to using top dressings, as described on page 83.

PHOSPHORUS

Small-grain plants require large quantities of phosphorus for the production of the seed and are dependent upon available phosphates for stooling. The interpretation of phosphorus deficiency symptoms in the field is difficult because there are no outstanding specific external symptoms that point directly to phosphorus hunger. Slow growth and lack of stooling are the common signs of phosphorus starvation, particularly when the plants are dark green and apparently healthy otherwise.

Figures 10, 11, 12, and 13 show the dwarfing effects of phosphorus deficiency on the wheat, oat, barley, and rye plants in the pots without phosphorus. The leaves were dark green, and some of those on the barley and wheat plants were purplish-tinged. Plate 10, C, shows the effects of phosphorus starvation on a wheat leaf. The tips of the older leaves die, and this dying of the tissues proceeds toward the base. This symptom so closely resembles the firing of nitrogen-starved (B) and potassium-starved (D) leaves that it is difficult to use it for diagnostic purposes in the field. Indeed, other factors may induce similar effects to complicate matters. Plate 8, B, shows oat leaves starved for phosphorus. The firing is very similar to that of the wheat in plate 10, C.

Small-grain plants growing vigorously contain reserves of inorganic phosphates in their tissues until the grain is formed. Any uncertainty regarding a deficiency may be cleared up quickly by making chemical tests for inorganic phosphates in the stem tissues of these plants. Of course the conclusion to be drawn from negative tests is that more available phosphates must be used in the fertilizer program for these crops.

POTASSIUM

The importance of potassium in small-grain plant economy is high although the quantities demanded are less than for corn and legume crops.

There is one common symptom of potassium deficiency that is found in small-grain plants and other grasses—the edge scorch of the leaves. In early stages the tips and margins of the older leaves turn yellow, then brown, and finally die, producing the scorch symptom. Later the stalks become weak and the plants show the weaknesses noted in the pots without potash in figures 10, 11, 12, and 13. Plate 10, D, shows a wheat leaf from a potassium-starved plant. The edge of the leaf shows the characteristic marginal scorch. The leaf is dying from the tip end.

The foliage symptoms shown in plate 10 for nitrogen, phosphorus, and potassium deficiencies, while definite when obtained under controlled nutrient conditions, are relatively unsuitable for field diagnosis. Unless the leaf symptoms are confirmed by chemical tissue tests (p. 83) it is practically impossible to guess their significance and use them to determine the fertilizer needs of these crops. Tissue tests for potassium are very reliable.

In barley, a deficiency of potassium results in the formation of small purplish-brown spots on leaves showing the marginal-scorch symptom. Plate 8, D, shows this typical symptom of potassium deficiency. The cause of the spotting is unknown. The spots do not develop on the leaves of plants grown with adequate potash fertilization.

Figure 14.—Wheat. Plants at left received 150 pounds of 0-20-10 fertilizer; those at right, 150 pounds 20-percent superphosphate only. Potassium strengthens the straw and prevents lodging. This demonstration was in a field where the available potassium had become depleted by crop removals following liming and the continued use of phosphates only.

A deficiency of potassium results in weak stem development in small-grain plants approaching maturity. Figure 14 shows the weakness of wheat stems starved for potassium. Both plots had received phosphate, and the plot to the left had received muriate of potash in addition.

The grain produced on potassium-starved plants is shriveled and immature. Since the same effect is induced by rusts and other factors, the causes of defective grains must be traced throughout the growing season.

MAGNESIUM

Little attention has been given to the symptoms induced by magnesium starvation on small-grain plants in this country. Most of the investigations have been made on corn and the larger-leaved crops. Chucka and Lovejoy (5) report increased yields of wheat, oats, barley, and rye from magnesium fertilizers. M. H. Lockwood, in private correspondence with the author, has supplied evidence of the response of oats to a spring application of magnesium sulfate (fig. 15). The magnesium-deficient plants were dwarfed and yellow. Thornton, at the Purdue Agricultural Experiment Station, has produced symptoms of magnesium starvation in wheat in controlled nutrient cultures (data unpublished). The plants were stunted in growth, and the leaves showed a distinct mottling of lighter yellowish-green patches in contrast to the normal green of the magnesium-fertilized plants. Plate 8, C, shows this symptom. Plate 9, B, shows magnesium-deficiency symptoms in oats.

Courtesy of M. H. Lockwood,
Eastern States Farmers' Exchange

Figure 15.—Oats. Aroostook County, Maine. Rows at right were magnesium-starved; plants yellow and stunted. Rows at left received a spring application of magnesium sulfate at the rate of 50 pounds per acre; plants growing normally and heading out.

At best these symptoms would be diagnosed with difficulty in the field. It is quite likely that magnesium deficiencies will be detected first in the larger-leaved crops in the rotation with small grains, and that the latter will benefit from the remedial measures for these other crops.

BORON

No reports have been noted of any symptoms attributed to boron deficiencies in fields of small grains in this country. Purvis (24) states that grasses and cereals apparently require very little boron.

MANGANESE

Manganese is an essential element for plant growth. Its role in plants presumably is that of a catalyst, although this is not definitely proved. Most investigations have been made on this element in relation to its influence on the chemical and biological reactions in the soil.   The processes of nitrogen fixation and ammonification in the soil are dependent upon its presence.   Manganese deficiencies are found mostly in soils high in calcium carbonate.

Albert (1) has reported on manganese deficiency in oats in South Carolina.   Oats growing in the heavily limed fertility plots at the Pee Dee Experiment Station displayed a bright yellow color of the leaves, with the leaves breaking down at their basal ends and dying slowly.   The tip ends remained yellowish green and alive.   These symptoms, according to Albert, are corrected by applications of 100 pounds of manganese sulfate per acre.

The "gray speck disease" of oats, described by Davies and Jones (6) in Wales, has not been reported in this country.

CHEMICAL TISSUE TESTS

TESTS FOR CORN

Nitrates

Cut out a small section of the stalk or slice a portion of a leaf into small bits. Place these pieces in a glass vial or on a clean porcelain plate and apply a few drops of concentrated sulfuric acid containing 1 percent of diphenylamine.   The older corn stalks in the field may be cut lengthwise and the freshly exposed tissues tested for nitrates by applying a few drops of the test solution as shown in figure 5.

The distribution of nitrates in the plant can be noted by testing the tissues of the stalk from the base to the top.

If nitrates are present in the tissue, a blue color is produced immediately. This positive result is typical of all dark-green corn plants.   If no blue color is produced, no reserve nitrates are present and the evidence confirms the yellowish-green symptoms (p. 60) indicating nitrogen deficiency.

The diphenylamine test solution for nitrates should be in every corn grower's cabinet, ready for quick service when needed.

Phosphates

Whenever possible, always make comparative tests of plant tissues from similar parts of phosphorus-starved plants and those growing normally in the same field.

It is suggested that tissues be taken from parts of the plants as follows:

Young plants—base of stalk.

Plants in tassel—tissue of stem below tassel.

Ear stage of development—compare tests of kernel tissues versus stem tissues of same plant.

Place a volume equivalent to a level teaspoonful of finely cut plant tissue in a glass vial, add 10 cc. of the phosphate-test solution (described later) and shake vigorously for 1 minute.

Then add the phosphate-test powder (also described later), in volume equal to a mustard seed, to the solution and shake thoroughly.

Refer to plate 11, A (page 97), the phosphate color chart, for interpretation of tests:

(A) *A dark-blue* solution indicates an abundant supply of inorganic phosphates in the plants at the time the test is made, as shown in plate 12, A, page 98. Note test of plant fertilized with phosphate (left).

(B) *A medium-dark blue* indicates an adequate supply for the present stage of growth of the plants.

(C) *A light-blue, greenish, or yellowish-green* color indicates an inadequate supply of phosphates for normal growth and development of the plants, as shown in plate 12, A. Note the absence of blue color in the test solution at right.

Ample reserves of inorganic phosphates are associated with health and vigor of corn plants. The reserves may be high in plants deficient in nitrogen or potassium or both. It is important always to ascertain the relation to these other plantfoods, reserves of which also are necessary for healthy growth.

Only when all three of these plant nutrients are found in reserve quantities should the *dark-blue* phosphate test be interpreted as indicating a satisfactory supply of available phosphates in the soil.

A negative test for phosphate indicates an inadequate supply of available phosphate in the soil. Tests for nitrates and potassium salts are important to complete the diagnosis and may help the interpretation of combined symptoms of nitrogen and phosphate hunger frequently found in plants in many acid soils. A negative potassium test on these phosphorus-deficient tissues indicates a deficient supply of this plant nutrient also.

Potassium

Two test reagents are required to detect the presence of potassium in corn-plant tissues. Their preparation is described on page 84. Reagent No. 1 consists of a solution of sodium cobaltinitrite and sodium nitrite in distilled water acidulated with acetic acid. Reagent No. 2 is 95-percent ethyl alcohol.

Whenever possible always make comparative tests of tissues selected from similar parts of plants that appear healthy and plants showing symptoms that indicate potassium hunger. If the tests are negative for the plant showing the symptoms while the healthy plant tissues contain potassium, the diagnosis of potassium deficiency is confirmed.

The following tissues are suggested for the tests:

Young plants—tissues from the lower part of the stalks.
Older plants—internodal stalk tissues or the basal portions of the leaves at the nodes bearing the developing ears.

After selecting the tissues to be tested, cut the material into small bits, place one-half teaspoonful in a glass vial, and add 10 cc. of Reagent No. 1. Shake vigorously for 1 minute. Then add carefully 5 cc. of Reagent No. 2 and mix thoroughly. Let the vial stand approximately 3 minutes and note the turbidity, if any, that develops.

Refer to plate 11, B, and compare the density of the cloudiness (turbidity) of the solution with the potassium-test chart.

(A) *Clear solution.* If the solution remains clear, as at the right in plate 12, B, there were no potassium salts in the tissue tested. A negative test of this kind confirms the diagnosis of potassium-hunger symptoms in such plants.

(B) *Turbid solution.* If the solution shows turbidity, as at the left in plate 12, B, its relative density may be approximated by noting whether the heavy black lines of the chart (plate 11, B) can be seen through the solution. Any turbidity whatever indicates the presence of potassium salts in the tissues, and the denser the turbidity, the higher is the potassium content. When the solution carries a dense precipitate, the plant was well supplied with potassium up to the time the test was made.

Any symptoms displayed by such plants are due to factors other than potassium starvation. No response to additional potash applied to the soil can be expected until the limiting factors are corrected.

If the solution carries only a slight turbidity, particularly when the tissues from young plants are tested, the soil supply of available potash may be just sufficient to meet the immediate needs of the plant. It may become deficient later when most needed to produce good yields of well-matured corn.

TESTS FOR SMALL GRAINS

Nitrates

The diphenylamine test solution is used in the same manner as recommended for corn tissues. By cutting several plants lengthwise, or by cutting several leaves into small pieces, and applying several drops of this test reagent, the presence of nitrates may be detected readily if a blue color develops. If none appears, the absence of reserve nitrates is indicated, and the yellowish-green symptom of nitrogen hunger (p. 76) is confirmed. Improvements in soil conditions favoring nitrification may change the nitrogen relations in a few days. These nitrate tests reveal such changes. In older plants the nitrate tests are useful up to the time the heads develop.

Phosphates

The same test reagents and procedure are used as described for corn tissues. Use leaf tissues of young plants and stem tissues of older plants for the tests. Refer to plate 11, A, and check the test results.

A positive test for phosphate in small-grain plants shows that the soil supply of available phosphates was sufficient for the plants at the time of making the tests, and that any symptoms shown by the plants are caused by factors other than phosphorus hunger.

A negative test shows that the available phosphate supply is inadequate and is the limiting factor or one of the limiting factors causing the symptoms. Usually such plants contain reserve nitrates and potassium.

Potassium

Use either stem or leaf tissues, preferably older tissues, and follow the procedure described for testing corn tissues for potassium.

A negative test for potassium indicates a deficiency and confirms any external symptoms that may be evident.

METHODS FOR PREPARING REAGENTS FOR THE CHEMICAL TISSUE TESTS

The reagents [4] for making the chemical tests on plant tissues for nitrates, phosphates, and potassium referred to in this article are prepared as follows:

Nitrate-Test Reagent

Dissolve 1 gram of diphenylamine in 100 cc. of concentrated sulfuric acid. Note: This solution is very corrosive and much care must be taken in using it. Do not use it if it becomes badly discolored—prepare a fresh solution.

Phosphate-Test Reagents

Reagent No. 1. Dissolve 4 grams of ammonium molybdate in 500 cc. of distilled water and add, slowly and with constant stirring, a mixture of 63 cc. of concentrated hydrochloric acid and 437 cc. of distilled water. As this solution may become unsuited for use after standing for a few months, it is desirable to prepare a solution of five times this concentration and dilute as needed.

Reagent No. 2. Dry powdered stannous chloride or stannous oxalate.

Potassium-Test Reagents

Reagent No. 1. Dissolve 5 grams of sodium cobaltinitrite and 30 grams of sodium nitrite in distilled water, add 5 cc. of glacial acetic acid, make to 100 cc. volume, and allow to stand for several days. Add 5 cc. of this solution to a solution of 15 grams of sodium nitrite in 100 cc. of distilled water and adjust to pH 5.0 with acetic acid. Sodium cobaltinitrite from different sources has been found to vary widely in cobalt content. The directions given here are based on the use of the Baker's Analyzed product. Cobaltinitrite concentration is an important factor in determining the sensitivity of the test.

Reagent No. 2. Ethyl alcohol (95 percent). When ethyl alcohol for use as a reagent is difficult to obtain, a mixture of 60 parts anhydrous methyl alcohol, 40 parts anhydrous isopropyl alcohol, and 5 parts of distilled water may be substituted. If this mixture becomes turbid it should be filtered. Completely denatured alcohol is not satisfactory.

Iron-Test Reagent

Prepare a 10-percent solution of potassium thiocyanate in distilled water. When ready to make the tests for iron in the joint tissues of the corn plant, mix 3 parts of this solution with 1 part of concentrated hydrochloric acid and apply several drops of the mixture directly to the tissues. This acidulated solution does not keep very well; prepare fresh mixtures when necessary. When used as indicated on page 66 a deep purplish-red color of the joint tissues indicates a severe deficiency of available potassium.

---

[4] The methods for preparing these reagents are taken directly from Purdue University Agricultural Experiment Station Circular 204 (27, pp. 8-9).

Other workers have described methods for chemically analyzing plant tissues and the composition of the sap of various plants. Gilbert and Hardin (13), Pettinger et al. (21, 22, 23), Emmert (10), Hester (14), Morgan (19, 20), Thomas et al. (25, 26), and others have described their respective techniques in detail. All involve the use of laboratory facilities and are very satisfactory for detailed comparative studies of healthy and malnourished plants of all kinds. Not only do these studies on the chemical compositions of plants provide facts for the interpretation of deficiency troubles, but also for the planning of extensive and effective programs for the fertilization of these crops. Canning companies and truck-crop growers are particularly interested in them.

LITERATURE CITED

(1) ALBERT, W. B.
 1931. AN ABNORMAL CONDITION OF OATS AND COWPEAS CAUSED BY INSUFFICIENT MANGANESE IN SOIL. S. C. Agr. Expt. Sta. Ann. Rpt. 44: 46-47. (Supplementary reports in 1932 and 1934 Ann. Rpts.)

(2) BARNETTE, R. M., CAMP, J. P., WARNER, J. D., and GALL, O. E.
 1936. THE USE OF ZINC SULPHATE UNDER CORN AND OTHER FIELD CROPS. Fla. Univ. Bul. 292: 3-52, illus.

(3) BRAY, R. H.
 1936. POTASSIUM AVAILABILITY IN ILLINOIS SOILS. Better Crops with Plant Food 20 (12): 11-15, illus.

(4) CAROLUS, R. L.
 1936. THE RELATION OF POTASSIUM, CALCIUM AND SODIUM TO MAGNESIUM DEFICIENCY. Amer. Soc. Hort. Sci. Proc. (1935) 33: 595-599.

(5) CHUCKA, J. A., and LOVEJOY, D. B.
 1933. FIELD CROP EXPERIMENTS IN MAINE. Maine Agr. Expt. Sta. Bul. 369: 529-539, illus.

(6) DAVIES, D. W., and JONES, E. T.
 1931. GREY SPECK DISEASE OF OATS. Welsh Jour. Agr. 7: 349-358, illus.

(7) DETURK, E. E.
 1940. THE PHYSIOLOGICAL BASIS OF PLANT NUTRIENT DEFICIENCY SYMPTOMS. Paper read before Division of Fertilizer Chemistry, American Chemical Society, Detroit. (Abstract in Amer. Chem. Soc., Abstracts of Papers 100: 15F-16F.)

(8) ECKSTEIN, O., BRUNO, A., and TURRENTINE, J. W.
 1937. POTASH DEFICIENCY SYMPTOMS. 235 pp., illus. Berlin.

(9) ELTINGE, ETHEL T.
 1936. EFFECT OF BORON DEFICIENCY UPON THE STRUCTURE OF ZEA MAYS. Plant Physiol. 11: 765-778, illus.

(10) EMMERT, E. M.
 1934. TESTS FOR PHOSPHATE, NITRATE AND SOLUBLE NITROGEN IN CONDUCTING TISSUE OF TOMATO AND LETTUCE PLANTS, AS INDICATORS OF AVAILABILITY AND YIELD. Ky. Agr. Expt. Sta. Cir. 43:25-40, illus.

(11) FERGUSON, WM., and WRIGHT, L. E.
 1940. MICROELEMENT STUDIES WITH SPECIAL REFERENCE TO THE ELEMENT BORON. Sci. Agr. 20: 1-8.

(12) GARRARD, H. L.
 1936. SIDE-DRESSING CORN WITH POTASH. Better Crops with Plant Food 20 (8): 6-9, illus.

(13) GILBERT, B. E., and HARDIN, LEO J.
 1927. THE CURRENT MINERAL NUTRIENT CONTENT OF THE PLANT SOLUTION AS A POSSIBLE MEANS OF CHEMICAL CONTROL OF OPTIMUM FERTILIZATION. Jour. Agr. Res. 35: 185-192.

(14) HESTER, JACKSON B.
 1934. MICROCHEMICAL SOIL TESTS IN CONNECTION WITH VEGETABLE CROP PRODUCTION. Va. Truck Expt. Sta. Bul. 82: 1121-1135.

(15) HOFFER, G. N.
 1930. TESTING CORN STALKS CHEMICALLY TO AID IN DETERMINING THEIR PLANT FOOD NEEDS. Purdue Univ. Agr. Expt. Sta. Bul. 298 (rev.): 1-31, illlus.

(16) ———
 1938. POTASH IN PLANT METABOLISM. Jour. Indus. and Engin. Chem. 30: 885-889, illus. (Bibliography, pp. 888-889.)

(17) JONES, J. P.
 1929. DEFICIENCY OF MAGNESIUM THE CAUSE OF A CHLOROSIS IN CORN. Jour. Agr. Res. 39: 873-892, illus.

(18) KILPATRICK, BRUCE M.
        1938. CORN ON ALKALI SOILS RESPONDS TO POTASH. Better Crops with Plant Food
              22 (4): 13-16, illus.
(19) MORGAN, M. F.
        1936. SOIL AND PLANT TISSUE TESTS FOR MINOR ELEMENT CONSTITUENTS. Soil Sci.
              Soc. Amer. Proc. 1: 255-257.
(20) ———
        1937. THE UNIVERSAL SOIL TESTING SYSTEM. Conn. Agr. Expt. Sta. Bul. 392: 129-
              159, illus.
(21) PETTINGER, N. A.
        1931. THE EXPRESSED SAP OF CORN PLANTS AS AN INDICATOR OF NUTRIENT NEEDS. Jour.
              Agr. Res. 43: 95-119, illus.
(22) ——— HENDERSON, R. G., and WINGARD, S. A.
        1932. SOME NUTRITIONAL DISORDERS IN CORN GROWN IN SAND CULTURES. Phyto-
              pathology 22: 33-51, illus.
(23) ——— and THORNTON, S. F.
        1934. A COMPARISON OF THE NEUBAUER, PLANT SAP ANALYSIS, AND HOFFER STALK TEST
              METHODS FOR DETERMINING THE NUTRIENT SUPPLY OF SOILS. Amer. Soc. Agron.
              Jour. 26: 547-561, illus.
(24) PURVIS, E. R.
        1939. THE PRESENT STATUS OF BORON IN AMERICAN AGRICULTURE. Soil. Sci. Soc. Amer.
              Proc. 4: 316-321.
(25) THOMAS, WALTER.
        1937. FOLIAR DIAGNOSIS, PRINCIPLES AND PRACTICE. Plant Physiol. 12: 571-599.
(26) ——— and MACK, W. B.
        1939. THE FOLIAR DIAGNOSIS OF ZEA MAYS SUBJECTED TO DIFFERENTIAL FERTILIZER
              TREATMENT. Jour. Agr. Res. 58: 477-491.
(27) THORNTON, S. F., CONNER, S. D., and FRASER, R.
        1939. THE USE OF RAPID CHEMICAL TESTS ON SOILS AND PLANTS AS AIDS IN DETERMINING
              FERTILIZER NEED. Purdue Univ. Agr. Expt. Sta. Cir. 204 (rev.), 16 pp., illus.

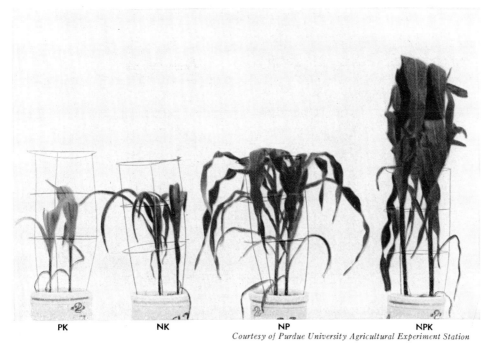

PK   NK   NP   NPK

Courtesy of Purdue University Agricultural Experiment Station

Plate 1.—A, Yellowish-green dwarfed corn plants in the PK pot are starved for nitrogen. The dark-green, stunted plants in the NK pot are starved for phosphorus. The slowly growing plants with the drooping, yellowish-green leaves in the NP pot are starved for potassium. The healthy, vigorous plants in the NPK pot serve as a check.

Plate 1.—B, Yellowish-green corn plants indicate need for available nitrogen. The dark-green plants in the background were side dressed with a nitrogen fertilizer.

[87]

A, courtesy of Florida Agricultural Experiment Station;
B and C, courtesy of Illinois Agricultural Experiment Station

Plate 2.—A, Zinc deficiency in corn. Advanced stage of "white bud" of the corn plant. The oldest leaves are dead, the upper leaves have yellow striping between the veins, and the plant is severely dwarfed. B, Calcium deficiency in corn. The tip ends of the leaves are gummed together. C, Phosphorus deficiency in corn. The yellowing of the leaves closely resembles that caused by nitrogen starvation. Tissue tests confirm phosphorus deficiency. D, Nitrogen-starved wheat. The yellowing of the tip ends and subsequent dying indicate nitrogen hunger. Nitrogen-starved leaves at right, normal leaf at left.

Plate 3.—Phosphorus hunger causes purpling of the leaves of many strains of corn.

Plate 4.—A, Corn in the three pots to the left, inbred CC5, lacking the purple-pigment factor, does not develop purple color at 30, 10, or 5 parts of phosphorus per million. Corn in the three pots to right, inbred CC7, has the purple factor but develops slight color only at 5 parts of phosphorus per million (pot at extreme right).

Plate 4.—B, Corn, inbred strain Hy, has the genetic factor for pigment production and the leaves become purple when starved for phosphorus.

Plate 5.—A, Potassium-starved young corn plant. The lower leaves show the typical marginal scorch. At this stage of growth in the field it is possible to apply remedial side dressings of potash salts profitably.

Courtesy of Massachusetts Agricultural Experiment Station

Plate 5.—B, Magnesium-starved corn. The regular yellowish-white stripes on the leaves indicate the deficiency.

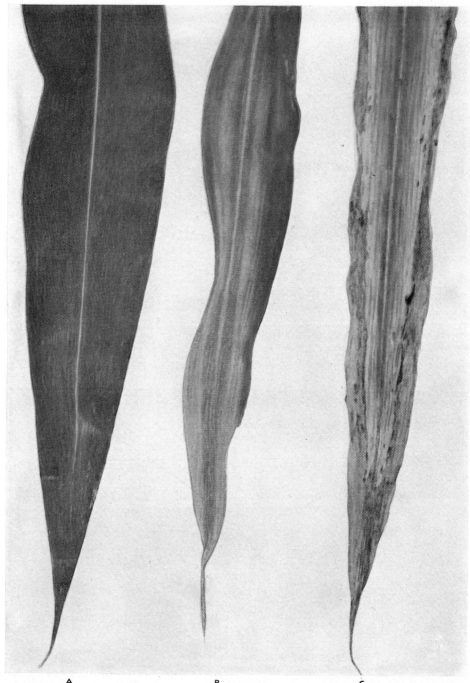

Plate 6.—A, Normal corn leaf. B, Nitrogen-starved leaf. The yellowing begins at tip end and progresses along the midrib. C, Potassium-starved leaf. Note characteristic brown edge scorch.

[92]

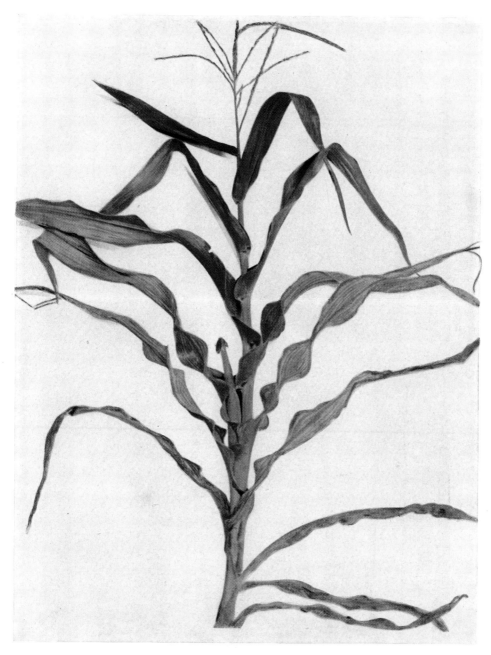

Plate 7.—Potassium starvation results in weak corn stalks with the leaves badly damaged. The marginal "firing" affects all the leaves.

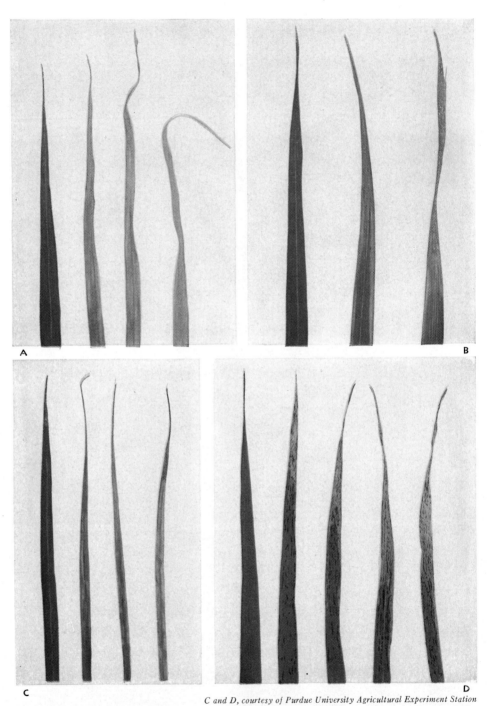

A

B

C

D

C and D, courtesy of Purdue University Agricultural Experiment Station

Plate 8.—A, Nitrogen-starved oat leaves. Nitrogen hunger causes the leaves to yellow and die. B, Phosphorus-starved oat leaves. The leaves die gradually from the tip ends with no particularly distinctive coloration. Note close similarity to the nitrogen-starved oat leaves. Chemical tests of the tissues are needed to confirm this symptom in the field. C, Magnesium-deficient wheat leaves. A slight mottling of the leaves was obtained in controlled nutrient cultures. D, Purplish-brown spots on barley leaves indicate potassium deficiency. These spots precede the usual marginal and tip-end "firing" of potassium-starved leaves. Cause of spots unknown.

Plate 9.—A, Nitrogen-starved oat plants. Yellowish-green plants seeded in disked corn stubble indicate a deficiency of nitrogen.

Courtesy of Eastern States Farmers' Exchange

Plate 9.—B, Magnesium-starved oat plants. The yellow-streaked, stunted plants indicate magnesium deficiency.

Plate 10.—A, Healthy green leaf of wheat showing balanced fertility. B, Yellowish-green leaf
with tip end turning yellow indicates nitrogen starvation. C, Dark-green leaf with the tip
end dying indicates possible deficiency of available phosphorus. D, Leaves with the tip ends
becoming yellow and scorched along the edges indicate a deficiency of potassium. These symptoms are diagnosed with difficulty under field conditions unless chemical tests for nitrates, inorganic phosphates, and potassium are made on the tissues.

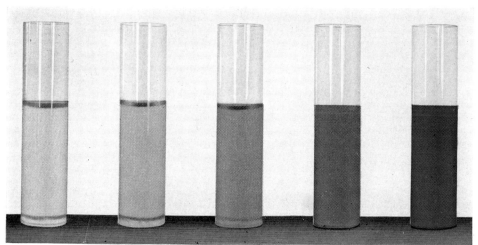

Plate 11.—A, Phosphorus-test chart. When making tissue tests compare test vials containing tissues with those in the chart. The density of the blue color of the test solution indicates the relative content of inorganic phosphates in the tissues.

Plate 11.—B, Potassium-test chart. When making tissue tests compare test vials containing tissues with those in the chart. The relative obliteration of the heavy black lines behind the test solution indicates the relative content of potassium in the tissues.

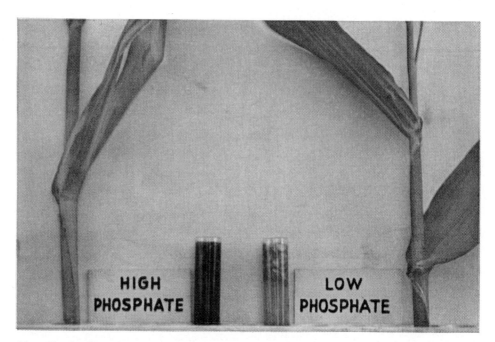

Plate 12.—A, Corn tissue test for inorganic phosphate. Left, high content of inorganic phosphate in stem tissues is indicated by the dark-blue color of the test solution in the vial. Right, a deficiency of inorganic phosphate is indicated by the light greenish-blue color of the test solution. The plants showed no definite symptoms to indicate these tissue-test differences other than in their relative sizes.

Plate 12.—B, Corn tissue test for potassium. Left, healthy leaf tissues contain an abundance of potassium, as shown by heavy turbidity of test solution in the vial. Right, the marginal-scorch symptom is confirmed by the negative (clear solution) test for potassium in the leaf tissues.

CHAPTER IV

Plant-Nutrient Deficiency Symptoms in the Potato

By H. A. Jones and B. E. Brown [1]

THE needs of the potato for the different nutrient elements are about the same as those of other crop plants, but this does not necessarily imply that the potato requires a given element in the same quantity as other plants. The potato may not have as big an appetite for certain elements as do other crops. Take, for example, the element boron. Some crops, including celery, cauliflower, turnip, and the sugar beet, appear to be much more susceptible to boron deficiency than is the potato. The greater response of cauliflower to boron has been used to ascertain whether a deficiency of boron could be detected in potato fields. This was accomplished by "spotting" cauliflower plants in the fields. Failure to get a response was assurance that boron was not deficient.

One may make a conjecture about the soil conditions responsible for nutrient deficiencies, but the forces at work are often apt to be so insidious that the final crop disturbance may not manifest itself definitely for some time. For example, when magnesium deficiency began to develop in a number of important potato-producing sections along the Atlantic seaboard, it was not until the supply of available magnesium hit rock bottom that definite symptoms of magnesium deficiency were generally observed. The continued use of certain fertilizers tended to increase the acidity, and the trouble spread rapidly. After considerable experimental work the remedy was found to be the addition of magnesium to the fertilizer mixture or directly to the soil. Combining the magnesium compound with the fertilizer gave a quicker effect and insured a supply of magnesium for the young potato plants.

The writers have been unable to find any reported case of a deficiency of boron, calcium, copper, or zinc affecting the potato when grown under field conditions. Manganese deficiency has been reported in naturally calcareous or overlimed soils because under such conditions this element is made comparatively unavailable for use by plants. Other elements—boron and zinc—are reported to be affected similarly by an excess of calcium carbonate. Potato

[1] H. A. Jones is Principal Olericulturist and B. E. Brown is Senior Biochemist, Division of Fruit and Vegetable Crops and Diseases, Bureau of Plant Industry, United States Department of Agriculture.

soils in the East, however, are generally acid in reaction, and perhaps this is why boron and zinc are not a problem.   For the same
reason iron and manganese present no problem.   Spray programs
tend to provide a supply of copper and arsenic.   In the more detailed
discussion to follow, no reference has been made to aluminum,
molybdenum, and a number of other so-called minor elements because there is no evidence at the present time to indicate that they
are essential to the potato.   The time may come, however, when
an element not now established as essential may turn out to be a
vital factor in potato production.   Potato investigators must be
alert to the importance of the many studies under way to determine
the requirements of economic crops for these minor elements.

The white or Irish potato is adapted to a wide range of soil and
climatic conditions.   In the United States it thrives from Maine to
the lower Rio Grande Valley of Texas, and from the Atlantic to the
Pacific coast (fig. 1).   Important commercial districts are located at
both high and low altitudes, under humid and semiarid conditions;
crops mature with different lengths of daylight, under light of different qualities and intensities, and on soils that vary widely in
texture and in natural fertility.   To each environmental complex
the potato plant responds in a somewhat different manner.   Deficiency symptoms due to the lack of any one or more than one
element are not always the same under all conditions, but certain
of the abnormalities seem to be characteristic, and these will be
given consideration here.

When the plants are grown under controlled conditions in sand
and water cultures there is much better agreement in the observations of various investigators, and these help to point the way to a
finer differentiation of deficiency symptoms under field conditions.

NITROGEN DEFICIENCY

A deficiency of available nitrogen is a distinctly limiting factor
in the growth of the potato plant—perhaps more generally so than
a deficiency of any other essential element.   Except possibly on
organic soils, such as muck and peat, some source of nitrogen—
manure, commercial fertilizer, green-manure crops, or a combination of these—is almost always utilized in commercial potato
production.

In Virginia an acre of potato plants during the first 50 days after
planting utilized less than 7 pounds of nitrogen as measured in the
growth above ground; during the next 10-day period absorption

of nitrogen averaged 1 pound a day, and during the next 20-day period it averaged 2 pounds a day. After about the eightieth day, when growth above ground had practically stopped, there occurred a gradual transfer of nitrogen from the foliage to the developing tubers (*3*).[2]

Figure 1.—Above, potato vines free from any nutrient deficiency. Normal foliage and growth. Splendid yields are the result of careful culture and plant feeding. Below, potato vines responsible for such a yield as this received a well-balanced diet with no deficiency of any nutrient element.

The reaction of the potato to nitrogen deficiency is similar to that of many other crops. The growth of the entire plant is re-

[2] Italic numbers in parentheses refer to Literature Cited, p. 118. The list of citations at the close of this chapter is by no means complete, however. Many instructive articles may be found in the literature on minor-element deficiencies affecting the potato alone, but lack of space precluded their inclusion herein. Anyone interested in more extensive reading is referred to "Bibliography of References to the Literature on the Minor Elements and Their Relation to Plant and Animal Nutrition," third edition, 1939, published by the Chilean Nitrate Educational Bureau, Inc., wherein appear 4,628 abstracts and references to minor-element deficiencies affecting crops in general.

stricted in accordance with the extent of the deficiency (plate 1, A, page 119), and this stunted condition is reflected in reduced yields and poor quality of tubers. The plant takes on a light-green to yellowish-green color. In advanced stages, the margins of the lower leaflets lose their chlorophyll, the color fading to a pale yellow (plate 1, lower right), and some shedding of foliage usually results.

Nitrogen deficiency is usually associated with sandy soils low in organic matter and acid enough to interfere with nitrification. A fertilizer practice that fails to offset the nitrogen losses usually results in acute nitrogen deficiency. Preventive measures include control of soil reaction, as by liming; addition of nitrogenous organic matter in the form of manure, composts, and green manures to supply a reservoir of nitrogen; and the use of commercial fertilizer at the proper time and rate to supply available nitrogen.

PHOSPHORUS DEFICIENCY

Phosphorus absorption runs parallel to that of nitrogen, but only about one-sixth as much of this element is used by the potato plant. After plants reach full growth, about one-half of the phosphorus in the aerial portion migrates to the developing tubers (3). An inadequate supply of available phosphorus generally causes pronounced growth reactions (plate 2, page 120). The plants are smaller, somewhat more spindling, and definitely retarded in growth, particularly during the early stage of development. At Aroostook Farm, Presque Isle, Maine, plants on plots receiving ample quantities of nitrogen and potassium but no phosphorus grow very slowly during the early part of the season and often appear no better and occasionally poorer than those on plots without fertilizer; but later, when they have developed a more extensive root system, they outgrow the plants without fertilizer. They also tend to continue growth in the fall longer than those on most of the other plots.

Tubers produced by plants grown on phosphorus-deficient soil show rusty-brown lesions in the form of isolated flecks which may join together to produce larger areas. The flecks occur in both the cortex, or outer region, and the pith, or central portion, and may cross the vascular ring located between these two regions. The pith is generally more susceptible than the cortex. The flecks vary in size from those that are scarcely visible to those almost half an inch in diameter. They also vary in number. If the crop is lightly affected, only a single small fleck may be apparent in a tuber; if it is badly affected, the lesions may occupy more than half the volume of the potato.   The arrangement of the flecks is generally irregular, but occasionally there is a tendency toward a radial pattern—streaks running out from a center.   In external appearance there is usually no distinction between healthy and diseased tubers.   Seldom do flecks occur so near the surface that they can be seen without cutting. When these potatoes are boiled, the flecks remain as hard, discolored masses in the softened tissue.   Brown flecks in the flesh of potato tubers have been described from most potato-growing countries, and they may be due to other causes besides phosphorus deficiency— for example, virus diseases or heat or frost injury.

When potato plants are grown in sand culture deficient in phosphorus, the leafstalks (petioles), leaflets, and leaf margins turn upward.   The leaflets are smaller and darker than normal and the plants are somewhat rigid (8).

Phosphorus deficiency occurs on a wide range of soil types—on heavy soils because of fixation, which makes the phosphorus unavailable; on light soils because of a naturally low phosphorus content; and on both types because of crop removal.   Lack of available phosphorus may be reflected more in low yields and poor quality than in distinctive foliage symptoms, but the latter will develop where continuous cropping is practiced without adequate phosphorus applications.

POTASSIUM DEFICIENCY

The potato plant must have a continuous supply of potassium for normal growth.   Where a deficiency exists, growth of the plant is first retarded and finally completely checked, and the internodes are somewhat shortened, which gives the plant a compact appearance.   The leaves are reduced in size, owing to a narrow arrangement of the leaflets, which form a sharper angle with the midrib. The leaflets lose their smooth surface, become crinkled, and droop.

The early appearance of abnormally dark green foliage is one of the most dependable signs of potassium hunger.   Then the older leaves become yellowish, and a brown or bronze color develops, starting from the tip and edge and gradually affecting the entire leaf, which finally dies (plate 3, page 121).   In a single plant this bronzing is not so striking, but it is quite prominent in mass effect. Under certain light conditions a distinct purplish cast is apparent. A number of the lower leaves may dry up at the same time, leaving for a time a tuft of dark-green leaves at the apex, or top, of the plant. Eventually, the entire plant dies (fig. 2).

Potatoes produced on potash-deficient soils have a tendency to develop a dark color after boiling.

Sand cultures have also been used to study potassium-deficiency symptoms of the potato, and the responses reported are similar to those described for plants growing in the field (8). The leaf, leaflets, and leaflet margins bend downward. The color of the leaves changes from a normal healthy green to a dark green and afterwards to a

Figure 2.—The final stage of potassium hunger—a plant completely collapsed through lack of vigor and resultant fungus attacks. Only small, low-quality tubers are produced by such plants.

peculiar bronze or yellow, beginning with the oldest leaves. Symptoms on the lower leaves may be pronounced while the top of the plant still has a normal appearance. The tissue between the veins of diseased leaves protrudes strongly. In severe cases the leaf margins break down, and discolored areas appear on various parts of the stems and petioles. The stolons are shorter than normal, and the roots and tubers are poorly developed.

Yields are decreased in proportion as the shortage of potassium increases. In the United States the area most generally affected is that lying east of the Appalachian Mountains, particularly the sandy soils of the Atlantic Coast States. Deficiency symptoms have been noted as far north as Aroostook County, Maine, being more prominent there on the Washburn than on the Caribou type of soil.

In general, deficiency occurs on light sandy soils of a leachy nature and on mucks and peats. Some heavy soils high in total potassium, however, are too low in available potassium to satisfy the needs of the potato crop, which requires from 100 to 200 pounds of potash per acre. During the World War, when the supply of potash fertilizer became very low, the deficiency became very serious (fig. 3).

Figure 3.—During the World War potash became a scarce article. Rows on left received 5-10-0 at rate of 1 ton per acre; rows on right, 4-8-4 at the same rate. Much earlier collapse of plants where no potash was in the mixture is very evident.

Fortunately, this country need no longer fear the pinch of potash hunger.

Obviously the remedy for potassium deficiency as it affects the potato is to utilize any available manure or fertilizer containing sufficient available potassium.

MAGNESIUM DEFICIENCY

Magnesium-deficiency symptoms have been reported on potatoes from practically all of the potato districts of the Atlantic Coastal Plain and as far north as Aroostook County, Maine.

The foliage of affected plants is lighter in color than normal. The lower leaves are the first to become affected, since some of their magnesium is withdrawn to be used over again by the new growth. In mild cases only the lower leaves of the plants show symptoms, while the new growth appears healthy. Loss of green color begins at the tips and margins of the lowermost leaves and progresses between the veins toward the center of the leaflets. In advanced stages of deficiency the central portion of the individual leaflets becomes chlorotic between the veins and eventually is filled with small brown dead areas. Break-down of the tissue, like loss of color, usually starts at the tip, and the terminal leaflet is generally the one most severely affected. The lower leaves of magnesium-deficient plants are brittle, which serves to distinguish them from leaves yellowing naturally through age.

In severe cases nearly the entire area of the leaves and all except the top growth of the plant are affected. The plants have a very marked chlorotic and stunted appearance with some upward rolling of the lower leaves, which show a definite bulging between the veins and become thick and brittle. These symptoms seem to be most conspicuous after a warm, dry spell when the potato plants are about 8-10 inches tall. Finally, the chlorotic leaves die, turn brown, and often drop off the plant (plate 4, page 122).

Magnesium-deficiency symptoms were observed in Virginia in 1931 at two distinct periods in the growth of the crop (4). Indications of the trouble were detected first in late April, during a period of rainy weather when foliage growth was rapid. Later, during a dry spell, the trouble disappeared to some extent as the plants were able to absorb sufficient amounts of magnesium from the soil. Deficiency symptoms appeared again during the latter part of May and were prevalent over a much wider area than at the time of the first outbreak. This recurrence of symptoms, which resulted in the premature death of many plants and greatly reduced yields, was probably caused by a transfer of magnesium from the foliage to the developing tubers where it was reused.

In Holland, when the potato variety President was grown under controlled conditions in glass sand in the absence of magnesium, the symptoms were more severe but similar to those observed in the field (8). Chlorosis developed at the tips of the lowermost leaves, then advanced along the margins and between the veins until the entire leaf was involved. The terminal leaflet was attacked first, then the other leaflets. Chlorosis progressed from the lowermost leaves upward, and in severe cases only the youngest leaves at the top remained green. The older leaves died prematurely, beginning at the tip and margin of the terminal leaflet. In severe cases the chlorotic tissue was almost pure white and protruded upward, while the tips and margins of the diseased leaflets bent downward. Growth of roots and tubers was also checked. In the presence of excess nitrogen, symptoms were still more severe.

Magnesium deficiency is associated with a very low magnesium content, rather low calcium content, and a relatively high nitrogen content in the lower leaves. In normal aging, the lower leaves have a high content of magnesium and calcium but are low in nitrogen (3). Investigations in Virginia show that plants containing over 0.4 percent of magnesium oxide normally accumulated throughout the entire growing season will not show symptoms of magnesium deficiency; but under conditions of excessive rainfall during the early months of the potato-growing season, coupled with the heavy use of acid-forming fertilizer, magnesium probably becomes a limiting factor on even the most fertile types of potato soil (4).

Results of experiments in Aroostook County, Maine, have shown that the so-called "potato sickness" prevalent in that district and specifically associated with magnesium deficiency may be effectively controlled by applying a magnesium compound to the soil. Substantial increases in the yield of Green Mountains and Irish Cobblers were obtained by incorporating magnesium sulfate[3] with the ordinary potato fertilizer (5, 6), or in the spray mixture (1), particularly in fields where severe chlorosis developed shortly after the emergence of the plants. Deficient plants sprayed with magnesium bordeaux showed recovery in the new growth, lived longer, and yielded more. In one test the yield from the use of magnesium bordeaux was 96 bushels an acre more than the yield in adjacent plots sprayed with high-calcium bordeaux. On less deficient soil in the same field, the yield was increased only 38 bushels per acre. In another test the magnesium bordeaux increased the yield 133 percent on deficient soil and 11 percent on better soil. It is suggested that some of the spray stimulation reported in the past may have been due to absorption of magnesium by the plants.

Magnesium deficiency generally occurs in highly acid soils, but it is not necessarily confined to those that are light and sandy, for its effects have been observed on soils of high fertility such as Caribou loam in Aroostook County. Heavy applications of acid-forming fertilizers, particularly those containing certain nitrogen materials

[3] Equivalent to 30 pounds of magnesium oxide (MgO) per acre.

of high plantfood concentration, increased the solubility of the magnesium compounds, which were subsequently leached away from the feeding range of the young potato plants.

Practical remedies for magnesium deficiency are direct light applications of dolomitic limestone to the soil; introduction of magnesium sulfate, generally a calcined form, into the fertilizer mixture, using 30 to 40 pounds of magnesium oxide per ton; addition of enough dolomitic limestone to the fertilizer mixture to make it neutral; or a combination of two or more of these.

CALCIUM DEFICIENCY

Though only about one-fourth as much calcium as potassium is used by the potato plant, calcium plays an important part in the plant's development besides creating a favorable soil environment for growth (3).   Calcium has an indirect effect on the growth of the plant by altering the availability of certain nutrients and preventing the toxic effect of others.

Potatoes grow well in acid soils—pH values between 5.0 and 5.5. When the soil is more acid than this, unfavorable conditions develop, such as aluminum toxicity and phosphate fixation.   Soils less acid may prove congenial for the growth of the scab organism; though yields may not be reduced, the tubers are less attractive and the crop may be valueless because of scab lesions.

The intake of calcium into the aerial portion of the potato plant is continuous, and the amount present reaches its peak at maturity. There seems to be very little migration of calcium from the older portions of the plant to the developing buds and shoots, and for this reason a continuous supply of available calcium from the soil to the growing regions of the plant is necessary if deficiencies are not to occur.   Also, the transfer of calcium from the aerial portion to the developing tubers seems to be negligible.   Studies in Virginia show that only about 7 percent of all the calcium absorbed by the plant is in the tubers (3).

One would naturally expect to find calcium-deficiency symptoms in the potato plant in regions where acid soils and heavy rainfall prevail.   Though such symptoms apparently have not been observed or reported in the literature, the possibility remains that certain abnormalities that have been ascribed to other causes may have been due to lack of calcium.   Because of lack of evidence under field conditions, it is necessary to refer to calcium-deficiency symptoms induced artificially (plate 5, A, page 123).

Deficiency symptoms on potato plants grown in sand culture with limited calcium are characteristic and pronounced (8). First a light-green band appears along the margins of the young leaves of the bud. The tissue in these light-colored areas may be killed; consequently, the leaves do not develop normally and often have a wrinkled appearance. In severe cases the young leaves at the top remain folded and later the tip of the plant dies. The axillary growth which develops later may show the same symptoms as the young leaves of the terminal bud.

In the medullary or pith region of the tubers, dead spots develop; these areas show first as a diffuse brown discoloration within the vascular ring at the stem end of the tuber. The symptoms may show up in tubers from plants that had healthy-looking foliage, which seems to indicate that when calcium becomes deficient late in the life of the plant the effect is primarily on the tuber, there being very little or no transfer of calcium from the aerial portions of the plant to the tubers to take care of the deficiency. Thus a continuous supply of calcium must be available as long as new organs are being formed and new tissue is being developed.

Calcium deficiency usually develops later than magnesium deficiency, owing to differences in solubility and leaching of the respective compounds. Potatoes on light sandy soils comparatively devoid of calcium compounds suffer first. The obvious remedies are to prevent excessive acidity by the use of limestone and to incorporate suitable calcium compounds with the fertilizer mixture when these are known to be lacking in the materials used.

BORON DEFICIENCY

Boron-deficiency symptoms of potato have been reported from time to time. In the field they have been described as occurring chiefly in tubers rather than on the vines. Only minute quantities of boron are needed for normal growth, and, so far as known, there are few published reports of vine injury under field conditions due to the lack of this element. Where a deficiency of boron does exist, field applications have given noticeable growth responses, such as hastening the emergence of the plants and bringing plants into bloom 10 to 14 days before those without boron applications.

A report of field experiments by the New York (Cornell) Agricultural Experiment Station indicates that boiled potato tubers grown without boron additions to the soil showed much sloughing (falling away of outer layer), were fairly soggy, and possessed a flat flavor definitely inferior to that of tubers grown with added boron. The effects of adding 20 pounds of borax per acre were to materially reduce sloughing, increase mealiness and dryness, and improve texture, flavor, and color (7).

During the World War period and for a time following, considerable injury occurred to the potato crop from excess amounts of borax in fertilizers. Experiments have shown, however, that the bad effects on yield were due largely to the manner in which borax was applied. On Caribou loam in Aroostook County, definite injury occurred when planting immediately followed applications as low as 5 pounds per acre in the furrow. Surplus borax may prevent sprouting of the seedpiece and thereby produce poor stands. Other effects are killing of the sprouts after some growth has occurred, failure of roots to form at the seedpiece, weak appearance of plants that finally do emerge, bleaching of the foliage or marginal yellowing of the leaves, and abnormally low yields (2).

Because of the inability to study satisfactorily the effect of boron deficiency on the behavior of the potato plant under field conditions, a number of investigators in both Europe and America have designed experiments whereby the plants could be grown with insufficient boron in water and sand cultures. It is doubtful, however, if many of the symptoms that appear in culture will ever appear in the field, because such a minute amount of this element is adequate for the normal functioning of the plant (plate 5, B, page 123).

The descriptive reports of most investigators regarding deficiency symptoms are in fairly close agreement. A killing of the growing points and the tips of the terminal shoots and a stimulation in growth of the lateral buds are characteristic. Internodes remain short and give the plant a short, bushy appearance. Leaves thicken and the margins roll upward, as in potato leaf roll. When the boron deficiency is not great, only a slight upward curling of the leaf margins of the older leaves is visible. With greater deficiency petioles become brittle, loss of green color (chlorosis) appears, and in severe cases anthocyanin (a purple pigment) is developed. The leaf points and margins, especially those of the older leaves, die prematurely. Starch congestion in the leaf tissue is conspicuous.

In an advanced stage of boron deficiency the roots are short and thick and have a brown appearance. Root tips die, and this stimulates the development of secondary rootlets, which in turn may die soon after emergence (fig. 4).

Internal symptoms of boron deficiency are first found at the growing points of the roots and afterwards at the growing point of the stem.   These symptoms appear as a brown discoloration and a breaking down of individual cells or cell complexes before the growing point is killed.   Later, the stem, the axillary buds, and the internal parts of the lateral shoots become diseased; next the tissue of the nodes is attacked, that of the highest first, then that of the internodes.

Courtesy of the New York (Cornell) Agricultural Experiment Station

Figure 4.—Lack of sufficient boron seriously interferes with root development of the potato plant. Fibrous roots are seen to be very much restricted in growth. (From work of Ora Smith and L. B. Nash.)

Boron-deficient tubers are smaller than normal and often have a ruptured surface.   The green portion of the plant may be markedly diseased, whereas the tissue within the tuber may show slight symptoms or none at all.   Again, the tubers may develop typical symptoms, such as a local brown discoloration below the skin, generally at the stem end of the tuber, or a brown discoloration of the vascular ring—most pronounced at the stem end but varying in the distance it extends toward the apex—or both.   In a few cases portions of the pith region were reported as having been affected.

Boron deficiency has not as yet become a problem for the potato grower unless boron is needed to prevent certain physiological disturbances within the tubers themselves. More experimental work will be required to determine whether the results reported by European investigators are applicable to conditions in the United States. Although authentic cases of boron deficiency have not been observed in the United States in the field, it is felt that under certain conditions a light broadcast application—10 to 15 pounds per acre—of sodium borate (ordinary borax) may be beneficial.

MANGANESE DEFICIENCY

Manganese has long been known to be present in plants, and in comparatively recent years it has been considered an essential element for plant growth (fig. 5). This element has been shown to

Courtesy of J. R. Neller, Florida Agricultural Experiment Station

Figure 5.—When the supply of manganese is insufficient, potato plants show it. Above, not enough manganese; below, enough manganese.

function in the synthesis of the green coloring matter (chlorophyll) and in photosynthesis—the manufacture of carbohydrate in the plant. To manganese are also ascribed certain stimulating (catalytic) functions, such as the activation of oxidizing enzymes. These functions would seem particularly important in the potato.

Symptoms of manganese deficiency have been noted especially in plants grown on highly calcareous or marly soils or on those that have been heavily overlimed. The first symptom is a chlorotic condition of the leaves, appearing first between the veins as an abnormal coloration which, depending upon the kind of plant, may be either pale green, yellow, or red.   Usually as the trouble becomes intensified the discolored areas between the green veins turn white (plate 6, page 124).   In Australia it has been shown that the "gray speck" or "white wilt" malnutritional disturbance of oats is associated with a lack of available manganese.

Manganese deficiency has been noted on certain truck soils of the Atlantic seaboard, but no clear-cut description of how it affects the potato has been given.

In water culture the deficiency symptoms on potato appear as light-green chlorotic areas in the interveinal tissue of the upper leaves.   Later, numerous little brown patches develop along the veins and these dead areas increase in both size and number.   When the lack of manganese is not severe, the upper parts of the plants become somewhat chlorotic but do not develop dead spots.

Even on highly calcareous or heavily overlimed soils it is likely that 50 to 75 pounds of manganese sulfate per acre would be sufficient to meet any deficiency of this element.   On acid soil there may be an excess of manganese in the soil solution sometimes great enough to create a toxic condition.

SULFUR DEFICIENCY

Sulfur-deficiency symptoms in the potato do not appear to have been recorded; at least, so far as this crop in the United States is concerned, no symptoms seem ever to have been observed under field conditions.   Until recent years the general use of superphosphate as a source of phosphorus in mixed fertilizers has been an insurance against sulfur hunger.   Observations on other plants show that when a shortage of sulfur exists the leaves may become yellow, the stems woody, and root development may decrease.   Sulfates have been found to increase nodular development of certain legumes, notably alfalfa and red clover.   Other researches tend to show that sulfur increases root development and may have a role in chlorophyll development.   Most investigations seem to indicate that symptoms resulting from a shortage of sulfur develop slowly.

In sections where fertilizers containing ordinary superphosphate are used in potato production, the large quantity of calcium sulfate associated with the superphosphate is insurance against a shortage of sulfur.   If, however, concentrated fertilizers are used which contain no sulfur compound, a deficiency on light sandy soils may develop. Obviously, the inclusion of appropriate sulfur compounds in the fertilizer mixtures would then be necessary.

IRON DEFICIENCY

A deficiency of available iron results in a malnutritional chlorosis which requires treatment with an iron salt to overcome the condition or at least to prevent further development. Like those of boron, manganese, and zinc, iron deficiency is usually found on highly calcareous or overlimed soils. This condition makes the iron less available and causes a so-called lime-induced chlorosis. On acid soils a deficiency of iron is a very remote possibility. A search of the agricultural literature fails to disclose any description of iron-deficiency symptoms in relation to potato plants in the field.

In water culture, with iron omitted the first symptom on potato is a slight chlorosis in the young leaves, rather regularly spread over the leaf blade. The points and margins of the leaflets keep their green color longest. Since both the green and yellow pigments are affected, the discolored tissue becomes a clear pale yellow, and in extreme cases almost pure white. The chlorotic tissue is curved in an upward direction. Leaves that develop before the symptom appears retain a normal green color.

Iron deficiency has not been reported on potato soils so far as is known. On acid soils there is usually sufficient iron in the soil solution to take care of growth requirements. As acid soils are usually preferred by potato growers because of the inhibitory effect on the development of the scab organism, there is little possibility of iron deficiency occurring in the production of this crop. To correct iron deficiency in other crops, the salt most generally used is ferrous sulfate.

COPPER DEFICIENCY

Copper is now considered by some to be essential to plant growth, but convincing proof is still lacking as to whether it is essential or indirectly beneficial. No authentic case of copper hunger except on organic soils seems to have been recorded in the agricultural literature. Potato soils of a mineral type rarely, if ever, suffer from lack of copper. This perhaps may be ascribable to the fact that sufficient copper is applied to potato plants in spray mixtures to prevent a deficiency. Some of the added copper gets into the soil, while some may be absorbed by the potato foliage.

Copper deficiency has not been known to occur in the general run of potato soils.   As mentioned, potato plants have the natural store of copper in the soil supplemented by the copper applied in sprays to prevent fungus diseases.

Copper sulfate is the copper salt usually applied to the soil to correct a deficiency of this element.

ZINC DEFICIENCY

Zinc is now accepted provisionally as an element essential for plant growth.   Apparently very little of this element is required by plants, but enough is known to indicate that either some plants need smaller amounts than others or they develop a more elaborate root system which enables them to obtain their needed supply of zinc more readily.   So far as is known, zinc-deficiency symptoms have never been reported as occurring on the potato under field conditions.   Very little of a positive nature is known about the metabolic activities of zinc, some investigators adhering to the belief that its action is indirect.

Potato plants growing in water solutions without zinc are reported to show distinct deficiency symptoms.   Growth of the plants is checked and they do not attain as large a size as those supplied with zinc; the top leaves assume a slightly vertical position, while the margins of some of the leaflets curl slightly upward, suggesting the early symptoms of leaf roll.   The leaves are smaller than those of the controls, the upper internodes are shorter, and the plants are more rigid.

Plants without zinc form grayish-brown to bronze-colored irregular spots, usually appearing first on leaves halfway up the plant, but sometimes on the older or on the younger leaves, and finally on almost all the leaves.   The affected tissue becomes sunken and finally dies.   Badly diseased plants have brownish-colored spots on the leaf petioles and stem.   Plants grown without zinc are significantly shorter than normal and they have a smaller weight of foliage and tubers.

On acid soils enough zinc goes into the soil solution to satisfy the needs of the potato.   It is possible that a deficiency might occur on highly calcareous soils or on those heavily limed.   To correct zinc deficiency in other crops, zinc sulfate has been commonly used.

WHEN MORE THAN ONE ELEMENT IS DEFICIENT

Potato plants grown in river sand with both potassium and phosphorus omitted have normal plant shape and color, but the growth of the stems, roots, and tubers is strongly checked (8).

With phosphorus and nitrogen omitted, the petioles, leaflets, and leaf margins are still more erect than in the case of phosphorus deficiency alone, but the leaves are lighter green in color. The plants are dwarfed and very stiff, the leaflets small, roots and tubers poorly developed.

With potassium and nitrogen omitted, the dark-green color characteristic of potassium deficiency is absent but the interveinal tissue protrudes upward and the leaves and margins of the leaflets are curved downward. The plants remain small and the roots and tubers are poorly developed.

Where all three of these important elements—potassium, phosphorus, and nitrogen—are omitted, growth is severely checked, but the shape and color of the plants are close to normal.

At present very little is known concerning the combined influence of a deficiency of two or more minor elements on the potato plant. For example, with both boron and calcium well below the optimum physiological requirements, the growth reactions might be expected to be a blending of the individual effects of the deficiencies of the two elements, or the symptoms of one deficiency might dominate or mask those of the other.

KEY TO PLANT-NUTRIENT DEFICIENCY SYMPTOMS OF THE POTATO

Reduced growth. More or less localized effects. Parasitic or virus disturbances absent.
Change in color of plant.

ELEMENT
DEFICIENT

A. Effects general on entire plant or confined to older or lower leaves.

   B. General on entire plant; also yellowing and drying up, or "firing," of lower
       leaves. Acute stages develop reddish to purplish color in lower leaves.

      C. Color fades, beginning with tips and margins of leaflets, until all foliage
         becomes a lighter green than normal. In time color may fade to pale-
         yellow. In extreme cases margins of lower leaves become devoid of
         chlorophyll and curl, sometimes "firing." Stunted growth and de-
         foliation are characteristic.................................... Nitrogen

      C. Foliage crinkly and dark green. In acute cases lower leaves become
         purplish. Plants stiffly erect. Petioles, leaflets, and leaf margins take
         an upward direction. Leaves fail to expand to normal size. Growth
         seriously affected when deficiency is acute. Tubers may have rust-
         brown lesions occurring internally.............................. Phosphorus

   B. Localized, occurring as mottling or chlorosis (loss of green color), with or
       without necrotic (dead) spots on lower leaves; practically no drying
       up of lower leaves.

      C. Lower leaves lighter green than normal. Chlorosis begins at tips and
         margins of lowermost leaves and progresses between veins toward
         center of leaflet. Eventually tissue between veins is filled with brown
         dead areas. A definite bulging between veins and thickening of
         foliage occur. Affected leaves are brittle....................... Magnesium

      C. Foliage darker green than normal. Leaf reduced in size. Internodes
         remain short. Plants have a humped-up, droopy appearance. Foliage
         becomes crinkled, and veins appear sunken. Later the older leaves
         become a trifle yellowish. Then a bronzing develops from tips and
         margins and gradually involves the entire plant. This bronzing is
         particularly evident in mass effect. In final stage plants are sus-
         ceptible to attack by parasitic organisms .... Potassium

      C. Lower leaves chlorotic, develop grayish-brown to bronze irregular spots,
         first usually on leaves midway of plant, eventually affecting practi-
         cally all foliage. Spots become sunken and involved tissue finally
         dies. In extreme cases internodes remain short and leaves small and
         thick. Spots develop on petioles and stem, top leaves assume a
         slightly vertical position, and margins of leaves may curl upward.... Zinc

A. Effects localized on newer leaves of plant.

   B. Terminal bud dies, preceded by unusual distortions at the tips or bases of
       the young leaves making up the terminal bud.

      C. The young leaves of the terminal bud are lighter green than normal, the
         light color being most pronounced at the base. Stem tip may die or
         make distorted growth. Internodes remain shortened, giving plant a
         bushy appearance. Leaves become thickened and roll upward, and
         leafstalks become brittle. Anthocyanin (purple pigment) may de-
         velop. Tips and margins, especially of lower leaflets, die prematurely.
         Tubers remain small and often have a ruptured surface............ Boron

      C. Earliest symptom is a light-green band along margins of young leaflets
         of terminal bud. Such areas often die (necrosis), giving leaflet a
         crinkled or buckled appearance. In some cases young leaves at top
         remain folded, causing tip to die. Leaflets often assume a cup shape
         due to upward roll of margin. Axillary buds may show same symp-
         toms as terminal bud. Tubers develop dead spots in the pith region.
         These first show as a diffuse brown discoloration within the vascular
         ring at stem end.. .... Calcium

ELEMENT
DEFICIENT

B. Terminal bud remains alive; chlorosis of newer leaves, with or without spots of dead tissue; veins light or dark green.

    C. Young leaves show loss of turgor and remain permanently wilted. Terminal bud tends to droop when flower buds are developing, especially if shortage is marked. Drying of leaflet tips occurs in advanced stage. No pronounced chlorosis develops... .... Copper

    C. A slight uniform chlorosis first develops in the young leaves. Tips and margins maintain green color longest. Principal veins retain normal green color. Affected tissue gradually becomes pale yellow. Foliage becomes white in extreme cases. No dead spots in evidence........ Iron

    C. Areas lighter green than normal first develop between veins of leaves and in tops of stems. These areas may become yellow to white. Numerous small brown patches develop which in time become more extensive. Lower leaves least affected. Mild shortage causes only slight chlorosis, chiefly confined to upper parts of the stem, and no dead spots develop... Manganese

    C. Symptoms develop slowly. A general yellowing of the leaves and veins occurs similar to that in nitrogen deficiency without the leaves drying up. Growth of the plant is materially checked. Some spotting of the leaves occurs if shortage is acute or prolonged..................... Sulfur

LITERATURE CITED

(1) BONDE, REINER.
    1934. POTATO SPRAYING—THE VALUE OF LATE APPLICATIONS OF MAGNESIUM-BORDEAUX. Amer. Potato Jour. 11:152-156.

(2) BROWN, B. E.
    1922. EFFECT OF BORAX IN FERTILIZER ON THE GROWTH AND YIELD OF POTATOES. U. S. Dept. Agr. Bul. 998, 8 pp.

(3) CAROLUS, R. L.
    1937. CHEMICAL ESTIMATIONS OF THE WEEKLY NUTRIENT LEVEL OF A POTATO CROP. Amer. Potato Jour. 14:141-153, illus.

(4) ———— and BROWN, B. E.
    1935. TRUCK CROP INVESTIGATIONS. MAGNESIUM DEFICIENCY. I. THE VALUE OF MAGNESIUM COMPOUNDS IN VEGETABLE PRODUCTION IN VIRGINIA. Va. Truck Expt. Sta. Bul. 89, pp. 1249-1288, illus.

(5) CHUCKA, JOSEPH A.
    1934. MAGNESIUM DEFICIENCY IN AROOSTOOK POTATO SOILS. Amer. Potato Jour. 11:29-35.

(6) ———— and BROWN, B. E.
    1938. MAGNESIUM STUDIES WITH THE POTATO. Amer. Potato Jour. 15:301-312.

(7) SMITH, ORA, and NASH, L. B.
    1937. EFFECT OF CERTAIN MINOR ELEMENTS ON CHEMICAL COMPOSITION AND COOKING QUALITY OF POTATO TUBERS. Amer. Soc. Hort. Sci. Proc. 34:530-533.

(8) VAN SCHREVEN, D. A.
    1935. PHYSIOLOGICAL EXPERIMENTS WITH POTATOES. Landbouwk. Tijdschr. (Amsterdam) 47:706-726, illus.

Courtesy of Virginia Truck Experiment Station and Bureau of Plant Industry,
United States Department of Agriculture

Plate 1.—Above: The potato plant at the left is normal. The one on the right shows incipient
stages of nitrogen deficiency, of which rolling of leaflets and general reduction in size and vigor
are predominant symptoms. Below: The leaf at the left is normal. The leaf at the right is
from a potato plant growing in soil highly deficient in nitrogen. It is characterized by light-
green color in the center of the leaflets and distinct loss of chlorophyll at the margins, with
tendency to "fire" and curl at the edges.

[119]

Plate 2.—A, Potatoes that received 2,000 pounds per acre of a 4-8-8 fertilizer.

Courtesy of Maine Agricultural Experiment Station

Plate 2.—B, These potatoes received the same applications of nitrogen and potash, but no phosphoric acid. They are darker green in color, stunted in growth, the foliage is crinkly, and the leaflets fail to expand normally. In such plants growth continues for an abnormally long time.

Plate 3.—A deficiency of potassium in the potato plant retards growth and reduces the size of leaves, which lose their smooth surface, becoming crinkled and droopy. In the early stage the plant takes on a dark-green color. Later the leaves become yellowish, with a characteristic bronzing which, starting from the tip and edge, gradually involves the entire leaf.

Virginia Truck Experiment Station and Bureau of Plant Industry,
United States Department of Agriculture

Plate 4.—Magnesium deficiency as it affects the potato. Four stages, including (1) normal leaf; (2) first symptom at tip of terminal leaflet; (3 and 4) advancing stages. Loss of color and "firing" of foliage are prominent symptoms. Foliage is characteristically brittle in advanced stages.

Courtesy of J. A. Chucka and S. M. Raleigh, Maine Agricultural Experiment Station

Plate 5.—A, Calcium deficiency (right) produces a light-green band along the margins of the young leaves of the potato plant and causes the terminal bud to cease to function, giving a rosetted effect. In serious cases the terminal bud dies and subsequent growth is from the sides. Normal plant at left.

Courtesy of J. W. Shive, New Jersey Agricultural Experiment Station

Plate 5.—B, Right, potato plant lacking boron in its diet. Leaves thicken and the margins roll upward. The main characteristic is death of the terminal bud. Some chlorosis develops, and petioles become brittle. Leaf points and margins die prematurely. Left, terminal growth of this plant was completely arrested by boron deficiency.

[123]

Plate 6.—A, Normal potato plant at the right. The plant at the left did not receive manganese, and the results of the deficiency are clearly shown. Light-green color developing in the interveinal tissue is the first symptom.

Plate 6.—B, The final stage of manganese deficiency is shown in the potato leaf on the left, which is practically devoid of chlorophyll. Normal potato leaf on right.

[124]

CHAPTER V

Plant-Nutrient Deficiency Symptoms in Cotton

By H. P. Cooper [1]

T HE climatic conditions and soil materials existing in the South-eastern States have resulted in the development of soil complexes which give marked response to applications of fertilizer. This has been an important determining factor in the many changes and drastic readjustments that have occurred in the agricultural pattern of the southeastern region. The virgin soils were capable of supporting a more or less diversified, self-sufficient type of agriculture. As long as suitable virgin land was available for clearing, the farm soils were abandoned when they became depleted and were allowed to return to trees. The lack of any more available areas of virgin soil finally forced farmers to use more chemical fertilizers. In addition to adjusting agriculture to depleted soils, it was necessary to meet the competition of other agricultural regions and also to develop a satisfactory economic and social system.

The agricultural systems in the Southeast during various periods have depended primarily on a single cash crop suitable for cultivation on an extensive scale and with relatively high value per acre, such as tobacco, rice, or cotton, or a small number of such crops at one time. This in itself has tended to bring about serious depletion of soil resources and to increase the necessity for using chemical fertilizers. The cash crops used had, in turn, to produce sufficient income to purchase the fertilizer necessary to maintain the productivity of the soil. The use of relatively large amounts of chemical fertilizers on crops of high acre value is widespread and is undoubtedly a sound economic practice. Large quantities may be used before reaching the point of diminishing returns.

The six Southeastern States from North Carolina to Mississippi use more than 50 percent of the fertilizer consumed in the United States. The cotton crop receives a very large proportion of this fertilizer. Prior to 1930, approximately 30 percent of the total tonnage of fertilizers used in the United States was used in the production of cotton. Reduction in the cotton acreage in recent years has decreased the amount to about 20 percent—slightly less than the

---

[1] H. P. Cooper is Dean of the School of Agriculture, Clemson Agricultural College, and Director of the South Carolina Agricultural Experiment Station.

total quantity used on corn. The use of complete fertilizers is more general in the Southeast than in the western section of the Cotton Belt. In the latter the river-bottom soils usually receive only nitrogen when fertilized, but the upland soils respond to complete fertilizers.

RESPONSES OF COTTON TO FERTILIZERS

Botanically cotton is a perennial plant, but it is grown as an annual crop in the main cotton-producing sections of this country. The plant has an indefinite growth period and is considered a long-season crop. Thus it is possible to study the appearance and extent of deficiency symptoms over a considerable period.

The deficiency symptoms in the cotton plant usually described are those commonly corrected by the addition of certain fertilizer materials. Growth response is usually attributed to a particular nutrient added to the soil. However, as most of the fertilizers commonly used contain a large number of nutrients as impurities, it is difficult to differentiate their effects clearly. Since there has been a very limited amount of carefully controlled experimental work with nutrient cultures in the case of cotton, it is not possible to state definitely that a particular symptom in the cotton plant results from the lack of a particular nutrient. Investigators may differ widely in their interpretation of the cause of a certain symptom. Because of the limitations of the experimental information available, it seems best at present to relate the deficiency symptoms observed in cotton to the fertilizer materials that correct them rather than to single elements.

It is also often impossible to differentiate between symptoms resulting from a lack of available nutrients in the soil and those due to diseases and insect pests. Even when there is an abundance of available nutrients, their absorption or utilization may be affected by injuries to plants caused by diseases or insects, and deficiency symptoms may appear. Such situations may lead to much confusion in interpreting experimental results unless all the factors involved are carefully considered.

Deficiencies of potassium and possibly of sulfur are most likely to occur during relatively dry growing seasons, whereas deficiencies of magnesium and manganese are more frequent during relatively wet growing seasons. Some important potassium and sulfur compounds are only slightly soluble in the soil solution, and there may not be sufficient amounts of these nutrients available when the season is dry. Certain magnesium and manganese compounds, on the other hand, are highly soluble and may be readily leached from the soil. This is true, for example, of magnesium nitrate, magnesium chloride, and magnesium sulfate. Magnesium-deficiency symptoms are particularly likely to occur in wet seasons if large amounts of nitrates, chlorides, or sulfates have been added to the soil in fertilizers.

The soil reaction also may be an important factor. The solubility of potassium, manganese, iron, and boron may be decreased by the addition of large amounts of lime material to the soil to decrease acidity. The strongly acid, highly leached, gray sandy-loam soils of the South Atlantic Coastal Plain are often very low in manganese, iron, and boron, and the availability of these nutrients may be reduced by the use of lime, resulting in deficiency symptoms in the plants.

The rate of growth of cotton may be another important factor in nutrient deficiencies. With slow growth, soil nutrients may dissolve fast enough to meet the needs of the plants and prevent marked deficiencies. Slow-growing plants in pot cultures in the greenhouse in winter may not show deficiency symptoms, whereas plants grown on the same soil in the field may show marked symptoms. Yield per acre has a similar effect. The rate at which nutrients become available may be adequate for small yields. This is very often true with potash; where the yields are low, there may be little response from the use of potash in the fertilizer, but where they are high, the response may be marked.

Deficiency symptoms in cotton will be described in the succeeding pages. A brief key to symptoms is given at the end of the chapter. In both the descriptions of symptoms and the key, the limitations already described should be kept in mind. Following the descriptions of symptoms, some important aspects of the relationship of soil characteristics and plant composition to nutritional deficiencies and the fertilizer needs of the cotton plant will be discussed.

DEFICIENCY SYMPTOMS

NITROGEN

Nitrogen-deficiency symptoms in cotton are characterized by relatively meager growth and yellowish-green color of foliage. The older leaves are the most severely affected, as is shown by the fact that the lower leaves dry up and are prematurely shed. The typical growth response of cotton to an application of 600 pounds per acre of a 6-10-4 fertilizer on Hartsells sandy loam at the Sand Mountain

Agricultural Experiment Station in Alabama is shown in figure 1. Figure 2 shows a plant suffering from nitrogen deficiency, grown in soil to which was added 600 pounds per acre of a 0-10-4 fertilizer (no nitrogen). The plant is small, but the individual leaves and flower buds are approximately normal in size.

Courtesy of Alabama Agricultural Experiment Station

Figure 1.—Normal cotton plant showing growth produced when fertilized with 600 pounds of 6-10-4 per acre.

The yellowish-green color of leaf resulting from a deficiency of nitrogen is illustrated in plate 1, page 143.

PHOSPHORUS

Phosphorus is usually the limiting nutrient in virgin cotton soils in humid climates. The symptoms of phosphorus deficiency in cotton are not so pronounced as those caused by a lack of nitrogen. The

Figure 2.—Effect of nitrogen deficiency on growth of cotton. This small, yellowish-green plant was grown on a plot receiving 600 pounds per acre of 0-10-4 fertilizer.

most outstanding are a dark-green color of the foliage and a generally dwarfed type of plant. The dwarfed plant shown in figure 3 was grown at the Sand Mountain station on Hartsells sandy loam to which 600 pounds per acre of a 6-0-4 fertilizer (no phosphate) was added. The dark-green color of an individual leaf is illustrated in plate 1 and in plate 2, B (pages 143, 144). Figure 4 shows the field condition of phosphorus-deficient plants grown on Orangeburg fine sandy loam at the South Carolina Agricultural Experiment Station. It is clear from figure 4 that a deficiency of phosphorus results in delayed fruiting and maturity—a very serious problem where boll-weevil damage is heavy.

POTASSIUM

The symptoms in cotton associated with a lack of potash in the fertilizer may be very pronounced, and the problem has been given much study. A lack of potash salts often results in a striking malnutritional symptom commonly called "cotton rust" or "potash hunger." Typical symptoms in the cotton leaf are illustrated in plate 3, A, page 145. The first symptom in the leaf is a yellowish-white mottling. The leaf color changes to light yellowish green, and yellow spots appear between the veins. The centers of these spots die, and numer-

Figure 3.—Effect of phosphorus deficiency on growth of cotton. This small dark-green plant was grown on a plot receiving 600 pounds per acre of a 6-0-4 fertilizer.

ous brown specks occur at the tip, around the margin, and between the veins. The tip and the margin of the leaf break down first and curl downward. As the physiological break-down progresses, the whole leaf finally becomes reddish brown in color, dries, and is shed prematurely. The premature shedding of leaves prevents the proper development of bolls, which are dwarfed and immature. Figure 5, and plates 3, B, and 4 (pages 145, 146) illustrate both leaf and boll

Figure 4.—Effect of phosphorus deficiency on maturity of cotton. Plot at left received 4-0-4 fertilizer and shows typical late maturity. Plot at right received 4-8-2 fertilizer.

conditions in plants grown on Orangeburg fine sandy loam at the South Carolina station. Many of the bolls fail to open and the fiber is of poor quality.

CALCIUM

In spite of the very large calcium requirement of the cotton plant discussed later in this article, no definite information is available on calcium-deficiency symptoms. The calcium oxide content is 2.17 percent of the plant and 26.53 percent of the ash left after the plant is burned. Considered on the basis of chemical equivalents, this is a larger percentage than that of any other element except nitrogen. Since sufficient quantities of calcium for the nutritional requirements of cotton are added to soils in superphosphate, there has been little need for a special consideration of this nutrient. The omission of calcium from the fertilizer, however, has markedly affected growth of cotton on some soils. The calcium content of superphosphate should always be considered in any cotton-fertilizer program, and much of the growth response on certain soils may be attributed to it.

MAGNESIUM

The characteristic magnesium-deficiency symptom in cotton is a purplish-red leaf with green veins. Late in the season it is some-

Figure 5.—Cotton showing potassium-deficiency symptoms. Plot at right received no potash. The leaves shed prematurely and the bolls are dwarfed. Plot at left received a complete fertilizer.

times difficult to distinguish between the color due to magnesium deficiency and that due to age or maturity, though the latter is apt to be orange red rather than purplish red. Magnesium-deficiency symptoms appear first on the lower leaves, as is shown in plate 5, A (page 147) and figures 6 and 7. The leaves are shed prematurely. This checks the growth of the plant and results in low production. The typical purplish-red leaves and the premature shedding of foliage are illustrated in plate 5, B.

SULFUR

Sulfur deficiency in cotton is not commonly observed in sections where the ordinary fertilizer materials are applied, since such materials as ammonium sulfate and the common superphosphates contain considerable quantities of this nutrient—enough, together with the sulfur from rain water, for most soils.   On certain unfertilized

Figure 6.—Magnesium-deficient leaf at right; normal leaf at left.

Courtesy of J. E. McMurtrey, Jr., United States Department of Agriculture

Figure 7.—Cotton plants illustrating magnesium-deficiency symptoms.   Note that lower leaves are affected first and are shed prematurely.

soils, or where there is no sulfur in the fertilizer used, sulfur deficiency may occur in cotton. Sulfur seems to be essential in the formation of chlorophyll, and plants grown in soil with an inadequate supply of this element develop a light-green color. Figure 8 and plate 6 (page 148) show the dwarfed growth and yellow color resulting from sulfur deficiency.

BORON

Boron deficiency has been observed in various plants under a wide variety of soil and climatic conditions. The deficiency symptoms in

Courtesy of F. L. Davis, Louisiana Agricultural Experiment Station

Figure 8.—Effect of sulfur deficiency on growth of cotton. The plot on the right received no sulfur in the fertilizer.

the cotton plant first appear in the terminal growth. The terminal buds often die, and this checks linear growth and may produce dwarfed, many-branched plants such as that illustrated in figure 9. The younger leaves are yellowish green in color. At a low boron level, flower buds become chlorotic, the bracts flare open, and the buds drop from the plant.

ZINC

Zinc deficiency in cotton is apparently not very common. Inadequate quantities of this element may result in the leaves becoming extremely chlorotic, with areas of dead tissue. The chlorosis resulting from a deficiency of zinc in water cultures is shown in figure 10.

Courtesy of K. T. Holley, Georgia Agricultural Experiment Station

Figure 9.—Right, dwarfed, many-branched cotton plant resulting from boron deficiency. Left, normal plant.

Figure 10.—Cotton leaf showing zinc-deficiency symptoms. Note extreme chlorotic condition and the darker colored veins.

MANGANESE

Manganese apparently tends to accumulate in the leaves of plants. In the absence of adequate quantities of this nutrient, the upper, or younger, leaves are the first to show a lack of chlorophyll. They become yellowish gray or reddish gray in color, with green veins. The characteristic deficiency symptoms observed in solution cultures are shown in figure 11. Manganese deficiency is not commonly observed under field conditions except on certain soil types or where relatively large quantities of lime material have been added to the soil.

Courtesy of New Jersey Agricultural Experiment Station

Figure 11.—Right, manganese-deficient leaves. Left, normal leaf.

PREVENTING NUTRIENT DEFICIENCIES IN COTTON

The occurrence of deficiency symptoms is most often observed in the regions where it is common practice to use commercial fertilizer in the production of cotton. It is usually possible at a relatively low cost to eliminate the symptoms by including the deficient nutrients in the fertilizer combination.

Suggested rates per acre for the application of various nutrients to prevent serious deficiencies are listed below:

Nitrogen—15 to 50 pounds of nitrogen.
Phosphorus—15 to 50 pounds of phosphoric acid.
Potassium—15 to 50 pounds of potash.
Magnesium—10 to 20 pounds of soluble magnesia or 100 to 200 pounds of dolomitic limestone in the row with the fertilizer.
Boron—2 to 5 pounds of boron.
Zinc—20 to 40 pounds of zinc sulfate or the equivalent.
Sulfur—use fertilizer materials containing sulfur.
Manganese—25 to 50 pounds of manganese sulfate or the equivalent.

RELATION OF SOIL CHARACTERISTICS TO DEFICIENCIES

The Red and Yellow Podzolic soils are the most common soils in the southeastern section of the Cotton Belt. The Piedmont and Coastal Plain soils are the predominant groups in the area. The parent rock material from which most of these soils were derived was acidic, though there are local areas of basic rock. The acid nature of the parent rock and the relief, climate, and cropping practices followed have all been favorable to excessive leaching and depletion of the nutrients in the soil. The group of Yellow soils particularly is relatively low in necessary plant nutrients. Under normal soil-formation processes—that is, without cultivation—the leaching of soluble material keeps the soil solution in balance and results in nutritional complexes of the soil suitable for the growth of plants.

The Red soils usually contain more nutrients than the Yellow soils. They are often well supplied with the elements that are needed in small quantities, such as manganese and iron. High acidity in Red soils, however, may result in the presence in the soil solution of toxic quantities of certain of these nutrients.

Excessive leaching of certain acid Yellow soils may reduce to a very low level both the major nutrients and those needed only in small quantities. Liming may then decrease the availability of what is left of some of the so-called minor nutrients, and this may account for the effect of liming in reducing the productivity of certain soils.

An understanding of the nutritional complexes that may develop in different soils under various conditions requires a careful consideration of the solubility, availability, and leachability of the nutrient materials that may be present.

INFLUENCE OF SOLUBILITY OF NUTRIENT COMPOUNDS

The data in table 1 on the solubility of important plant nutrients may make it possible to predict the relative amount of leaching of various materials and to know the general characteristics of the resultant nutritional complexes that are likely to develop. Most of the solubility values were taken from the International Critical Tables.[2]

The simple acids, such as hydrochloric, sulfuric, nitric, phosphoric, and boric, are very soluble in water. The presence of these acids in the soil results in ready solubility and availability of such nutrients as manganese, iron, and boron; whereas in limed soils, in

---

[2] Published by the National Research Council in 7 volumes, 1926-30. See v. 3.

which calcium and hydroxides (combinations of chemicals with hydrogen and oxygen) are increased, there may be a marked decrease in the solubility and availability of certain so-called minor nutrients.

The order of insolubility of hydroxides (the last line of table 1) is as follows: Copper, manganese, iron, and magnesium. Heavy applications of lime materials often reduce the availability of such nutrients and limit plant growth to such an extent that crop yields are significantly lowered. On the other hand, the solubility of nitrates, chlorides, and sulfates of manganese is 7.66, 5.93, and 4.49 moles respectively. (A mole is a unit of measurement in chemistry, based on the molecule.) Likewise, the solubility of the chlorides, nitrates, and sulfates of iron is 5.18, 4.67, and 1.74 moles respectively.

Increasing the calcium content of the soil will also affect the solubility and availability of the boron in the soil. This is shown by the relative solubilities of potassium borate, boric acid (shown opposite the line Borate under the column Hydrogen), sodium borate, and calcium borate, which are 0.825, 0.809, 0.129, and 0.0247 moles respectively. Excessive amounts of lime in the soil may result in a marked boron deficiency in cotton as shown in figure 9.

TABLE 1.—APPROXIMATE SOLUBILITY OF CERTAIN PLANT-NUTRIENT MATERIALS, EXPRESSED IN MOLES [1]

Ion	Potassium	Sodium	Calcium	Magnesium	Hydrogen	Manganese[2]	Iron[2]	Copper[3]
Chloride	4.61	6.13	6.70	5.76	[4]	5.93	5.18	5.58
Sulfate	.637	1.33	.015	2.88	[4]	4.49	1.74	1.30
Nitrate	3.08	10.31	7.88	5.00	[4]	7.66	4.67	6.56
Phosphate	9.10	.68	.00009	.0006	[5]	[6]	[7]	[7]
Borate	.825	.129	.0247	[7]	0.809			
Hydroxide	19.90	27.20	.0218	.0002		.000005	.00007	[7]

[1] Most determinations made at temperatures between 20° and 30° C.
[2] Manganese and iron at lower valence.
[3] Copper as cupric compounds.
[4] Infinitely soluble.
[5] Very soluble.
[6] Slightly soluble.
[7] Insoluble.

An increase in the content of potassium or sodium in the soil solution may markedly increase the solubility and availability of both major and so-called minor nutrients, as is indicated by the high solubility values for the compounds of these elements included in table 1.

THE COMPOSITION OF THE COTTON PLANT

The interrelation between nutrients, particularly in a group or family of elements, should be given consideration in studying the nutrition and chemical analysis of plants. An abundance of one member of a family of elements may enable the plant to grow successfully with a minimum quantity of an essential nutrient belonging to the same family.

In the alkali-earth family there may be a supplemental relation between calcium and strontium in their effects on the productivity of soils. In the alkali family the presence of rubidium or sodium may affect the growth response of cotton to potassium. Likewise, under certain conditions there may be some interrelation between nitrogen, phosphorus, and arsenic in the nitrogen family.

The effect of the sodium content of fertilizer on the growth response of cotton to various rates of application of potash is discussed in the next section of this chapter. It clearly illustrates the possible relationships between nutrients, which must be considered in a critical study of nutritional-deficiency symptoms in plants.

The average chemical analysis of 28 samples of cotton plants collected from different soil series extensively utilized for cotton production in South Carolina is shown in table 2. As already noted,

TABLE 2.—AVERAGE CHEMICAL ANALYSES OF 28 SAMPLES OF COTTON PLANTS

(South Carolina Agricultural Experiment Station)

Material	Percent of plant	Percent of ash
Potash (K_2O)...............	0.907	11.09
Soda (Na_2O)...............	.557	6.81
Lime (CaO)...............	2.170	26.53
Magnesia (MgO)...........	.686	8.39
Alumina (Al_2O_3)...........	.050	.611
Manganic oxide (Mn_3O_4)....	.037	.452
Ferric oxide (Fe_2O_3)	.073	.892
Nitrogen (N)...............	1.733	21.18
Chlorine (Cl)...............	.679	8.301
Phosphoric acid (P_2O_5)......	.500	6.113
Sulfur (S).................	.255	3.117
Silica (SiO_2)...............	.133	1.626
Ash......................	8.179	....
Moisture..................	9.09	....

calcium oxide makes up 26.53 percent of the ash of these plants. This high content of calcium in the cotton plant is interesting and significant. Cotton is tolerant of rather high soil acidity, but it has a high calcium requirement, and this explains in part why cotton yields have been greatly increased by applications of superphosphate. The sulfur supplied by superphosphate is also required by the plant in rather large quantities. The omission of either calcium or sulfur from the fertilizer may have a marked effect upon the yield of cotton.

The high sodium oxide content of cotton plants—6.81 percent of the ash—is also interesting. If the sodium is considered on a chemical-equivalent basis, it would be equal to approximately 10.28 percent of potassium oxide. This chemical-equivalent value for the sodium is very nearly equal to the 11.09 percent of potassium oxide actually found in the ash. It should be understood that nutrients are utilized by plants on a chemical-equivalent rather than a weight basis.

USE OF SODIUM BY COTTON

The capacity of the cotton plant to utilize sodium probably accounts in part for the increase in yields observed from the use of fertilizers containing this element. The seed-cotton yields shown in table 3 were obtained when the cotton was fertilized with 600 pounds per acre of a 5-10-0 fertilizer in addition to the potash indicated, and side dressed with 15 pounds of nitrogen per acre. On half the plots sodium nitrate was used as the source of nitrogen. The amount of sodium added as sodium nitrate was equivalent to approximately 200 pounds of sodium oxide per acre.

TABLE 3.—COMPARATIVE YIELDS OF SEED COTTON WHEN THE EQUIVALENT OF 200 POUNDS PER ACRE OF SODIUM OXIDE WAS INCLUDED IN A 600-POUND APPLICATION OF 7.5-10-0 FERTILIZER IN ADDITION TO THE POTASH INDICATED

Potash in fertilizer (pounds per acre), with and without sodium	Average yield per acre	Increase due to use of sodium with varying amounts of potash		Yield expressed as percentage of that with no potash and no sodium
	Pounds	*Pounds*	*Percent*	*Percent*
No potash:				
No sodium.........	311			100
Sodium............	535	224	72	172
15 pounds potash:				
No sodium.........	772			248
Sodium............	988	216	28	318
45 pounds potash:				
No sodium.........	1,133			364
Sodium............	1,340	207	18	431
60 pounds potash:				
No sodium.........	1,243			400
Sodium............	1,450	207	17	466

The data in table 3 represent the average yield of four plots for each treatment over a 9-year period. Where no potash was used there was a 72-percent increase in yield from the use of sodium in the fertilizer. There was a gradual decrease in the response from the use of sodium as the amount of potash was increased. This suggests that when sufficient potash is added to the soil, there is less growth response from the addition of sodium. The available data on the relation of the use of sodium and potassium by the cotton plant indicate that, after the addition of about 20 to 25 pounds of potash to the soil, sodium may be almost as effective as additional potash in increasing the yields of cotton on many cotton soils.

A lack of consideration of the capacity of the cotton plant to utilize sodium where potassium is deficient has led to a misinterpretation of the significance of certain experimental data. This is strikingly illustrated by the increased yields and the absence of potassium-deficiency symptoms in experiments involving the application of varying amounts of potash when sodium was also included in the fertilizer.

KEY TO PLANT-NUTRIENT DEFICIENCY SYMPTOMS OF COTTON

Causal parasites or viruses absent. More or less localized effects and decreased growth.

ELEMENT
DEFICIENT

A. Effects localized on older or lower leaves or more or less general on whole plant.

  B. Symptoms local, occurring as mottling or chlorosis with or without necrotic spotting (areas of dead tissue) on lower leaves; little or no drying up of lower leaves.

    C. Lower leaves brittle, curved or cupped under, with yellowish-white mottling between veins. Necrotic spots present................... Potassium

    C. Lower leaves purplish red with green veins...................... Magnesium

  B. Symptoms general, with yellowing and drying, or "firing," of lower leaves.

    C. Plants light green; lower leaves yellow, drying to brownish color...... Nitrogen

    C. Plants dark green, leaves and plants small, maturity delayed......... Phosphorus

A. Effects localized on terminal growth (upper and bud leaves).

  B. Dieback involving terminal buds, resulting in many-branched plant. Young leaves yellowish green, flower buds chlorotic.................. Boron

  B. Terminal buds remain alive; chlorosis of upper or bud leaves.

    C. Leaves yellowish gray or reddish gray with green veins.............. Manganese

    C. Leaves green in color, plant dwarfed............................ Sulfur

SELECTED REFERENCES

(1) COOPER, H. P.
  1931. SAND DROWN OR MAGNESIUM DEFICIENCY IN COTTON. S. C. Agr. Expt. Sta. Ann. Rpt. 44: 36.

(2) ——
  1932. SYMPTOMS OF MAGNESIUM DEFICIENCY IN CROPS. S. C. Agr. Expt. Sta. Ann. Rpt. 45: 30-35, illus.

(3) ——
  1933. NUTRIENT DEFICIENCY SYMPTOMS IN CERTAIN PLANTS. Assoc. South. Agr. Workers Proc. 34: 80-81.

(4) —— ROGERS, W. B., and WALLACE, R. W.
  1934. EXPERIMENTS WITH POTASH FERTILIZER FOR COTTON. S. C. Agr. Expt. Sta. Ann. Rpt. 47: 16-18.

(5) —— WALLACE, R. W., and ROGERS, W. B.
  1932. EXPERIMENTS WITH POTASH FERTILIZERS. S. C. Agr. Expt. Sta. Ann. Rpt. 45: 28-30, illus.

(6) EATON, F. M.
  1932. BORON REQUIREMENTS OF COTTON. Soil Sci. 34: 301-305.

(7) GEORGIA EXPERIMENT STATION.
  1933-34. COTTON NUTRITION. Ga. Expt. Sta. Ann. Rpt. 46: 29.

(8) GILBERT, W. W.
  1924. COTTON DISEASES AND THEIR CONTROL. U. S. Dept. Agr. Farmers' Bul. 1187, 32 pp., illus.

(9) HIBBARD, R. P.
  1910. COTTON DISEASES IN MISSISSIPPI. Miss. Agr. Expt. Sta. Bul. 140, 27 pp., illus.

(10) HOAGLAND, D. R., CHANDLER, W. H., and HIBBARD, P. L.
  1936. LITTLE-LEAF OR ROSETTE OF FRUIT TREES. V. EFFECT OF ZINC ON THE GROWTH OF PLANTS OF VARIOUS TYPES IN CONTROLLED SOIL AND WATER CULTURE EXPERIMENTS. Amer. Soc. Hort. Sci. Proc. 33: 131-141, illus.

(11) HOLLEY, K. T., and DULIN, T. G.
  1939. INFLUENCE OF BORON ON FLOWER-BUD DEVELOPMENT IN COTTON. Jour. Agr. Res. 59: 541-545, illus.

(12) Jones, L. H.
      1936. diagnosis of plant troubles with diphénylamine. Plant Physiol. 11: 207-209.

(13) King, B. M.
      1931. cotton production in missouri. Mo. Agr. Expt. Sta. Bul. 299, 34 pp., illus.

(14) McMurtrey, J. E., Jr.
      1938. distinctive plant symptoms caused by deficiency of any one of the chemical elements essential for normal development. Bot. Rev. 4: 183-203.

(15) Maddux, H. T.
      1933. extra potash controls rust and wilt. Com. Fert. 46(1): 14-17, illus.

(16) Milad, Y.
      1939. physiological studies in lime-induced chlorosis. Chem. Abs. 33: 7462.

(17) Miller, E. C.
      1938. plant physiology, with reference to the green plant. Ed. 2, 1201 pp., illus. New York. (See especially pp. 324, 328.)

(18) Moore, J. H., and Rankin, W. H.
      1937. influence of "rust" on quality and yield of cotton and the relation of potash applications to control. N. C. Agr. Expt. Sta. Bul. 308, 18 pp., illus.

(19) Neal, D. C.
      1928. cotton diseases in mississippi and their control. Miss. Agr. Expt. Sta. Bul. 248, 30 pp., illus.

(20) ——— and Gilbert, W. W.
      1935. cotton diseases and methods of control. U. S. Dept. Agr. Farmers' Bul. 1745, 34 pp., illus.

(21) New Jersey State Agricultural Experiment Station.
      1936. boron and manganese deficiency. N. J. Agr. Expt. Sta. Ann. Rpt. 57: 78-80.

(22) ———
      1937. level of the boron supply in relation to nitrogen metabolism in cotton. N. J. Agr. Expt. Sta. Ann. Rpt. 58: 84-85.

(23) Novikov, V. A., and Sadovskaya, R. O.
      1939. soaking of cotton seed in boric acid as a means to satisfy its boron requirement and increase salt resistance. Chem. Abs. 33: 8891.

(24) Oakes, J. Y.
      1938. the effects of potash fertilizer on cotton in louisiana. La. Agr. Expt. Sta. Bul. 291, 11 pp., illus.

(25) Reynolds, E. B.
      1930. the effect of sulphur on yield of certain crops. Tex. Agr. Expt. Sta. Bul. 408, 23 pp., illus.

(26) Russell, Sir E. John.
      1937. soil conditions and plant growth. Ed. 7, 655 pp., illus. London, New York, [etc.]. (See especially p. 65.)

(27) Shive, J. W.
      1936. the adequacy of the boron and manganese content of natural nitrate of soda to support plant growth in sand culture. N. J. Agr. Expt. Sta. Bul. 603, 36 pp., illus.

(28) Wadleigh, C. H., and Shive, J. W.
      1939. a microchemical study of the effects of boron deficiency in cotton seedlings. Soil Sci. 47: 33-36.

(29) Walker, M. N.
      1930. cotton diseases in florida. Fla. Agr. Expt. Sta. Bul. 214, 32 pp., illus.

(30) Ware, J. O., and Young, V. H.
      1934. control of cotton wilt and "rust." Ark. Agr. Expt. Sta. Bul. 308, 23 pp.

(31) Williams, C. B.
      1937. study starvation signs on tobacco and cotton. Better Crops with Plant Food 21 (10): 14-15, 40-41, illus.

Courtesy of Alabama Agricultural Experiment Station

Plate 1.—Cotton leaves showing normal condition and nitrogen- and phosphorus-deficiency symptoms. Left, normal green color. Center, yellowish-green color due to nitrogen deficiency. Right, dark-green color characteristic of phosphorus deficiency.

Courtesy of Pee Dee Experiment Station, Florence, S. C.

Plate 2.—A, Nitrogen deficiency in cotton is characterized by yellow color of foliage and slow growth. The plot on the left did not receive nitrogen in the fertilizer; the plot on the right received a complete fertilizer.

Courtesy of Alabama Agricultural Experiment Station

Plate 2.—B, Effect of phosphorus on color and growth of cotton. Right, the small, dark-green plants exhibiting phosphorus deficiency received a 6-0-4 fertilizer. Left, normal green plants that received a 6-10-4 fertilizer.

Plate 3.—A, Cotton leaves showing potassium-deficiency symptoms. Left, normal green leaf. Right, reddish-brown leaves with ragged margins due to potassium deficiency.

Plate 3.—B, Cotton boll showing potassium-deficiency symptoms. Left, normal, large, well-opened boll. Right, small, immature, partly opened boll resulting from a deficiency of potassium.

[145]

Courtesy of Pee Dee Experiment Station, Florence, S. C.

Plate 4.—Growth characteristics due to potassium deficiency. The plot at the top did not receive potash in the fertilizer. Note the premature shedding of the leaves and the immature, partly opened bolls. The normal growth of plants that received a complete fertilizer is shown at the bottom.

Plate 5.—A, Cotton leaves showing purplish-red color with green veins resulting from magnesium deficiency. Leaf at left is normal.

Courtesy of J. E. McMurtrey, Jr., United States Department of Agriculture

Plate 5.—B, The plants in the foreground did not receive magnesium. Note the purplish-red color of the lower leaves and premature shedding of foliage. The normal plants in the background received a complete fertilizer, including magnesium.

[147]

Courtesy of F. L. Davis, Louisiana Agricultural Experiment Station.

Plate 6.—Sulfur deficiency in cotton. The plant on the right did not receive sulfur in the fertilizer. Note the dwarfed growth and yellow leaves with green veins. These characteristics are similar to nitrogen-deficiency symptoms, though the green color of the veins may be more distinct in the case of sulfur deficiency. The large, normal green plant on the left received sulfur.

CHAPTER VI

Plant-Nutrient Deficiencies in Vegetable or Truck-Crop Plants

By J. J. Skinner [1]

IN THE larger truck-crop or vegetable-growing areas of the United States the soils are generally sandy, and because of the way they were formed they are naturally low in mineral constituents. Plantfood minerals are possibly leached more readily from soils of this character than from other kinds. In the growing of vegetable crops, therefore, it is common practice and necessary for successful production to add commercial fertilizers to supply the so-called major plantfoods—nitrogen, phosphorus, potassium, calcium, and sulfur—which are needed in relatively large quantities in such soils. If any of these nutrients is deficient in the soil, malnutrition will in all probability be manifested in abnormalities of the plant and in decreased yields.

Until recent years nitrogen, phosphorus, potassium, and calcium were the only plant nutrients it was considered necessary to supply to meet the requirements of vegetable crops. But in certain local areas throughout the country abnormal plant development and partial crop failures have occurred which are now attributed to deficiencies of essential plantfoods other than those ordinarily supplied in commercial fertilizers. Such deficiencies occur most frequently in the belt of sandy soils along the Atlantic seaboard. Deficiencies of the so-called minor plant nutrients are not confined to this region, however, for reports have been made of truck-crop failures due to such deficiencies on soils in limited areas from the Atlantic to the Pacific.

Evaluation of the plantfood content of a soil and of the quantity and quality of nutrients required for normal growth and profitable yields of vegetable crops is essential to efficient production and indispensable to fertilizer practice. The nutrient requirements of vegetable crops vary, although many plants in this group must have large quantities of plantfoods available for the rapid growth necessary to produce large yields of good-quality products. The symptoms of malnutrition due to a deficiency of an essential plantfood may, of course, be manifested differently in different crops. Nevertheless there is a similarity in the nutrient

---

[1] J. J. Skinner is Senior Biochemist, Bureau of Plant Industry, United States Department of Agriculture.

requirements, growth characteristics, plant development, and foliage coloration in many of the vegetable plants.

In this chapter more consideration is given to symptoms in tomatoes than in other vegetables because the nutritional problems of this crop have been widely studied. The deficiency symptoms in the tomato are similar in many respects to those in other vegetable plants. In addition, however, outstanding symptoms of deficiencies that have become economically important in other vegetable crops are discussed and illustrated.

NITROGEN DEFICIENCY

It is well known that nitrogen is essential to the maintenance of soil fertility and to the growth of all plants. It is especially important for the production of vegetable crops of good quality. For rapid growth and the synthesis of essential proteins, these plants require an available supply of nitrogen in the soil at all periods of development. At the same time, the content of total nitrogen in most truck-crop soils is relatively low, and available inorganic nitrogen compounds may be easily lost from the soil through crop removal, leaching, and erosion. A deficiency of nitrogen in soils used for growing vegetables results in retarded growth, poor color, appearance, and quality of plants, and low production. A sufficient supply of available nitrogen in the soil, maintained by the growing of leguminous crops, the turning under of vegetation, or the use of nitrogen fertilizers, helps in getting plants off to a quick start and has a tendency to encourage stem and leaf development. Plants grown with plenty of nitrogen available will make more rapid growth and have a normal deep-green color.

For the development of most vegetables, adequate amounts of phosphorus, potassium, and certain other plantfoods as well as of nitrogen are essential. For the normal growth of turnips, for instance, experiments have indicated the necessity of potassium in conjunction with nitrogen. No amount of available phosphorus and potassium, however, will overcome a deficiency of nitrogen in any vegetable crop.

Tomato plants and vegetable plants in general may show indications of nitrogen deficiency at any period of growth. In most cases a general indication of deficiency is retarded growth with lack of green color in the stems and leaves. The symptoms may become acute at any stage of development; if the soil is very deficient in nitrogen they may appear early in the seedling stage. If there is sufficient nitrogen to support early growth only, the deficiency symptoms may appear later. If the available supply is maintained through the growth period but becomes exhausted at the time of fruiting, the symptoms appear suddenly, too late for correction, and the result is economic loss.

The first symptom of nitrogen deficiency in tomatoes is very slow growth, followed by a change in color. The green of the leaves becomes lighter than normal, fading through shades of green to pale yellow. An early indication is a lighter green color in the tips of the leaves at the top of the plant. These leaves remain small and thin. From a yellowish green the color of the veins changes to a deep purple, which is accentuated on the under side of the leaf. The stems become hard and fibrous, and they too may become deep purple in color, like the veins of the leaves (plate 1, page 179).

Roots of nitrogen-deficient tomato plants may be more fully developed than the tops in early growth, but they finally become stunted, turn brown, and die. Flower buds turn yellow and shed, a symptom apparently associated with the reduced leaf area, which limits the amount of chlorophyll. In turn, less carbohydrate is manufactured to support fruiting. The fruit that does develop on nitrogen-deficient plants is small, firm, and pale green in color when unripe but highly colored when ripe. The yield is reduced.

In cucumbers also early symptoms of nitrogen deficiency are exhibited by a stunted growth and a change in color of foliage. The normal green of the leaves eventually fades to a yellow green after passing through several stages of green and yellow. In extreme cases practically all the chlorophyll is broken down and the final color is yellow. The stems are slender and become hard and fibrous. The roots may be more fully developed than the tops, but they finally become stunted and in time turn brown and die.

Cucumber fruit on nitrogen-deficient plants is frequently light in color. As the effects of the deficiency become more pronounced, the cucumbers become pointed at the blossom end and the pale color is intensified (plate 2, page 180). Such cucumbers are marketed as low-grade products. A lack of nitrogen in the soil is one of the principal causes of low cucumber yields.

Nitrogen deficiency in radishes is likewise indicated by retarded growth, which affects both tops and roots. The leaves are small, narrow, and thin, and they become yellow. The stems are slender and weak. The roots are small and imperfectly developed and have a faded reddish color compared with radishes grown with an abundant supply of nitrogen (plate 3, page 181).

The nitrogen-deficiency symptoms exhibited in the tomato leaflets in plate 1 are from experiments of the New Jersey Agricultural Experiment Station. The plants were grown in the greenhouse in sand cultures supplied with nutrient solutions. The symptoms pictured are similar to those observed in the field. The cucumber plants (in plate 2) showing nitrogen-deficiency as well as potassium-deficiency symptoms were grown in field plots at the Ohio Agricultural Experiment Station. The radishes, exhibiting potassium-, phosphorus-, and nitrogen-deficiency symptoms, shown in plate 3, were grown in a sand-soil mixture in pots at the Indiana Agricultural Experiment Station.

POTASSIUM DEFICIENCY

Potassium starvation has been observed in almost all truck crops and occurs generally in truck-crop soils unless they are properly fertilized. Potassium is perhaps removed from soils by vegetable crops in larger amounts than are other nutrients, and it is readily leached from the kind of soils found in the large trucking areas. Most vegetable crops quickly reflect any shortage of this element. Without sufficient available potassium in the soil, truck or vegetable plants suffer in reduced vigor, greater susceptibility to disease, impairment of growth processes, and failure to develop normally and to translocate starch, i.e., move it from one part of the plant to another in response to internal needs. On the other hand, the presence of an adequate supply of available potassium in the soil promotes the health and improves the quality of the plant, increases resistance to certain diseases, and offsets the effect of an over-supply of nitrogen.

Potassium-deficiency symptoms in vegetable plants are indicative of a very limited supply of available potassium in the soil. Early symptoms indicate danger, which may be avoided under some circumstances by applying potassium to the soil. If the deficiency is not corrected, the result may be defective plants, retarded growth, reduced yields, and economic loss.

A deficiency of potassium is recognizable by a change in the color of the vegetative parts as a whole and the occurrence of spots caused by a breaking down of the tissues. Symptoms may vary with the age of plants. In soils extremely low in potash the symptoms may appear in the seedling stage, but in those with a supply that is moderate but not sufficient to support normal growth to maturity they may not appear until the fruiting stage. In soils with a medium content of potash and an abundant supply of nitrogen, potassium-deficiency symptoms may develop after a period of rapid growth. Where there is a moderate supply in the soil, potassium starvation in tomato plants may appear first at the middle of the plant and work upward, but in very deficient soils the symptoms usually appear first in the older leaves at the base of the plants.

Potassium-starved tomato plants grow slowly. The plant is stunted and the yield is small. The young leaves become finely crinkled. Older leaves turn an ashen grayish green at first, developing a yellowish green along the margins. The injury progresses from the margin toward the center of the leaflet, causing a bronzing of the tissue which is followed by the development of large, light-colored spots between the larger veins. The affected areas often turn a bright orange color and frequently become brittle. The leaves turn brown and finally die. The stems become hard and woody and fail to increase greatly in diameter, remaining slender. (Plate 4, A, page 182.) The roots are not well developed; they remain slender and are often brown in color, and secondary thickening does not occur.

Potassium deficiency may have a decided effect on the shape, solidity, and quality of tomato fruit. The fruit on plants showing extreme deficiency may ripen unevenly and lack solidity (plate 4, B).

Cabbage plants showing potassium deficiency in its earliest stage become bronzed on the border of the leaf, and the bronzing spreads inward. As the deficiency becomes acute, the symptoms progress and are manifested by a parching of the leaf rim and the development of brown spots in the interior of the leaf (plate 5, page 183).

Potassium deficiency in brussels sprouts causes symptoms very similar to those in cabbages. In carrots, the symptoms are manifested first in curled leaves. The rim of the leaf becomes brown, and the green of the inner portion fades to a grayish green and finally becomes bronzed.

In cucumber plants, potassium-deficiency symptoms are the characteristic bronzing and dying of the leaf margin. The bronzing gradually spreads into the leaf area between the veins. Fruit with an enlarged tip end is characteristic (plate 2).

Radishes grown in potash-deficient soil exhibit a dark-green color in the center of the leaf, a very early symptom of potassium deficiency, while the edges curl and become pale yellow to brown. Extreme deficiency is exhibited in the deep yellow to bronze color

of the lower leaves and the stems.   The leaves are thick and
leathery.   The roots are more bulbous than they would be normally
(plate 3, page 181).   In beets the deficiency is manifested in a
tapered root, which is nonbulbous and poorly developed.

Potassium-deficiency symptoms in the tomato leaves shown in plate 4, A, page
182, are from experiments of the New Jersey Agricultural Experiment Station.
The plants were grown in sand cultures supplied with nutrient solutions.   The
symptoms developed in these greenhouse experiments are similar to those of
potassium deficiency which have developed under field conditions.   The tomatoes
in plate 4, B, were from field plots in experiments conducted at the Ohio
Agricultural Experiment Station on a potash-deficient soil, with no potash
included in the fertilizer.   The several stages of potassium deficiency in cabbage
leaves shown in plate 5, page 183, are from field-plot experiments of the Virginia
Truck Experiment Station.

PHOSPHORUS DEFICIENCY

Phosphorus deficiency is most likely to become evident after
land has been farmed for a number of years.   For this reason the
soils of the eastern trucking areas of the United States have shown
the need of phosphorus first.   The custom of using large quantities
of phosphate fertilizer is so general in the large areas of extensive
truck-crop farming, however, that phosphorus deficiency is seldom
of economic importance.   If commercial phosphate was not abundantly supplied to sandy truck-crop soils of low phosphate content
and to the heavy truck soils of high colloidal (clay) content, which
have a high fixation power for phosphorus that makes it unavailable, phosphorus deficiency in vegetables would in all probability
become serious and result in great loss.

The symptoms of phosphorus deficiency in vegetable crops are
slow growth and delayed maturity.   Characteristic foliage symptoms are generally less pronounced than those resulting from deficiencies of some of the other plantfoods.   Phosphorus hastens
fruiting and maturity in most vegetables, however, and it aids
plants in absorbing other nutrients.   Phosphorus-deficiency symptoms appear most readily on young plants a few weeks old and
may continue to maturity.

An early symptom in tomatoes is the development of a reddish-
purple color on the under side of the leaf.   The color in the web
of the leaf may first appear in spots and later spread over the
entire leaf, with the veins finally becoming reddish purple.   The
foliage eventually assumes a purplish tinge.   The stems are slender
and fibrous.   The leaves are small, and the plant is late in setting

fruit (plate 6, page 184). The leaves of phosphorus-deficient radishes also exhibit a reddish-purple color on the under side (plate 3, page 181). In celery the deficiency is exhibited by poor root development and slender stalks. The roots are stunted in many phosphorus-deficient vegetable crops, which is perhaps responsible for the slow growth and delayed maturity.

The phosphorus-deficiency symptoms exhibited in the tomato leaves shown in plate 6 are from experiments of the New Jersey Agricultural Experiment Station, and the plants were grown in sand cultures supplied with nutrient solutions. The symptoms exhibited here are very similar to those secured by P. L. Fisher in nutrient-solution cultures at the Maryland Agricultural Experiment Station. These symptoms from sand and nutrient solutions do not differ widely from those secured by Hester and Shelton (3)[2] in work in the field.

CALCIUM DEFICIENCY

Soils of the important trucking areas are universally supplied with calcium in the form of lime or in fertilizers containing calcium. The latter are used generally in quantities sufficient to supply the calcium necessary for the growth of vegetable or truck crops. A deficiency may become prevalent in these soils if fertilizers that do not contain calcium are used for a period of years.

Much research work has been reported on the growth of plants in calcium-free nutrient solutions. From such experiments the symptoms of calcium deficiency in some vegetable plants are well known, though its occurrence under field conditions is unusual.

A lack of calcium results in retarded vegetative growth and thick woody stems. The root tips are affected. Tomato plants suffering from the deficiency have yellow leaves on the upper part of the plant, while the lower leaves remain green. This is a distinctive characteristic; in deficiency of nitrogen, phosphorus, or potassium, the lower portion of the plant exhibits discolored foliage while the upper leaves and stems remain normal. The indications are that calcium is not transferred from the older leaves at the base of the plant to the newer leaves at the top. Calcium-deficient tomato plants are weak, flabby, and lacking in firmness or turgidity. The terminal buds die and the stem near the terminal becomes spotted with dead areas. Roots are short, much branched, stubby, bulbous. and dark brown in color.

Calcium deficiency in garden peas is shown by the appearance of red patches on the leaves, first near the midrib and at the ends of the small veins. As the injury increases it spreads out

[2] Italic numbers in parentheses refer to Literature Cited, p. 178.

towards the leaf margin until the whole leaf is involved. The color changes gradually, the healthy green turning to pale green and then to white. The basal portion of the leaf loses color first, the margin remaining green longest. Calcium deficiency causes a very slow growth and a dwarfing of the plant (figs. 1 and 2).

The symptoms of calcium deficiency in tomatoes are based on the work of P. L. Fisher, who conducted experiments in nutrient-solution cultures with deficiencies and excesses of a number of essential plantfoods at the Maryland Agricultural Experiment Station, and on the work of Nightingale, Addoms, Robbins, and Schermerhorn, who also conducted experiments in sand cultures to which nutrient solutions were added at the New Jersey Agricultural Experiment Station. Symptoms in garden peas likewise are based on results of nutrient-solution cultures. The latter work was by Hibbard and Grigsby (4).

Courtesy of R. P. Hibbard and B. H. Grigsby,
Michigan Agricultural Experiment Station

Figure 1.—Garden-pea plants, growing in water cultures, showing calcium deficiency. Plants on the left are growing in a complete nutrient solution, those on the right in a solution lacking calcium. Lack of calcium early retards the elongation of stem; 2 weeks' growth produced the difference in height. The leaves are drying and curling under, the tendrils shriveling, and the young tissue changing to pale green or yellow (4).

SULFUR DEFICIENCY

Sulfur starvation in vegetable plants in the field is unusual. A deficiency of this plantfood is seldom found in soils used for vegetable crops, particularly soils of the large trucking areas. This is perhaps because sulfur is supplied in commercial fertilizers, which are used in large quantities on most truck-crop soils, and also because the sulfur in the atmosphere is brought down by rain. Sulfur deficiency may occur in local areas where the soil conditions are unusual. Serious injury to vegetable crops in the large trucking areas from sulfur deficiency is improbable unless present fertilizer practices are radically altered.

Sulfur-deficiency symptoms develop slowly in tomato plants. The appearance of the plants is similar to that of plants suffering from an incomplete supply of nitrogen. The lower leaves become yellowish green, the stems are hard and woody, and the roots are well developed and extensive. Both roots and stems are small in diameter. Sulfur-deficient tomato plants have a remarkable capacity for elongation of the stem, which is not the case with plants grown with an incomplete supply of nitrogen, phosphorus, or potassium. Stems of sulfur-deficient plants, though woody and hard, increase in length but not in diameter. The plants are high in carbohydrates and sometimes in nitrogen.

The description of sulfur-deficiency symptoms given for tomato plants is based on the work of Nightingale, Schermerhorn, and Robbins of the New Jersey Agricultural Experiment Station. In these experiments tomato plants were grown in pots in the greenhouse in sand to which nutrient solutions were applied.

MAGNESIUM DEFICIENCY

Magnesium deficiency in truck-crop soils is widespread in many sections of the country. Soils of the Atlantic and Gulf Coastal Plains, where extensive areas are devoted to vegetable growing, are very low in magnesium content. The causes of the deficiency are a natural lack of magnesium rock material in the soil, extensive leaching due to heavy rainfall, the removal of large quantities of magnesium in crops, and the use of fertilizers containing no mag-

Courtesy of R. P. Hibbard and B. H. Grigsby, Michigan Agricultural Experiment Station

Figure 2.—A detailed comparison of the difference between the shoots of young pea plants grown in a complete nutrient solution, on the left, and in one lacking calcium, on the right. The color of the leaves on the left is a deep green and the tendrils are long and active. The margins of the leaves on the right are green but the centers are white. The tendrils are short, tough, and shriveled (4).

nesium. Losses due to magnesium deficiency are of economic importance not only in the Atlantic and Gulf trucking belts, but also in many other sections throughout the country. Periodic applications of soluble magnesium fertilizer or magnesium limestone to magnesium-deficient soils are necessary to produce truck or vegetable crops of good quality. The growing of cover crops for green manure tends to conserve the magnesium supply in the sandy soils of the Atlantic seaboard trucking belt, which are subject to excessive leaching. It is essential to maintain an adequate supply of magnesium in truck-crop soils at all times.

Magnesium influences the earliness and the uniformity with which vegetable crops mature, the size of the root, the size of the fruit, and the quality of the marketable portion of the crop. Vegetable plants develop a characteristic chlorosis, or lack of normal green color, when the magnesium supply is insufficient. The lower leaves are affected first, and in some vegetables these are practically the only leaves that become chlorotic.

Tomato plants grown in soil or in sand-nutrient solutions deficient in magnesium develop leaves that are very brittle and have a tendency to curve upwards. The veins remain dark green while the areas between them become yellow, the yellow color increasing in intensity with distance from the vein. The yellow areas become deeper in color and finally turn brown and break down. The symptoms are most common in the older leaves of mature plants. From time of fruiting the deficiency may become increasingly severe. There is little effect on the stems or the fruit (plate 7, page 185).

Early stages of magnesium deficiency in cabbages are manifested by a chlorotic, mottled, puckered appearance of the lower leaves (fig. 3). The advanced stage is a more severe mottling which develops into white or very pale yellow areas around the rim and at the center of the leaf. These areas decay and die. The white and yellow area at the rim of the leaf turns brown when extreme deficiency has developed (plate 5, page 183). If magnesium deficiency is the only one present, the entire leaf becomes marked with areas of dead tissue. If nitrogen is also a limiting factor, the entire leaf will first turn a light-green color and then become yellow before the break-down occurs in the central portions of the areas between the veins.

Potassium deficiency is sometimes confused with a lack of magnesium. The former, however, appears as a bronzing of the leaf, the color developing into brown before the break-down of tissue occurs.

Turnip leaves from plants grown under conditions of magnesium deficiency develop brown areas around the rim which dry up and fall out, while the inner areas are chlorotic and mottled (plate 8, A, page 186).

Most vegetables are susceptible to a shortage of magnesium in the soil and show the general characteristics described here.

Magnesium deficiency in carrots is characterized by a lightening of the foliage color and the appearance of light-yellow or brown spots on the tips of the lobes of the leaflets. Deficient plants are generally smaller than those with an adequate supply of magnesium. In beets, magnesium deficiency has seldom been observed. Cucumbers and squash are very sensitive to any condition that may unbalance the supply of nutrients in the soil solution. These two

Figure 3.—Overwintered cabbage plant from field experiments showing symptoms of magnesium deficiency. Note the white, puckered, spotted area of the lower leaves, indicative of early stages of the deficiency (2).

Courtesy of R. L. Carolus, Virginia Truck Experiment Station, and
B. E. Brown, United States Department of Agriculture

vegetables show similar responses to magnesium deficiency. Snap beans (plate 8, B, page 186) and lima beans deficient in magnesium show the characteristic mottling and browning of the foliage described for other vegetables.

Magnesium-deficiency symptoms shown in tomato plants in plate 7, page 185, are from experiments in sand-nutrient solution cultures at the New Jersey Agricultural Experiment Station. The symptoms exhibited in these greenhouse experiments are identical with those described for field-grown tomato plants at the Virginia Truck Experiment Station.

The symptoms of early magnesium deficiency in cabbages, illustrated in figure 3, are from field plots of the Virginia Truck Experiment Station, while the leaf in plate 5, showing an advanced stage of magnesium deficiency, is from nutrient solution-sand experiments made in the greenhouse of the New Jersey Agricultural Experiment Station. The symptoms in greenhouse and field-grown plants are very similar.

Magnesium-deficiency symptoms of turnips, illustrated in plate 8, A, page 186, are from cooperative field experiments of the Virginia Truck Experiment Station and the Bureau of Plant Industry of the United States Department of Agriculture. The symptoms of snap beans shown in plate 8, B, page 186, were secured in pot experiments at the Central Experimental Farm, Department of Agriculture, Ottawa, Ontario, Canada.

BORON DEFICIENCY

Small quantities of boron are necessary for the normal growth of most, if not all, vegetable plants. The addition of 5 to 20 pounds of borax per acre to boron-deficient soils is usually adequate for normal growth of vegetables. The range between quantities necessary for normal growth and amounts that are toxic is very narrow.

In recent years boron has been found to be an essential plant-food of vegetable crops; previously it was considered that soils ordinarily contained sufficient boron to support plant growth. Authentic cases of boron deficiency in vegetable as well as other crops have been reported from various sections of the United States and Canada—in fact from most parts of the world. Plants become adversely affected or die if deprived of boron. Crop failure from this cause has actually occurred in many widely separated sections, often causing considerable economic loss.

Boron deficiency has been noted on soils differing in physical and chemical characteristics. It is common on soils to which lime has been applied and on sandy, leachy soils, as well as on those that are heavy and silty. The crack stem of celery on sandy soils in Florida, attributed to boron deficiency, is among the earliest cases known of the failure of a field crop from this cause. During the past few years it has been reported in Eastern, Middle Western, and Western States. Malnutrition of beets, turnips, rutabagas, cauliflower, lettuce, and spinach, due to a lack of boron, has been observed in Virginia, New Jersey, New York, and Michigan, where it occurs in sufficiently large areas to be of economic importance. Boron deficiency is also economically important in Canada and in European countries.

The severity of boron-deficiency diseases in the field may depend on other factors besides the boron content of the soil. Soil moisture is an influential factor—in dry seasons there is greater injury from this cause. Excessive amounts of lime in the soil increase injury. The injury to vegetable crops caused by overliming has been attributed in some cases to boron deficiency, but the mechanism involved in rendering boron unavailable has not been explained.

Characteristic symptoms of boron deficiency in specific vegetable plants vary widely.   The crack stem of celery and the brown heart of table beets and turnips are very different, but both are due to a lack of boron.

In celery, boron deficiency first manifests itself by a brownish mottling of the leaf, usually appearing first along the margins of the bud leaves.   The mottling is accompanied by brittleness of the stem and by the appearance of brown stripes in the epidermis along the ribs.   Finally crosswise cracks appear on the surface of the stalk and the tissue curls outward from these breaks.   The disrupted tissue soon becomes dark brown in color.   Roots of affected plants turn brown, the laterals dying back, and form small knoblike appendages at their extremities.   In the final stages the plant dies. Under field conditions the deformed plant may remain alive and new growth may appear later. (Plate 9, A, page 187.)

Boron deficiency in table beets, turnips, and other root crops, commonly known as brown-heart disease, is manifested first by dark spots on the roots, usually on the thickest parts.   The plant gradually becomes stunted or dwarfed.   The leaves are smaller than normal and less numerous, and they gradually assume a variegated color, which appears as a mixture of yellow and purplish-red blotches over part or all of the leaf, while the stalks of such leaves usually show a longitudinal splitting.   Frequently the affected plants have twisted leaves and exhibit a slight shortening and discoloring of the leaf stalks in the center of the crown. The growing point may die and decay.   The root does not grow to full size and under conditions of severe boron deficiency remains very small and distorted, with a rough, unhealthy, grayish appearance instead of a clean, smooth surface.   Often the surface will be wrinkled and cracked. (Plate 9, B.)

On cutting through a root, boron deficiency may be seen as the familiar brown heart—dark-brown, water-soaked areas in the flesh at the center (fig. 4).   According to the severity of the deficiency, brown heart may vary from a few small, scattered, isolated spots to a large water-soaked area, or even a hollow center with all the inner flesh badly discolored.

In tomatoes boron deficiency has not been of economic importance and has not occurred generally.   The deficiency has been observed when plants were grown in nutrient solutions free of boron.   An early symptom is a blackened appearance at the growing point of the stem.   The plant looks bushy owing to the growth of new leaves below the growing point of the stem. The cotyledons, or seedling leaves, and the true leaves turn a distinctly purple color while the plant is young. The stems become stunted and the terminal shoot curls inward, yellows, and dies. The conductive tissue breaks down. A striking characteristic is the extreme brittleness of the petioles, or leaf stems, and the midribs. The roots show extremely poor growth and become yellow or brown in color. The fruit is frequently covered with darkened or dried areas, apparently owing to the break-down of the tissue.

Boron deficiency in lettuce is characterized by malformation of the more rapidly growing leaves, spotting and burning of the leaf

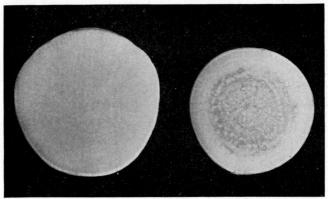

Figure 4.—Interior of turnip roots showing dark center, or hollow heart, caused by a deficiency of boron. Left, normal turnip; right, boron-deficient turnip.

Courtesy of R. W. Donaldson, Massachusetts Agricultural Experiment Station

tips, and death of the growing point of the plant (figs. 5 and 6). The first symptoms are retardation of growth and malformation of the younger leaves. Marginal growth ceases, and this results in a folding back of the leaf tip. The spots on the leaves increase in size and number, involving the entire leaf tip and giving it a scorched appearance. The older leaves are not noticeably affected, but all young leaves, from those first affected to the growing point itself, are involved.

Boron deficiency in cauliflower first appears as small, concentric, water-soaked areas in the stem and in the center of the small branches of the curd (plate 10, A, page 188). The external appearance may resemble the browning in brown heart of turnips. When browning is severe, both the outer and the inner portions of the head are affected. The discoloration of the curd may appear at various stages of maturity, and it increases with growth. In a cauliflower plant affected with boron deficiency the smaller leaves around the curd may be deformed and stunted.

Courtesy of J. S. McHargue and R. K. Calfee, Kentucky Agricultural Experiment Station

Figure 5.—Growing point of lettuce plant showing symptoms of boron deficiency. Note the curling or folding back of the young leaves and the scorched appearance of the disfigured leaf tips (*8*).

Figure 6.—Normal leaf (left) and boron-deficient leaf (right) resulting from growing lettuce in sand and nutrient - solution cultures.

Courtesy of D. I. Arnon and S. B. Johnson, California Agricultural Experiment Station

Much research work has been in progress on the effects of an excess or a deficiency of boron in soils on the growth of vegetable plants. Purvis and Ruprecht (9) were among the first to detect the deficiency in Florida celery soils and to describe the symptoms of crack stem. Their work was in field plots and the symptoms described here follow their discussion. They were working with a sand which received large applications of commercial fertilizers. The illustration in plate 9, A, page 187, shows the results of experiments at the Oregon Agricultural Experiment Station. The deficiency was observed in field plots. Likewise boron-deficiency symptoms in celery have been reported by the Oregon Agricultural Experiment Station (1), where the deficiency has been observed in widespread areas on peat land as well as on sandy and silt-loam soils. Under these soil conditions crack stem is characterized by small transverse cracks of the outer tissues on the ribs of the stalk. The cracks may extend only a short distance on the stems of a lightly affected plant but up to the full length of the stalks in a plant that is badly diseased. The cracked tissues of the ribs become brown and curl outward and backward. There is often a browning of the tissue along the inner or concave surface of the stalks. The stalks become very brittle. Plants that are badly affected have a stunted growth.

The boron-deficient beets shown in plate 9, B, page 187, are from field experiments of the Oregon Agricultural Experiment Station, and the turnip in figure 4, showing interior symptoms, is from experiments conducted at the Massachusetts Agricultural Experiment Station.

Boron-deficiency symptoms in lettuce, exhibited in figures 5 and 6, are from experiments in sand-nutrient solutions conducted at the Kentucky Agricultural Experiment Station and the California Agricultural Experiment Station, respectively.

The boron-deficiency symptoms in cauliflower shown in plate 10, A, page 188, were developed in pot experiments of the New York (Cornell) Agricultural Experiment Station, using soil from a field in which bronzing and hollow stem occurred the preceding year. The deficiency symptoms in bean plants (plate 10, B) are from experiments in soil in pots at the Central Experimental Farm, Department of Agriculture, Ottawa, Ontario, Canada.

IRON DEFICIENCY

Iron is indispensable for plants and is abundantly supplied in nearly all soils except those that are calcareous and alkaline. The solubility of iron is governed by the soil reaction; in acid soils it is comparatively soluble. The addition of organic matter, such as crop residues and stable manure, increases the supply of iron available to crops.

Iron deficiency in truck or vegetable crops is not of economic importance on the acid soils of the large trucking belts. In the alkaline regions of the United States, however, a chlorosis due to iron deficiency is important with some plants.

The outstanding symptom of iron deficiency is usually the development of yellow leaves on the upper parts of the plants. The terminal growth is the first part affected.   In tomato plants (fig. 7), chlorosis of the young leaves, with little necrosis or dying of tissues, appears to be the dominant symptom.

Iron occurs in greatest concentration in the leaves of vegetable plants.   These plants vary in their susceptibility to chlorosis associated with inactivity of iron induced by the presence of lime.

Figure 7.—Iron-deficiency symptoms shown by tomato plants grown in nutrient solutions. The leaf on the left is from a plant grown in a complete nutrient solution; the one on the right was grown in a solution containing no iron (*5*).

Courtesy of D. R. Hoagland and D. I. Arnon,
California Agricultural Experiment Station

The symptoms of iron deficiency of tomatoes shown in figure 7 were secured in nutrient-solution cultures in experiments at the California Agricultural Experiment Station, where an extensive study has been made of the nutrient requirements of plants.

COPPER DEFICIENCY

Results of recent studies confirm the belief that copper is an essential plantfood for vegetable or truck crops.   Applying it to some kinds of soils stimulates growth and results in the production of normal plants, when without it crops fail. Copper is a normal constituent of all plants. The fact that seeds are high in copper suggests that this mineral is especially important in the case of plants grown for seed.

Available evidence indicates that copper deficiency in vegetables is confined to those grown on dark-colored soils, such as the Portsmouth soil types, and on peat and muck. Abnormal growth of vegetable crops on peat soils of Michigan and Delaware, caused by copper deficiency, has been noted. The addition of 100 to 200 pounds of copper sulfate per acre to peat soils in western New York was found necessary to produce normal truck crops. On the saw-grass peat soils of the Everglades of Florida vegetable crops will not make normal growth without the addition of 20 to 30 pounds of copper sulfate per acre. There have been reports of copper deficiency in plants growing on peat soils in many other parts of the world. Copper deficiency is of economic importance in vegetable production in large areas of this class of soils.

Most mineral soils contain sufficient copper to support normal crops of vegetables, except possibly some that are very sandy and leachable.

The quantities of copper sulfate that have been used on soils to correct the deficiencies noted vary from 20 to 200 pounds per acre. Some peat soils have a high fixing power for copper compounds so that relatively heavy applications are necessary to produce the desired effect.

A deficiency of copper may not cause as distinct color characteristics in the foliage of vegetable crops as do deficiencies of other plantfoods. There are some outstanding characteristics noted in field-grown plants in dark-colored soils, however, as well as some definite characteristics observed in plants grown in nutrient solutions in the greenhouse. The leaves of affected plants do not maintain their firmness. The foliage exhibits a chlorotic condition which gives it a bleached appearance; this may be corrected by washing or spraying the leaves with a weak copper sulfate solution. Chlorotic lettuce grown on unproductive muck soil deficient in copper has become normal after being dusted with copper sulfate.

Copper-deficiency symptoms in tomatoes include very stunted growth of shoots and exceedingly poor root development, dark bluish-green color of foliage, curling of leaves and absence of flower formation, development of chlorosis, and a lack of firmness in leaves and stems (fig. 8). Leaves of copper-deficient lettuce plants become bleached and chlorotic, the stem of the leaf and the rim being affected first (fig. 9).

Onions grown in peat soils in New York exhibit copper deficiency in an abnormal, thin scale of a pale yellow color (plate 11, A, page 189). The application of copper sulfate at the rate of 100 to 300 pounds per acre increased the thickness of the onion scales and

Courtesy of D. R. Hoagland and D. I. Arnon, California Agricultural Experiment Station

Figure 8.—Tomato leaves from plants grown in nutrient solutions. On left, leaflet from plant grown in copper-deficient solution; in center, in a complete nutrient solution; and on right, in a zinc-deficient solution. A deficiency of either copper or zinc has produced small leaflets as compared to those of the normal plant. The copper-deficient plant has small stems and chlorotic leaves which are curled inward. The zinc-deficient plant has normal-size stems with leaves resembling those in little leaf of fruit trees (5).

changed the color from pale yellow to a brilliant brown. Copper-deficient onions lack solidity and firmness.

In cases of copper deficiency as extreme as on the Florida soils mentioned, truck-crop plants fail entirely to grow. In less extreme cases growth is very slow and stunted.

The copper-deficiency symptoms described for tomato plants, the copper-deficient tomato leaflet in figure 8, and the copper-deficient lettuce leaf in figure 9 are from experiments conducted at the California Agricultural Experiment

Station.   The plants were grown in nutrient-solution sand cultures in the green-house.   Symptoms exhibited in these nutrient-solution experiments are similar in many details to characteristics of field-grown vegetable plants on large areas of peat and muck soils.

The onions shown in plate 11, A, page 189, exhibiting an increasing intensity of tan or brown color with increasing amounts of copper sulfate added to the soil, were grown in copper-deficient muck soil in field plots by the New York (Cornell) Agricultural Experiment Station (7).   The color of onion scales grown in different muck soils in New York is correlated with the amount of copper in the soil.

Courtesy of D. I. Arnon and S. B. Johnson, California Agricultural Experiment Station

Figure 9.—Lettuce leaflets from plants grown in nutrient solutions.   Left, leaflet from normal plant grown in a complete nutrient solution; right, leaflet grown in copper-deficient solution. Copper deficiency has caused reduced growth and malformation of the leaf, which exhibits chlorosis; the plant is weak and lacks firmness.   The chlorosis appeared first on the stem and the outer rim of the leaf.

ZINC DEFICIENCY

Only a few cases of zinc deficiency in vegetable crops have been reported.   It has been proved by greenhouse demonstrations that zinc is essential to the normal development of some plants, including beans, squash, and mustard, but in field-grown vegetables zinc deficiency has not become of economic importance except on unusual soils.   The application of zinc salts to the soil or the culture medium was effective in producing normal growth.

Squash (fig. 10), mustard, and tomato plants grown in zinc-deficient soils in the greenhouse at the California Agricultural Experiment Station exhibited zinc-deficiency symptoms. Some of the plants had extremely mottled leaves with necrotic, or dead, areas. Squash was especially affected. Other plants had leaves of a uniform chlorotic appearance. Abnormally small leaves, yellow or mottled, were frequently produced, especially by tomato and mustard plants, which resembled those in "little leaf" of zinc-deficient fruit trees. Tomato plants sometimes gave evidence of leaf injury (fig. 8) when only a few inches high.   Symptoms developed by plants grown in nutrient solutions containing no zinc have characteristics similar to those shown by the same kind of plant on zinc-deficient soil in the field.

Zinc deficiency in bean plants, as observed in the field on peat soils of Florida by the Florida Everglades Experiment Station, is exhibited in symptoms similar to those discussed for squash and tomatoes in nutrient solutions and in soil in pots.

Courtesy of D. R. Hoagland, W. H. Chandler, and P. L. Hibbard, University of California

Figure 10.—Leaf of squash plant, showing zinc-deficiency symptoms, grown in nutrient solution without the addition of zinc (6).

MANGANESE DEFICIENCY

Manganese is a common constituent of soils and plants. The quantities present in both vary greatly, but there is little correlation between the total manganese in soils and that in the plants growing in the soils.   The availability of manganese to the crop is governed more by the acidity of the soil and the reducing action of manganese in the soil than by the quantity present.

Deficiency of manganese in soils, as demonstrated by the growth of plants, is confined principally to soils that are nonacid or calcareous.   The deficiency has been noted in local sections of the trucking areas of various parts of the country and is of economic importance in some places, especially on overlimed and calcareous soils of the Atlantic seaboard. Manganese is sometimes deficient in acid soils, and when the deficiency occurs in decidedly acid soils it is thought to result from the leaching of soluble manganese, which may be pronounced in soils that are very sandy.

Application of manganese to the soil has prevented chlorosis of tomatoes and other truck crops on the calcareous soils of Florida where crops failed to grow without it. Normal growth and good yields have resulted.

Manganese deficiency in soils can be corrected by annual applications of 50 to 100 pounds of manganese sulfate per acre. The requirement, however, may vary widely. Highly calcareous soils, overlimed soils, and very acid, leachable, sandy soils will in all probability require more frequent applications and larger quantities for successful vegetable production.

In the foliage of tomato plants, manganese deficiency manifests itself first as a lightening of the green color, which gradually turns to yellow, in the leaf areas farthest from the major veins. As the condition progresses the yellow becomes more marked and extensive. The veins remain green, which gives a characteristic mottled appearance to the leaf. Eventually the foliage may become completely yellow, and in many cases necrosis sets in, appearing at first as small brown pin points centering in the yellow areas farthest from the veins and expanding until larger dead areas indicate complete break-down of the tissue. Growth is spindling, little or no blossoming takes place, and no fruit forms. Retardation of growth and chlorosis indicate failure of the leaves to function normally owing to inadequate synthesis of chlorophyll.

Manganese starvation in tomatoes has been widespread, having been observed in regions extending from Florida to the northern trucking belt. In severe cases, as in the calcareous soils of Florida, plants fail and do not produce fruit (fig. 11).

The characteristic, striking form of chlorosis in manganese-deficient tomatoes manifests itself in greenhouse-grown plants and in plants grown in nutrient solutions (figs. 12 and 13) just as it does in plants grown in various types of soil in the field.

In spinach the chlorosis appears first at the growing tips and gradually extends throughout the plant. The normal green color fades from the web of the leaf, leaving it pale green to golden yellow. The green color persists longest along the principal veins. After some time white dead areas may appear between the veins of the leaves. The gradual yellowing of spinach leaves has caused some confusion of manganese deficiency with "spinach yellow," a mosaic disease.

In table beets the symptoms are somewhat different owing to the large amount of red and purple pigments in the plants. When

*From work of J. J. Skinner, U. S. Department of Agriculture, and
R. W. Ruprecht, Florida Agricultural Experiment Station*

Figure 11.—Tomatoes on calcareous soil of Florida on which vegetables do not grow unless manganese is supplied. Center, commercial fertilizers were applied at the rate of 1,200 pounds per acre. On sections of the field to the left and right, 100 pounds per acre of manganese sulfate was added to the commercial fertilizer (*10*).

manganese is deficient, the leaf gradually takes on a deep red to purple color instead of becoming progressively yellow. As with spinach, the color change is most definite between the veins, where eventually dead areas appear. Beets in soils extremely deficient in manganese make little growth of either roots or tops.

Manganese-deficient snap beans grow normally for a short period, the first symptom to appear being a loss of green color in the trifoliate leaves. The yellowing does not spread to the cotyledonary or seed leaves until late in the development of the deficiency. At first the trifoliate leaves show a faint mottling, the tissue near the veins remaining green longer than the islets of tissues between the veins. Growth is retarded when these symptoms appear, and the chlorotic leaves do not attain normal size. A

*Courtesy of D. R. Hoagland and D. I. Arnon,
California Agricultural Experiment Station*

Figure 12.—Characteristic mottling on a tomato leaflet as a result of manganese deficiency. On left, leaflet from a plant grown in a manganese-free nutrient solution; on right, in a similar solution containing manganese.

few days only may elapse between the appearance of the first mottling until the whole leaf turns a golden yellow. Small brown spots, near and parallel to each side of the midrib and veins between the lateral branches, may appear before the leaf becomes completely yellow (plate 11, B, page 189).

When manganese becomes deficient in cucumbers, the web of the leaf begins to change from green to yellowish white, while the regions along the veins and midribs remain green. The stems and leaves remain small in size, weak, and slender. Frequently the

Courtesy of D. R. Hoagland and D. I. Arnon, California Agricultural Experiment Station

Figure 13.—Manganese deficiency as exhibited in tomato leaves from plants grown in nutrient solutions in the greenhouse. Left to right, progressive stages of manganese-deficiency symptoms in tomato leaflets.

blossom bud turns yellow. Cabbages (fig. 14) and peppers exhibit somewhat similar characteristics. In all these plants growth is stunted and yields are reduced.

The manganese-deficiency symptoms described and illustrated are characteristic for most vegetable crops. The foliage symptoms exhibited in plants grown in nutrient solutions, in soil in pots in the greenhouse, and in the field are very similar.

The effect of manganese deficiency in retarding growth and reducing production of tomatoes in certain calcareous soils as shown in figure 11 is from cooperative work of the Florida Agricultural Experiment Station and the United States Department of Agriculture. The work was performed in calcareous soils of south Florida in a region devoted to the growing of vegetable crops.

Manganese-deficiency symptoms in tomatoes and other vegetable plants have been observed by means of pot and field-plot experiments in a wide range of soils in various parts of the country. The progressive stages of manganese deficiency in tomatoes shown in figures 12 and 13 are from plants grown in nutrient solutions at the California Agricultural Experiment Station.

The cabbage leaf in figure 14 showing manganese deficiency is from cooperative work of the Florida Agricultural Experiment Station and the United States Department of Agriculture.

The manganese-deficient beans shown in plate 11, B, were grown in light sandy soils in field plots of the Virginia Truck Experiment Station.

From work of J. J. Skinner, U. S. Department of Agriculture, and
R. W. Ruprecht, Florida Agricultural Experiment Station

Figure 14.—Cabbage leaves from plants grown on field plots in manganese-deficient calcareous soil of Florida. Left, from plot fertilized with nitrogen, phosphorus, and potassium but no manganese. Right, from plot fertilized with manganese in addition to the other nutrients (*10*).

SUMMARY OF DEFICIENCY SYMPTOMS IN VEGETABLES

Mineral deficiency in plants may be modified to some extent by factors other than soil composition. Light, temperature, and distribution of the moisture supply have an influence on growth and may affect the nutrients required by vegetable plants and the quantities absorbed. These environmental influences, however, are perhaps not so great as to alter materially the characteristic symptoms due to the deficiency of an element. Many of the symptoms of nutrient deficiencies described in vegetable crops were secured in nutrient solutions and in soil in pots in the greenhouse under controlled climatic conditions. These have been compared with symptoms in the field on soils of known deficiency and on soils that produce normal vegetables when the plantfood indicated as deficient is supplied.

When an essential plant nutrient is deficient in the soil or present in an unavailable form, the symptoms exhibited by the plant are in all probability characteristic for that element.

A key to nutritional-deficiency symptoms in tomato plants is appended. Many symptoms described for tomatoes are similar to those in other vegetable plants. A symptom common to all the vegetables and all deficiencies is slow growth.

Nitrogen-deficiency symptoms characteristic of many vegetables, including tomatoes, beans, cucumbers, celery, and others, include small leaves, slender and fibrous stems, pale-green foliage fading to yellow, and a complete cessation of growth in extreme cases.

Phosphorous-deficiency symptoms are likewise similar in a number of vegetable plants. This deficiency is also exhibited by small leaves and slender, fibrous stems. The under side of the leaves, however, assumes a reddish-purple color. The plants are slow to set fruit, and maturity is delayed.

The symptoms of potassium deficiency are possibly more alike in the various vegetable plants than are those of other deficiencies. The ashen gray-green leaves, developing edges of brown, which crinkle, curl, and become bronzed, are characteristic in many cases.

Sulfur-deficiency symptoms have not been observed in many vegetable plants. The development of long, slender stems and yellowish foliage is characteristic in several instances.

Copper deficiency is confined principally to peat or muck soils, and a characteristic symptom in vegetable plants is slow growth or complete cessation of growth, so that the plants are weak and unproductive. Insofar as symptoms have been observed, they are specific for several vegetables. In the case of onions the scale is thin and pale cream in color when copper is deficient, in contrast to the thick scale and deep brown color when the plants are grown with a plentiful supply of copper. In carrots, copper deficiency is exhibited by a faded yellow color. A lack of turgor in leaves and stalks is a general characteristic of copper deficiency in many vegetables.

Magnesium- and manganese-deficiency symptoms are more or less uniform for most vegetable plants. The deficiency symptoms of magnesium are exhibited by brittle leaves which curl upward after the areas between the green veins have become first yellow and then dark brown. The deficiency results in nonuniformity of the marketable portion of the vegetable and delayed maturity. Manganese-deficiency symptoms differ from those due to magnesium deficiency in that in manganese deficiency necrosis sets in, appearing as small brown pin points on the leaf farthest from the veins, the surrounding area losing its green color, turning yellow, and developing a mottled appearance.

A deficiency of boron affects various vegetable plants quite differently. In celery, crack stem develops, while in beets and turnips the deficiency results in a corklike area in the roots and in cauliflower in a hollow stem and discoloration of the curd. The foliage symptoms may be common to many vegetable plants. The leaves are stunted and their growth is retarded; they are lighter in color than normal, and dark spots, which increase in size, appear on the tips of young leaves. Frequently the affected plants have twisted leaves, and the growing point of the stems may die.

Deficiencies of zinc and iron have not been observed in a sufficient variety of vegetables to make possible descriptions of the symptoms in different cases. The most characteristic effect of zinc starvation is on the leaf, which becomes long and narrow, as in the case of little leaf in fruit trees. Iron deficiency is exhibited by a chlorotic appearance of young leaves without the development of necrosis.

KEY TO PLANT-NUTRIENT DEFICIENCY SYMPTOMS OF TOMATOES

Retarded growth. Localized effects causing abnormal plants. Reduced yields.

ELEMENT
DEFICIENT

A. Effects general on whole plant.

  B. Leaves small.

    C. Stems slender, fibrous, and hard. Early indication, light green on tips of leaves. Leaves fade through stages from green to pale yellow. Under side of stems and leaves becomes bluish purple. Symptoms may appear in seedlings or later if supply is exhausted. Fruit small, pale green before ripening, highly colored when ripe . . . .   Nitrogen

    C. Stems slender, fibrous, and hard. Under side of leaf turns reddish purple. Color in web of leaf appears first in spots and then spreads to entire leaf. May appear in plants a few weeks old and continue to maturity. Roots stunted. Fruit late to set and mature . . . .   Phosphorus

    C. Stems and plant bushy. Leaves turn dark purple to black while young. Terminal shoot curls inward, turns dark, and dies. Bushy appearance due to growth of new leaves below stem. Fruit darkens and has dried areas . . . .   Boron

  B. Leaves normal in size.

    C. Stems fibrous and hard. First indication, upper leaves turn dark green and may curl upward. Edges turn yellow, and leaves dry up and fall. Lower leaves normal. Roots stubby and bulbous. Terminal bud dies. Plant loses turgor, becoming weak and flabby. Roots short and much branched, turn brown . . . .   Calcium

    C. Symptoms develop slowly. Leaves become thick and firm. Lower leaves become yellowish green. Stems grow long but slender. Roots long and slender . . . .   Sulfur

    C. Stems slender and woody. Foliage becomes chlorotic. Leaves lack turgor. Plants not vigorous—little or no growth . . . .   Copper

A. Effects principally on foliage.

  B. Leaves normal in size.

    C. First indication, ashen gray-green leaves at base of plant. Leaves develop a bronze and yellowish-brown color. Young leaves become crinkled and curl. Leaf margin becomes brown. Specks develop along veins of leaf. Tissue deteriorates and dies. Roots poorly developed and brown. Stems slender, become hard and woody. Fruit ripens unevenly . . . .   Potassium

    C. Lower leaves first affected. Veins of leaves remain dark green, area between veins becomes yellow and finally dark brown. Leaves are brittle and curl upward. Tissue breaks down. Fruit uniform, maturity delayed . . . .   Magnesium

    C. Leaf area farthest from veins turns light green, then yellow. Leaves have mottled appearance, eventually becoming entirely yellow. Necrosis sets in, appearing as small brown pin points. Tissue finally breaks down completely. Stems slender . . . .   Manganese

    C. Leaves on upper section of plant become yellow. Terminal growth first affected. Young leaves chlorotic, but with little necrosis . . . .   Iron

  B. Leaves small.

    C. Yellow or mottled leaf, similar to "little leaf" of fruit trees. Plants affected in seedling stage . . . .   Zinc

NOTES ON OCCURRENCE AND CORRECTION OF PLANTFOOD DEFICIENCIES IN TRUCK-CROP SOILS

Deficiencies of nitrogen, phosphorus, and potassium may occur in general on intensively cultivated and light, leachable, sandy soils unless the elements are supplied in commercial plantfood and leguminous crops are grown and turned under.

Deficiencies of calcium and sulfur are unusual on tillable truck-crop soils, where common fertilizer practice is followed. They possibly might become general on acid, leachable, sandy soils if fertilizers containing no calcium or sulfur were used.

Copper deficiency occurs most frequently on peat soils of high organic-matter content. It may be remedied by small applications of copper sulfate.

Magnesium is deficient over a wide area in the large eastern trucking belt. The deficiency is most severe and most general on light, acid, sandy soils. It may be remedied by applying soluble magnesium or dolomitic limestone.

Manganese deficiency occurs in local sections of the eastern trucking belt on nonacid and calcareous soils, occasionally in acid soils. Remedy is annual application of manganese sulfate, 50 to 100 pounds per acre.

Boron deficiency is general, but in local sections of the trucking belts. It is not confined to any class of soils, but its effect is accentuated in overlimed soils. Remedy is application of 5 to 30 pounds of borax per acre.

Zinc deficiency is unusual in vegetables, but common in some fruit and nut trees and field crops on acid, leachable, sandy soils and alkaline soils. Remedied by applying zinc sulfate to acid soils and spraying it on plants in alkaline soils.

Iron deficiency is unusual in vegetables except on alkaline soils. Remedied by spraying iron sulfate solution on the foliage.

LITERATURE CITED

(1) Bouquet, A. G. B., and Powers, W. L.
   1939. CELERY STEM CRACK AND THE USE OF BORON IN ITS CONTROL. Oreg. Agr. Expt. Sta. Cir. Inform. 194, 4 pp., illus.

(2) Carolus, R. L., and Brown, B. E.
   1935. MAGNESIUM DEFICIENCY. I. THE VALUE OF MAGNESIUM COMPOUNDS IN VEGETABLE PRODUCTION IN VIRGINIA. Va. Truck Expt. Sta. Bul. 89, pp. 1250-1288, illus.

(3) Hester, Jackson B., and Shelton, Florence A.
   1939. THE SOIL SIDE OF TOMATO GROWING. Campbell Soup Co. Bul. 1, 61 pp., illus.

(4) Hibbard, R. P., and Grigsby, B. H.
   1934. RELATION OF LIGHT, POTASSIUM, AND CALCIUM DEFICIENCIES TO PHOTOSYNTHESIS, PROTEIN SYNTHESIS, AND TRANSLOCATION. Mich. Agr. Expt. Sta. Tech. Bul. 141, 39 pp., illus.

(5) Hoagland, D. R., and Arnon, D. I.
   1938. THE WATER-CULTURE METHOD FOR GROWING PLANTS WITHOUT SOIL. Calif. Agr. Expt. Sta. Cir. 347, 39 pp., illus.

(6) ——— Chandler, W. H., and Hibbard, P. L.
   1936. LITTLE-LEAF OR ROSETTE OF FRUIT TREES. V. EFFECT OF ZINC ON THE GROWTH OF PLANTS OF VARIOUS TYPES IN CONTROLLED SOIL AND WATER CULTURE EXPERIMENTS. Amer. Soc. Hort. Sci. Proc. 33: 131-141, illus.

(7) Knott, J. E.
   1933. THE EFFECT OF CERTAIN MINERAL ELEMENTS ON THE COLOR AND THICKNESS OF ONION SCALES. N. Y. (Cornell) Agr. Expt. Sta. Bul. 552, 13 pp., illus.

(8) McHargue, J. S., and Calfee, R. K.
   1933. FURTHER EVIDENCE THAT BORON IS ESSENTIAL FOR THE GROWTH OF LETTUCE. Plant Physiol. 8: 305-313, illus.

(9) Purvis, E. R., and Ruprecht, R. W.
   1937. CRACKED STEM OF CELERY CAUSED BY A BORON DEFICIENCY IN THE SOIL. Fla. Agr. Expt. Sta. Bul. 307, 16 pp., illus.

(10) Skinner, J. J., and Ruprecht, R. W.
   1930. FERTILIZER EXPERIMENTS WITH TRUCK CROPS. Fla. Agr. Expt. Sta. Bul. 218, 65 pp., illus.

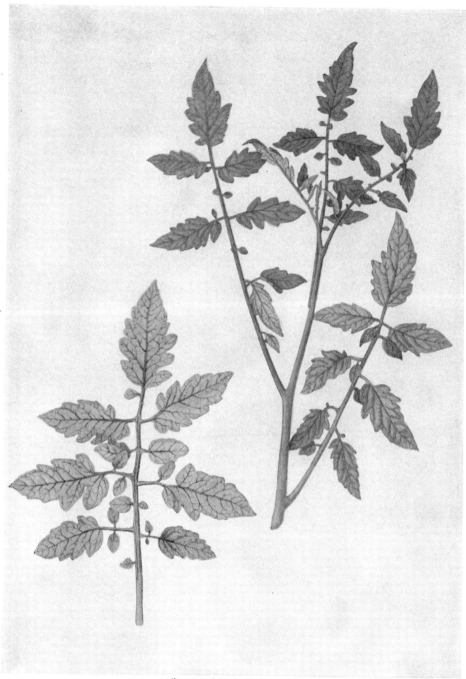

Courtesy of V. A. Tiedjens, New Jersey Agricultural Experiment Station

Plate 1.—Stems and leaves of tomato plants grown under conditions of nitrogen shortage, showing, in the specimen on the right, the pale-green color of the tips of plants, the purple ribs of the under side of the leaves and stems, and the pale-green leaves fading to yellow; and, on the left, the golden-yellow leaves with hard, fibrous, bronzed stems manifesting extreme nitrogen deficiency.

[179]

Courtesy of I. C. Hoffman, Ohio Agricultural Experiment Station

Plate 2.—Cucumbers and leaves grown in field plots on Wooster silt loam, with (1) complete fertilizer, (2) no potash, and (3) no nitrogen. Nitrogen-deficient plants are small, leaf veins are pale green with areas between pale yellow or light brown. Blossom ends of cucumbers are pale yellow to brown and pointed. Potassium deficiency is exhibited by a bronzed, decayed area around the rim of the leaf and by fruit with enlarged tip end and undeveloped stem end.

1   2   3   4

Courtesy of S. F. Thornton and Mack Drake, Indiana Agricultural Experiment Station

Plate 3.—Radishes grown in a sand-soil mixture in pots, fertilized with (1) ammonium nitrate, dicalcium phosphate, and potassium chloride; (2) potassium omitted; (3) phosphate omitted; and (4) nitrogen omitted.

[181]

A

B

A, courtesy of V. A. Tiedjens, New Jersey Agricultural Experiment Station;
B, Courtesy of I. C. Hoffman, Ohio Agricultural Experiment Station

Plate 4.—A, Potassium shortage in tomato leaves. Upper left and lower right, early stages; center, later stage; upper right and lower left, well-developed symptoms. B, Tomatoes from potassium-deficient plants, left, and from normal plants, right.

[182]

A, B, and C, courtesy of J. B. Hester, Virginia Truck Experiment Station;
D, courtesy of V. A. Tiedjens, New Jersey Agricultural Experiment Station

Plate 5.—A, Early stage, and B, late stage of potassium deficiency in cabbage leaves from plants grown in field plots on a typical southeastern truck soil. C is a normal cabbage leaf. Leaf A shows bronzing between the veins of the inner part. Leaf B shows brown spots. D, Advanced stage of magnesium-deficiency symptoms developed in sand culture. The mottled spots have turned pale yellow to white, and, with the rim of the leaf, will turn brown, decay, and die.

[183]

Plate 6.—Tomato leaflets, stalk, and leaves exhibiting phosphorus-deficiency symptoms, showing reddish-purple veins on the under side of the leaflets and on the stems of tomato plants grown in nutrient solution-sand cultures.

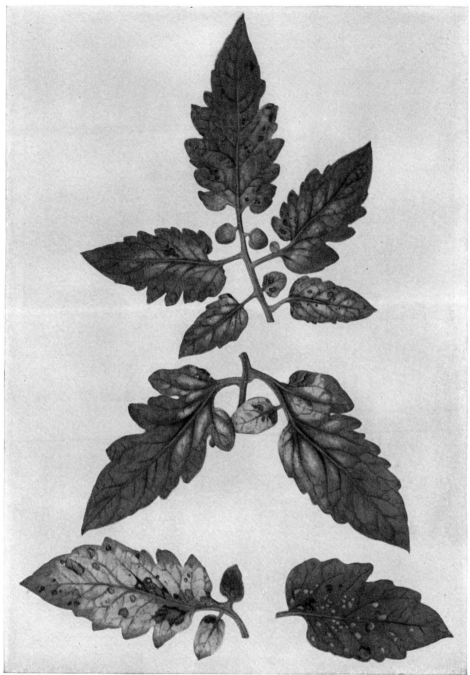

Courtesy of V. A. Tiedjens, New Jersey Agricultural Experiment Station

Plate 7.—Various stages of magnesium-deficiency symptoms in tomato leaves from plants grown in nutrient solution and sand cultures—early stage in leaf at the top and severe stage in leaflet at lower left; center and lower right, intermediate stages. The early deficiency symptoms are exhibited by pale-yellow areas between the veins of the leaves. In the later stage, these develop into brown and black areas.

[185]

Courtesy of R. L. Carolus, Virginia Truck Experiment Station, and
B. E. Brown, United States Department of Agriculture

Plate 8.—A, Leaves (left) from normal and (right) from magnesium-deficient turnip plants, both grown in field plots at the Virginia Truck Experiment Station. The outline of the magnesium-deficient leaf is ragged owing to disintegration of the outer edge. The inner areas are very chlorotic.

Courtesy of M. B. Davis, Central Experimental Farm, Ottawa, Ontario, Canada

Plate 8.—B, Magnesium deficiency in snap beans grown in soil in pots, showing characteristic chlorosis of foliage caused by a lack of magnesium. Right, magnesium-deficient plant; left, normal plant.

Courtesy of W. L. Powers, Oregon Agricultural Experiment Station

Plate 9.—A, Celery plants grown in boron-deficient soil. (1) Healthy plant grown in soil to which boron was added; (2) and (3) plants showing crack stem and decay due to boron deficiency.

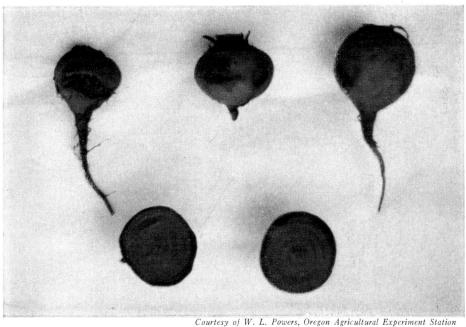

Courtesy of W. L. Powers, Oregon Agricultural Experiment Station

Plate 9.—B, External and internal appearance of beets grown in a boron-deficient soil.

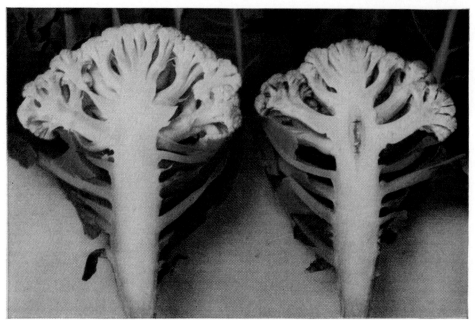

Courtesy of C. H. Dearborn, H. C. Thompson, and G. J. Raleigh,
New York (Cornell) Agricultural Experiment Station

Plate 10.—A, Cauliflower grown in a boron-deficient soil, showing hollow stem and bronzing, symptoms of boron deficiency. Left, normal plant grown in soil receiving 10 pounds of borax per acre; right, plant grown in soil to which no borax was added.

Courtesy of M. B. Davis, Central Experimental Farm, Ottawa, Ontario, Canada

Plate 10.—B, Boron-deficiency symptoms in snap-bean plants grown in soil in pots. Right, plant showing boron deficiency; left, normal plant.

[188]

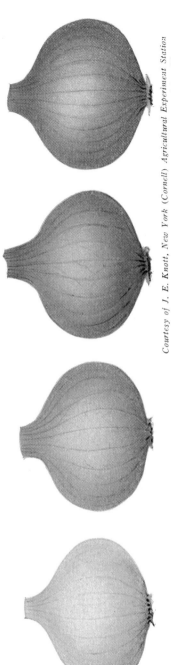

Plate 11.—A, effect of copper sulfate on color of onion scales. (Onions grown on copper-deficient peat soil.) Left to right: No copper, 100 pounds, 200 pounds, and 300 pounds of copper sulfate per acre. The thickness of the scale of the onions as well as the brown color increased as more copper was added to the soil.

Plate 11.—B, Leaves from normal and manganese-deficient bean plants grown on a neutral truck-crop soil at the Virginia Truck Experiment Station. Left, normal leaf; center, leaf showing early stages of manganese deficiency; right, leaf showing late stages of manganese deficiency.

CHAPTER VII

Nutrient-Deficiency Symptoms in Deciduous Fruits

By O. W. Davidson [1]

THIS chapter describes in some detail the symptoms of nutrient deficiencies observed in apples, peaches, and strawberries. Other deciduous fruits are included only indirectly, primarily because of the author's lack of specific experience with them, and secondarily because of the infrequency with which nutrient deficiencies, other than that of nitrogen, have been encountered in these fruits.

In general, the symptoms described for apples resemble very closely those for corresponding deficiencies in other pome fruits, and those described for the peach resemble the symptoms found in other stone fruits. Differences in manifestation are more a matter of degree than of kind. In fact, one who is familiar with the symptoms of a particular nutrient deficiency in the apple or the peach should be able to identify a lack of the corresponding nutrient in deciduous small fruits as well as in other deciduous tree fruits.

A key to deficiency symptoms in deciduous tree fruits is given at the end of the chapter.

When different kinds of fruit are grown in the same district, it is not uncommon to find different species affected by the same deficiency. Nevertheless, there may be marked differences in susceptibility. Thus, on light sandy soils, peaches, apples, and pears are prone to develop nitrogen deficiency. In regions where boron troubles are common and apples, pears, and cherries are grown, all may develop a deficiency of this nutrient. Likewise, in parts of California where zinc deficiency is common, apples, peaches, cherries, apricots, and walnuts are affected.

[1] O. W. Davidson is Associate Biochemist in Horticulture at the New Jersey Agricultural Experiment Station.

The author wishes to express his appreciation to M. A. Blake and J. H. Clark for helpful suggestions and criticisms given during the preparation of this manuscript. He also wishes to express gratitude for the cooperation of the New Jersey Peach Council in making it possible to secure the paintings by Mary E. Eaton of nutrient-deficiency symptoms used for color plates, and to thank A. B. Burrell of the New York (Cornell) Agricultural Experiment Station, R. D. Dickey and G. H. Blackmon of the Florida Agricultural Experiment Station, and H. W. Ridgway of the Hampton Institute, for providing some of the photographs used.

APPLES

Bearing apple trees are large plants and as such have the capacity to store comparatively large quantities of nutrients. Moreover, their seasonal period of rapid vegetative growth may be short, whereas the absorption of nutrients by the roots is known to continue throughout nearly the entire year in some fruit regions and during a much longer time than top growth in all locations. Because of these conditions, apple trees require only a moderate degree of soil fertility, and they are relatively slow in responding to a nutrient deficiency. For the same reason numerous and contradictory recommendations are found concerning the fertilization of this crop.

Deficiencies of all the major and most of the minor nutrients have been known to occur in various commercial apple orchards throughout the United States. The manifestations of these deficiencies are not greatly unlike those described for tobacco. In well-developed stages, each nutrient deficiency may be recognized readily by the trained observer. In the early stages, however, deficiencies other than those of nitrogen and boron may be difficult to identify with assurance by means of the tree symptoms alone. For the identification of such deficiencies it may be convenient to refer to plant-tissue tests or to indications in cover-crop or sod plants.

Nitrogen Deficiency

Most apple growers are familiar, in a general way, with some of the symptoms of nitrogen deficiency in their trees. This is the most common nutrient deficiency in commercial apple orchards, and the one that is most readily corrected. There are, however, an infinite number of degrees of nitrogen deficiency. Only a severe deficiency of this nutrient causes injury to the tissues of a tree, but all degrees of nitrogen deficiency result in a retardation of growth. Depending upon circumstances, this may be advantageous or disadvantageous. In the hands of experienced fruit growers, nitrogen manipulation becomes a valuable means of exercising a high degree of control over the quality of growth produced by trees. Control over nitrogen supply results in an indirect control over carbohydrate reserves in the trees, which, in turn, assists in improving bud set, fruit color, and winter hardiness. Because of this, nitrogen is sometimes referred to as "the balance wheel in plant nutrition." If other nutrients, water, light, and temperature are favorable, tree growth can usually be accelerated or re-tarded by controlling the nitrogen supply.

A deficiency of nitrogen may occur at any time during the growing season in trees of any age. The symptoms are manifested in various ways according to the part of the season at which the deficiency develops and its severity.

In the early spring, when a rapid renewal of growth is taking place, a deficiency of nitrogen may result in a relatively small set of fruit and be associated with leaves that mature without attaining normal size. Nitrogen deficiency at this stage frequently is overlooked, for the young foliage and twigs do not then exhibit the hard growth condition and pronounced discoloration usually associated with a lack of nitrogen later in the growing season. For the most part, this form of nitrogen deficiency is avoided by early spring fertilization. In general, the deficiency may be foretold the previous summer or early fall by the appearance of symptoms of nitrogen hunger.

Throughout most of the spring and summer, nitrogen deficiency is indicated by a gradual decrease in greenness and an associated increase in yellowness of mature leaves. In all instances, the symptoms appear first near the base of the current growth and progress toward the tip. If the deficiency is a severe one, however, as in orchards in which it has been allowed to develop over a period of a year or more, or if the trees are young, yellow foliage may appear at the tips of twigs soon after the basal leaves are affected. At the same time, new leaves fail to attain their normal size for the variety, and the leafstalks (petioles) tend to form narrow angles with the stems. Nitrogen deficiency is associated with a gradual accumulation of carbohydrates and anthocyanin (purple) pigments, and with a general decrease in vegetative activity. Twig growth therefore becomes stiff and woody, limited in length and diameter, and reddish or brownish in color. These symptoms are illustrated in plate 1, page 227. Elongation of twigs and spurs stops early.

Trees affected by a mild lack of nitrogen may mature fruits of normal or nearly normal size and improved color. When the nitrogen deficiency is very pronounced, fruits become drastically reduced in size and tend to ripen and drop prematurely. Such trees, moreover, are apt to set fruit poorly in the spring.

In many instances, a deficiency of nitrogen may be forecast by the appearance of surrounding vegetation. Where apple trees develop a pronounced deficiency of nitrogen, nonleguminous sod plants, cover crops, or weeds in the orchard usually are stunted in size and yellowish in color.

PHOSPHORUS DEFICIENCY

Many cover-crop and sod failures in orchards are caused by insufficient phosphorus. This condition leads in time to unsatisfactory tree growth. Phosphorus, however, is not required by apple trees in such large quantities as nitrogen, potassium, or calcium. Mature apple trees, moreover, may store amounts of phosphorus adequate to sustain apparently normal growth for several years after the soil has become deficient in this element. Such growth is often accomplished by the redistribution of phosphorus from mature tissues to growing parts, where it is used over again. This is attended by the death of many cells and the weakening of others to such an extent that the hardiness of the tree is seriously affected. When the supplies of phosphorus in the tree and in the soil are no longer sufficient to meet the requirements for this apparently normal growth, deficiency symptoms appear.

Nursery apple trees have small reserves of phosphorus and, owing to their relatively rapid growth, are likely to exhibit deficiency symptoms within 2 or 3 months when planted on soils lacking in this nutrient.

As the phosphorus supplies of apple trees fail to meet the requirements for growth, the foliage retains a good color, or it may appear somewhat darker than usual. New leaves do not attain normal size, and the twigs—which may or may not be curtailed in linear growth, depending upon the severity of the deficiency— do not reach normal thickness. At the same time branching becomes obviously restricted. Phosphorus-deficient trees, like nitrogen-deficient ones, develop leaves with narrow petiole angles. The petioles and the veins of the lower leaf surfaces may become conspicuously purplish. These symptoms are illustrated in plate 2, page 228. In the early phases of phosphorus deficiency the utilization of sugars appears to be retarded and hence they accumulate. This results in the development of abnormal amounts of anthocyanin pigments, so that, particularly during cool spring or summer weather, all of the current-season growth may appear purplish or purplish red.

If the deficiency is allowed to become severe, the oldest leaves develop a mottled appearance with yellowish-green and dark-green areas. These mottled leaves soon drop. Twig diameter on such trees is conspicuously small, and fruit-bud formation is seriously reduced.

There is also some evidence of a lack of normal winter hardiness in phosphorus-deficient trees.

POTASSIUM DEFICIENCY

Potassium requirements of apple trees are about as large as those for nitrogen. Nevertheless, in many commercial orchards the amounts of potassium applied are small in comparison with those of nitrogen used. Under such conditions, apple trees are dependent upon the inherent and residual supplies of potassium in the soil. When these fail to meet the requirement for new growth, symptoms of potassium deficiency develop. The relative ease with which these symptoms may be identified is dependent upon the severity of the deficiency.

Apple trees affected by a mild deficiency of potassium may easily be confused with trees slightly lacking in nitrogen. Indeed, the symptoms exhibited may actually be those of nitrogen deficiency, since it has been found that trees lacking adequate amounts of potassium cannot utilize nitrates efficiently. Moreover, in the early stages of potassium deficiency, carbohydrates accumulate in the tree. Associated with this is a slightly yellowish-green color of the foliage, and the amount of yellow (or red, depending on the variety) in the twigs also may increase.

In apple orchards in which pronounced symptoms of potassium deficiency have appeared a characteristic type of foliage necrosis (death of tissues), or "scorch," develops after the terminals have made several inches of growth. The first leaves to be affected are those located near the middle or slightly below the middle of the current-season growth. From this portion, the injury spreads toward the tips and bases of affected twigs. The areas which later develop scorch are usually located along or near the leaf margins, and are preceded by dark-purplish discolorations as shown in plate 3, page 229. These discolored portions are plasmolyzed areas (that is, cell sap is extruded into the spaces between the cells, giving the tissue a water-soaked appearance) and they usually develop into scorched ones within a few hours or a day during warm summer weather. As a result of the relative inelasticity of the dead areas, subsequent growth in adjoining tissue causes crinkling and curling. The intensity of leaf scorch varies with the severity of potassium deficiency. Thus trees in which potassium is moderately deficient exhibit a type of scorching that is very largely confined to the leaf margins, as shown in plate 3, page 229. When there is a severe deficiency, scorched areas develop throughout the blade tissue, as shown in plate 4, page 230.

The symptoms of potassium-deficiency scorch on apple foliage are shown in plates 3 and 4. The plants from which these illustrations were made were grown in a greenhouse, where it is possible to obtain leaf specimens that are free from spray burning as well as from insect and disease injury. Nevertheless, the final color developed by the scorched areas is somewhat lighter and brighter than that of leaves found in the orchard. When the scorched areas are exposed to rain in the orchard they assume a dull brown color that is several shades darker than that illustrated.

Following the development of scorch, new leaves fail to attain normal size. This reduction in leaf size becomes more pronounced as potassium deficiency increases in severity.

It is characteristic of the necrotic or scorched leaves of the apple, as well as of those of most plants affected by potassium deficiency, to remain attached to the stems or twigs for some time after they have dried up.

Preceding the plasmolysis and purpling, potassium is withdrawn from the affected areas and moved to the growing tips and newly expanding leaves. This transfer and reuse enables trees that are not too deficient in potassium to make as much or nearly as much linear growth as normal trees. The growth produced by the deficient trees, however, is characteristically slender. Moreover, limited observations both in the United States and in England have shown that potassium-deficient apple trees are abnormally susceptible to wilting.

If the deficiency is not too severe, scorched trees may set an abnormally large number of small fruit buds. These buds blossom and set a fair amount of fruit, but owing to the weak condition of the trees and the reduced leaf area, the mature fruits are abnormally small.

Calcium Deficiency

The role of calcium in the apple orchard is often confused with that of lime. Calcium comprises a large portion of the ash of apple trees and is absolutely indispensable to growing tissues. On the other hand, the fact that productive apple orchards are found on strongly acid as well as neutral soils has led some people to underestimate the importance of calcium in practical fruit growing. For the most part, the occurrence of calcium deficiency is confined to soils having an inherently low supply of the element rather than to those that are strongly acid. The latter condition is conducive to rapid losses of calcium, but, since some acid soils are derived from rocks well supplied with this element, soil reaction alone is not necessarily an indication of the calcium supply. The influence of soil acidity on plant nutrition in general has been discussed in the first article in this book.

Because apple trees grow to be large plants and because they succeed best on well-aerated soils, they are dependent on the subsoil for much of their moisture supply during the summer season. It is important, therefore, that the trees develop their roots to such a depth and extent that they can procure whatever soil moisture is available during drought periods. For this reason an adequate supply of calcium is very important, since a deficiency has a retarding effect on root growth.

The symptoms of calcium hunger in apple trees usually become evident in the roots before they do in the tops. The extent to which roots manifest calcium-deficiency symptoms is dependent upon the degree to which the calcium supply is limited. Calcium-deficient roots are abnormally short and stubby. In mild deficiency symptoms, the tips of new roots stop elongating early, while the cortex— the outer cell layer—continues to thicken and new roots emerge in abnormal numbers a short distance behind the tip. When the calcium supply actually fails to meet the demands for growth, apple roots die back from the tips to the old, woody portions. Many new rootlets usually emerge from the live tissues a short distance behind the dead tips. Masses of short, stubby, excessively branched roots, as illustrated in figure 1, are indicative of calcium deficiency.

Symptoms of mild calcium hunger may be exhibited by apple-tree roots without the occurrence of distinctive deficiency characteristics in the top, although the growth of affected trees becomes retarded. This form of calcium deficiency occurs more frequently than that associated with foliage necrosis. Inasmuch as the roots of apple trees may be expected to reveal symptoms of calcium deficiency soon after such a condition develops in the soil, root growth is a more reliable index of the adequacy of the calcium supply than is top growth.

If young trees are planted in a soil very deficient in calcium, they may make several inches or a foot of growth and then form terminal buds. The foliage on these trees may show none of the specific symptoms of calcium hunger but may appear relatively normal except for a reduction in size. This has occurred repeatedly under experimental conditions and has been observed to occur in orchards. Calcium is required primarily in regions of new growth,

Figure 1.—Symptoms of calcium deficiency in apple roots. Roots tend to be short and somewhat bulbous, and usually die back from the tips after making a short growth.

and it is not transferred in significant amounts during the growing season from old tissues to new ones. Thus there may be considerable amounts of calcium compounds present in mature portions of plants whose tip growth has been inhibited by a lack of calcium. During the dormant season, some supplies of calcium are liberated in a soluble form by the break-down (hydrolysis) of previously insoluble calcium compounds in mature tissues and by the death of some cells. The liberated calcium is available for new top and root growth the following spring. As a result the young trees may make much more growth during the second season than they did in the first, and they are apt to grow much faster.

After several inches or a foot of new twig growth has formed, discolorations and necrotic areas develop on the young leaves (plate 5, page 231). The tips and sometimes the margins of affected young leaves may curve downward. Injury to the tip leaves is soon followed by the appearance of areas of dead tissue on nearly mature leaves that are still growing. Death of the discolored areas of leaf tissues is preceded by the development of light-green areas that usually turn a dull dark brown in a day or two.

When young apple trees are planted on soils which, although lacking an adequate supply of calcium, provide very limited amounts to the roots, the symptoms of deficiency are the same as those just described for young trees in their second season.

The supplies of calcium available to the growing twigs of mature apple trees are depleted only gradually. Consequently the rather sudden arresting of growth described for newly planted apples is not likely to occur. The writer has had an opportunity to observe definite symptoms of calcium deficiency in only one mature apple orchard, and they were similar to those shown in plate 6, page 232. Here again, an abundance of confirmatory evidence was shown by the roots of the mature trees.

Magnesium Deficiency

Although magnesium hunger, or "blotch," seldom develops in apple orchards in the United States, it has caused serious damage to commercial orchards in New Zealand. It is most apt to be encountered on light soils that are acid or have received excessive amounts of nitrate of soda, potash, or high-calcium forms of lime. It is especially favored by heavy, leaching summer rains.

Symptoms of magnesium shortage are very distinctive. When the deficiency first develops and before any foliage necrosis occurs, leaves have the lush, dark-green color of trees abundantly supplied with nitrogen. Under some conditions and with certain varieties, this stage is accompanied or followed by the appearance of chlorosis on the young terminal leaves. Later, mature leaves near the base of the current season's growth develop light-green or grayish-green blotches between the veins. These blotches frequently extend to the leaf margins, although they may occur near the middle of the blades. The light-green or grayish areas soon turn a fawn color and then a dark brown. Progressive stages of leaf blotching caused by magnesium deficiency in mature twig foliage are shown in plate 7, page 233. This is followed in a day or two by the shriveling and falling of affected leaves. The defoliation progresses rapidly toward the terminals until only a rosette of soft, thin, light-green leaves may remain. The effect of magnesium deficiency in defoliating 1-year-old apple trees is illustrated strikingly in figure 2.

The spur leaves on seriously deficient trees develop blotches similar to those on twig leaves. Defoliation of the spurs soon follows. A large portion of magnesium in the affected or blotched leaves is translocated to the growing tips. This enables twig growth to continue even on trees that show severe defoliation. Since leaves as well as magnesium are essential to carbohydrate manufacture by trees, however, the defoliation and blotching that accompany

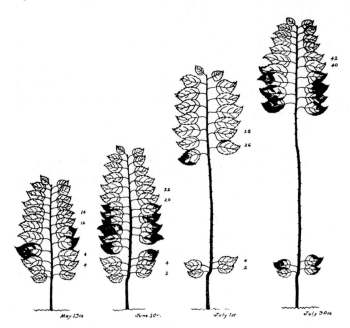

Figure 2.—Diagrammatic illustration of progressive leaf fall as a result of magnesium deficiency on 1-year-old apple trees. Black areas indicate blotched portions of leaves.

magnesium hunger result in a soft type of growth. Fruits on such trees, therefore, are abnormally small and poor in color and in edible quality. Experience with 1-year-old trees, moreover, indicates that magnesium deficiency greatly reduces their resistance to winter injury.

Boron Deficiency

It seems very likely that during the past decade deficiencies of boron in apple orchards have occurred more commonly than deficiencies of any other nutrient except nitrogen. Lack of this so-called minor element causes serious damage each year to apple crops in many fruit regions in the United States as well as in other parts of the world. Various types of boron deficiency have been given descriptive names by growers and investigators. "Drought spot," or external cork, "corky core," or internal cork, and "drought dieback" in apple trees are known to be due directly to boron deficiency.

This ailment occurs on a wide variety of orchard soils. It is found on limestone soils, on acid soils, on sandy soils, on stony soils in hilly regions, on dry soils, and on excessively wet soils. In regions affected by the deficiency, it is most common during dry years. Applications of nitrogen, by increasing the growth of apple trees, also increase the boron requirement, thereby augmenting the deficiency. It has been shown also that in some regions excessive liming, especially on strongly acid soils, is conducive to the development of this trouble.

As long as any part of an apple tree is growing, it needs a continuous supply of boron. This nutrient is not stored in plant tissues and transferred to regions of new growth as is the case with some other nutrients. Because of this, a deficiency of boron may develop at almost any time during the growing season. Moreover, the ailment may develop for the first time in either a mild or a severe form. It may be manifested one year by one group of symptoms and another year by a different group. Thus it is not uncommon for a tree to develop internal cork on the fruit one year and external cork the following year.

Internal cork may develop in the fruit on boron-deficient trees any time from 2 weeks after petal fall until harvest. Roundish water-soaked areas develop in the flesh and change quickly to brown-colored lesions which dry and become corky. These areas may develop anywhere throughout the flesh. When internal cork develops early in the growing season, the affected fruits become deformed and tend to drop badly. Apples developing internal cork late in the season show larger and more diffused brown lesions, but they are not misshapen. McIntosh fruits affected by late internal cork are illustrated in figure 3. The brown lesions developed in mature fruits have a decidedly bitter taste, the apples mature early and drop prematurely, and red varieties often show more or less bronzing.

External cork always develops early in the growing season and may appear within 2 weeks after petal fall. The first symptom is the occurrence of water-soaked, dead areas on the surface of the young fruits. Although these areas may appear on any portion of the fruit, they are most apt to occur on the inner or green side. The lesions become brown and hard and, since they are on the surface, subsequent growth of the fruit causes cracking, wrinkling, and scurfing of the skin, as shown in figure 4. Affected fruits may drop when they are little more than an inch in diameter or they may adhere to the trees. Fruits that are only slightly affected may attain normal size.

According to A. B. Burrell (2),[2] when a serious deficiency of

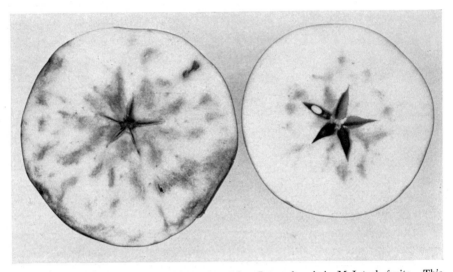

Figure 3.—Symptoms of boron deficiency in apples: Internal cork in McIntosh fruits. This type of boron deficiency usually develops during the late summer.

Figure 4.—External cork in McIntosh fruits at harvest time. This type of boron deficiency usually develops within 2 weeks after petal fall.

Courtesy of A. B. Burrell, Cornell University

boron develops within 8 weeks of petal fall, it is usually manifested in the fruit as external cork in the McIntosh, Baldwin, Rome, Northwestern Greening, and Jonathan varieties. With the varieties Fameuse, Ben Davis, Cortland, and Rhode Island Greening, the internal type of cork develops and the surface remains intact. On

[2] Italic numbers in parentheses refer to the list of Selected References, page 225.

the other hand, the varieties Wealthy, Duchess of Oldenburg, and Spy, when affected by the deficiency at this time, develop both the external and the internal types of cork, as shown in figure 5. Burrell has found that, regardless of the variety, cork developing more than 8 weeks after petal fall is usually manifested as the internal type.

Figure 5.—Oldenburg apples about 5 weeks after petal fall, showing symptoms of both internal and external cork due to boron deficiency.

Although the losses to apple growers from boron deficiency have been due mainly to direct injury to the fruits, considerable damage sometimes occurs to the vegetative portions of the trees. Injury to the wood may be due to boron deficiency alone, or to a combination of its direct effects and winter injury caused indirectly by the reduced vigor associated with the deficiency.

Burrell (2) has described three types of boron deficiency in apple twigs and leaves in the Champlain Valley region of New York State. The first of these, known as "incipient dieback," appears on twigs in the late summer. Leaves on current-season twigs affected by this form of boron deficiency appear yellowish with red veins and are somewhat convex and otherwise distorted in shape. Necrotic areas subsequently develop at the tips and margins. A distinctive symptom of incipient dieback is the occurrence of small necrotic areas in the phloem and cambium tissues (bark, and tissue between bark and wood) near the twig tips.

Burrell reports that this necrosis is found especially under axillary leaf buds. The enlargement of these areas results in death of the twigs from the tips downward.

A second type, known as dieback, has been found in boron-deficient orchards in New York State and in the Provinces of New Brunswick and British Columbia. The first indication of this form of the deficiency may be observed in the spring when otherwise normal buds fail to develop or make a delayed and feeble growth and soon die. Affected twigs may die back from their tips to wood that is several years old. Subsequently, an abnormal number of small twigs may branch out from wood just below the dead portion. These new branches may soon die back in a similar manner and tend to stimulate the development of another set. This process gives rise to an excessively branched condition often known as "witch's broom," which is also common in boron-deficient roses and tomatoes. Boron deficiency of this type may kill an apple tree in a few years.

Another form of boron hunger is manifested by the production of dwarfed, thickened, and brittle leaves arising from nodes separated by abnormally short internodes. The effect produced is that of a rosette of leaves, and hence Burrell has applied the term "rosette" to this form of the deficiency, which also occurs in roses and other plants. Burrell has made the interesting observation that the rosette leaves have smooth rather than serrated margins. Rosette and dieback may develop on the same branch, as shown in figure 6.

ZINC DEFICIENCY

Zinc deficiency in fruit trees has occurred in several parts of the United States and on vastly different types of soil. In some of the sandy areas it seems likely that the zinc supply of the soil is depleted, but in some other regions this has not occurred. It is known, however, that some soils have a high capacity for zinc fixation, which may possibly account for the development of zinc deficiency in trees growing on them. The deficiency is responsible for rosette of apple and pecan trees, "little leaf" of stone fruits and grapes, "mottle-leaf" of citrus, and "yellows" of walnuts. The symptoms of zinc deficiency in these various fruits show marked similarities.

Apple rosette, caused by zinc deficiency developing in the spring, is characterized by whorls of small, stiff, and sometimes mottled leaves near the tips of current-season twigs. Many of the leaves, in fact, may be no more than an inch in length and a quarter of an inch in width. Except for these terminal rosettes, the twigs may be bare for some time. Following this, branches arise from below the affected twigs; these usually produce leaves that are nearly normal early in the season but later become mottled and misshapen. Fruit-bud formation is severely reduced, and the fruits that develop are usually small and malformed. Twigs may begin to die back after the first year.

Less severe types of zinc deficiency are associated with the formation of prominent rosettes of small, narrow, chlorotic, or mottled leaves after twigs have grown several inches. Most of the leaves formed before the development of the rosette tend to drop off. Twigs are spindling and short. Few fruit buds are formed on affected branches. Just as in severe cases, branches arise from below the affected twigs and produce fairly good leaves. These symptoms are illustrated in figure 7.

PEACHES

Nutrient deficiencies are more common in peaches than in apples. This is due primarily to three factors: (1) Peaches are frequently grown on soils that are lighter and inherently less fertile than those ordinarily used for apples. (2) In general, peach trees, especially young ones, grow at a faster rate than do apple trees. Moreover, they normally continue rapid growth for a longer period than do apple trees. Other things being equal, the

Courtesy of A. B. Burrell, Cornell University

Figure 6.—Rosette and dieback of McIntosh apple tree caused by boron deficiency. Leaves are narrow, thick, and have smooth rather than serrated margins.

nutrient requirement of a plant increases in proportion to its rate of growth. (3) Peach trees are poorer competitor plants than are apples; consequently they soon show signs of starvation when crowded by weeds or cover crops on inadequately tilled soil.

It may be indicated at this point that peach trees on very light, sandy soils may be prone to exhibit symptoms of nitrogen deficiency periodically even when well fertilized with nitrogen. When

Figure 7.—Symptoms of zinc deficiency in apple. Branch on left shows normal growth a year after treatment with zinc sulfate. Branch on right was not treated with zinc sulfate and shows dieback, rosette, and small foliage due to zinc deficiency.

Courtesy of H. W. Ridgway, Hampton Institute

soil moisture is not provided in adequate amounts the utilization of nitrogen by the trees is inhibited. Likewise, peaches on very acid soil may make an unsatisfactory growth except when abnormally large amounts of fertilizer are used, and even then, in some instances, they may grow poorly. When endeavoring to account for unsatisfactory growth of peach trees, these limitations must be considered.

Nitrogen Deficiency

In peaches, deficiency of nitrogen occurs more commonly than that of any other nutrient. The symptoms of pronounced nitrogen hunger are familiar to commercial peach growers, for even on relatively good soils the trees may develop the symptoms within a very short time if they are forced to compete with weeds on untilled or inadequately tilled land. Young, rapidly growing peach trees in sand cultures are sufficiently responsive to nitrogen deficiency to enable an experienced observer to detect deficiency symptoms within a day after the nutrient is withheld. Although trees in the orchard are not suddenly subjected to conditions that deprive them of all sources of nitrogen, a deficiency of this nutrient can develop during May, June, or early July, and the characteristic growth symptoms may appear within a week. Prompt and appropriate care usually corrects the deficiency with little or no damage. A delay of 2 weeks, on the other hand, may seriously weaken young trees.

In the initial stages of nitrogen deficiency, mature leaves located near the bases of current-season twigs gradually become yellowish green and then greenish yellow. This is followed by a retardation of growth and a readily discernible stiffening of growing shoots 2 to 4 inches behind their tips. These symptoms may appear very quickly. If the deficiency continues to develop, leaves become yellowish green progressively from the bases to the tips of current growth. Simultaneously, twigs become spindling, short, and stiff, with brownish-red or purplish-red bark.

Nitrogen is translocated from mature or slowly growing tissues to regions of active growth. Consequently, the deficiency symptoms may develop to a pronounced degree on the older and lower twigs of a peach tree while well-exposed upper branches show only mild symptoms.

When linear growth on short twigs is checked considerably or when the young leaves on long current-season twigs are yellowish and fail to attain normal size, nitrogen deficiency in the old leaves is acute. Leaf color at this stage varies from yellowish green at the tips of growing twigs to reddish yellow at the bases, where red and brown spots characteristically develop. Depending upon the activity of the twigs and the location of the leaves, foliage will vary in color from yellowish green, through greenish yellow and yellow, to reddish yellow. Red spots or necrotic brown spots are common on all but the yellowish-green leaves, and some may be found on these. Leaf discolorations characteristic of nitrogen deficiency are illustrated in plate 8, A, page 234.

When nitrogen deficiency in peach trees reaches the stage at which reddish, spindling twigs with red-spotted leaves are found, fruit-bud formation may be severely curtailed. In fact, any deficiency of nitrogen that causes a reduction in twig growth is apt to decrease fruit-bud formation. Moreover, the winter hardiness of both twigs and buds may be reduced. Fruits formed on branches producing these twigs are usually small and abnormally astringent for the variety. With red varieties, the color may become dark and unattractive.

PHOSPHORUS DEFICIENCY

Phosphorus deficiency is responsible for considerable losses to peach growers each year. It is particularly serious in young and in replanted peach orchards, where a deficiency of phosphorus reduces the vigor of the trees to such an extent that losses during the first winter are often very high. Acid soils and light sandy soils are particularly susceptible to the deficiency, as well as soils with a high phosphorus-fixing power.

Since phosphorus can be reutilized in peach trees, symptoms of an inadequate supply would be expected to appear first on the old leaves of current-season twigs. While this is apt to be the case, characteristic symptoms also appear on young foliage at about the same time. At the onset of deficiency symptoms, peach foliage, young and old, attains a dark-green color that might cause it to be mistaken for that of a tree well fertilized with nitrogen. If the prevailing temperatures are rather cool at this time, careful observation should reveal a purple or bronze pigmentation on the veins of the lower leaf surfaces and on the petioles. Regardless of temperatures, this stage is followed by a bronzing and tanning of the upper leaf surfaces, as illustrated in plate 9, A, page 235. Moreover, if cool weather prevails during this stage, the leaves will show more or less reddish or purplish pigmentation, especially along the margins of blades and on leafstalks.

Associated with the bronze or tan discoloration on the foliage, the uppermost new leaves tend to become more erect than usual, while those just below the tip stand out approximately at right angles to the twigs. The leaves characteristically curve downward near the margins and at the tips; this is shown in plate 9, B. In general, the newly matured leaves do not attain normal width.

At about the same time that changes occur in the conformation and position of leaves at the tips of current-season twigs, mottling develops on foliage at the bases of twigs and progresses upward. In some respects this mottling is not unlike that which may normally precede the dropping (abscission) of basal leaves. The mottling shown in plate 9, C, page 235, however, is characteristic of phosphorus-deficient peach trees and may appear weeks or months in advance of abscission, depending upon the degree to which the nutrient is lacking. Instances have been observed in which peach trees deficient in phosphorus lost nearly all leaves except those near the tips of twigs. Afterward, the trees renewed their growth and developed leaves which, although they showed symptoms characteristic of phosphorus hunger, held through most of the season.

Peach trees only slightly lacking in phosphorus may make a fair growth, but they develop relatively few branches. The latter, moreover, are rather slender. If the deficiency is severe, whorls of leaves form at the tips of twigs after little more than a quarter of the normal growth has been produced.

Potassium Deficiency

In the United States, potassium deficiency has been encountered much more often in the peach than in the apple. Peach trees, in fact, may show symptoms of severe potassium deficiency in the same orchard with apples that show little or no definite evidence of a lack of the nutrient. This is probably due to the fact that peaches usually require as much if not more potassium than do apples, as well as because their period of rapid growth is normally longer than that of apples.

Potassium deficiency occurs in commercial peach orchards planted on light sandy soils, droughty shales, limestone soils, acid soils, soils with high potash-fixing power, and also on soils that for one reason or another are abnormally low in organic-matter content. On light sandy soils, potassium deficiency can be induced in peaches by excessive applications of lime. This should not be interpreted to indicate that liming is apt to cause potassium deficiency on light soil, for lime in moderate applications may be highly beneficial. The use of nitrogenous fertilizers on soils that are slightly deficient in potassium also is likely to intensify the deficiency symptoms. This is due in part to the fact that any stimulus to growth is apt to increase the tree's nutrient requirements.

The first diagnostic symptom of potassium hunger in peach trees is the development of crinkled leaves near the middle portion of current-season twigs. The crinkling is caused by uneven growth of blade tissue, and is particularly noticeable along the midrib. As the deficiency increases in severity the crinkling becomes more pronounced and more extensive over the tree, and is often associated with more or less rolling of the leaves, as shown in figure 8. The rolling is apt to develop particularly during dry weather. This may be an adaptation to reduce transpiration, since it has been shown that potassium-deficient trees are particularly subject to wilting. The rolling of peach leaves due to potassium deficiency is always associated with crinkling and curling of the blade tissues. This type of rolling should not be confused with that caused by some stages of calcium deficiency, by cold injury, and by girdling, and by some other translocation abnormalities that cause rolling without crinkling.

Figure 8.—Crinkling and curling, together with some rolling of leaves, preceding the development of foliage necrosis on a potassium-deficient peach tree grown in sand culture.

Simultaneously with the appearance of crinkling, peach trees may exhibit some of the symptoms of nitrogen deficiency. This is because a deficiency of potassium restricts the utilization of nitrogen in the plant. The twig tips tend to stiffen, and the leaves acquire a yellowish-green color that is more prominent with the yellow-fleshed than with the white varieties. This stage is usually followed by the development of small straw-colored areas of dead tissue in the leaf blade (see plate 10, E, page 236). These areas may remain small and straw-colored for a few days or they may expand into larger areas that become brown. These stages are illustrated in plate 10, F. The necrotic areas are usually bordered by definite lines, or abscission zones, which, in the field, are often discolored reddish brown or purplish red. The dropping out, or abscission, of many of the necrotic areas in the blades and along the margins leaves holes—not unlike those formed by the "shothole" disease of peaches—and scalloped edges. Careful examination will usually reveal dark-green water-soaked (plasmolyzed) areas that are the initial stages of necrosis in the blades. The withdrawal of potassium from these areas and its reutilization at the growing tips are sometimes followed by an improvement in the color of immature and recently matured leaves, and an increase in rate of growth. Leaves maturing throughout the remainder of the season fail to attain normal size, especially in length. Young peach trees in a greenhouse have been observed in a single season to undergo three successive cycles of leaf necrosis followed by renewal of growth. The first cycle was the most pronounced of the three.

If potassium is supplied to and absorbed by the affected trees at this stage they utilize it readily, as might be supposed from the fact that they quickly reutilize the potassium withdrawn from necrotic leaves. Necrotic areas in mature foliage may continue to develop, however, for several weeks after potassium has been supplied to the trees, even though tip growth is rapid and normal.

In orchards lacking adequate potassium, the deficiency symptoms increase in severity throughout the growing season. Areas of dead tissue along the leaf margins, particularly, become more prominent. The affected foliage also develops cracks and tears as a result of the action of wind on the inelastic dead areas. At the same time, light-red or purplish-red pigmentation develops on affected leaves, especially on the exposed lower surface of the longitudinally rolled blades.

Unlike nitrogen- or phosphorus-deficient leaves, the tattered and discolored leaves on trees lacking potassium adhere to the twigs for a long time. If active growth is renewed after considerable foliage necrosis has occurred, the affected leaves may drop off prematurely. Likewise, if the deficiency develops in the early summer and continues throughout the season, many leaves may fall early. On the other hand, when the deficiency symptoms first develop rather late in the season, the affected leaves usually adhere until normal leaf fall occurs, or even later.

As a consequence of the reutilization of potassium in peach trees, linear growth of deficient trees is not always greatly curtailed. In fact, trees exhibiting only the mild deficiency symptoms may make nearly as much growth as those abundantly supplied with potassium. The twigs on deficient trees, however, are usually slender.

The effects of potassium hunger on peach fruit-bud formation are most severe. Even in relatively mild cases, when only a small portion of the foliage develops necrosis and little defoliation occurs, the trees may fail to form a single fruit bud. If the deficiency symptoms do not appear until late in the summer, fruit buds may form, but only on the most vigorous twigs, and yields consequently are very small.

If potash is not supplied to peach trees that developed symptoms of a severe deficiency during the previous season, dead areas may appear on newly expanding foliage at the time at which growth is renewed in the spring or very shortly thereafter. In this case, the necrosis may occur with or without crinkling of the foliage, as shown in plate 10, A and B, page 236.

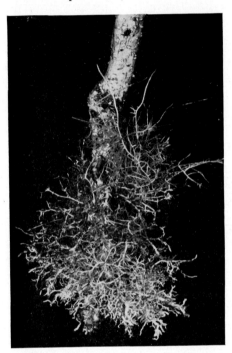

Figure 9.—Symptoms of calcium deficiency in roots of a 1-year-old peach tree. Roots are short, sometimes bulbous, and die back after making comparatively little linear growth. New roots emerge profusely behind the dead root tips.

CALCIUM DEFICIENCY

Peach trees may lack adequate supplies of calcium irrespective of the pH values of the soil on which they are growing. The excessive use of potash fertilizer or nitrate of soda on light soils inherently low in calcium may induce a deficiency of the latter. Nevertheless, peaches growing on such soils require considerable nitrogen and potash and their efficient use, therefore, is dependent upon an adequate supply of calcium.

Calcium hunger in peaches, as in most other plants, is revealed very quickly by its effect on root growth. New roots are abnormally short, thick, and crooked. Most of the roots die back from their tips after making a growth of 1/2 inch to 3 inches. Moreover, there is a very pronounced and characteristic tendency for new roots to arise in profusion a short distance behind the tips of deficient roots (figure 9). Although a few roots may make a fair amount of growth, root extension in general is drastically curtailed.

If peach trees are suddenly subjected to a lack of calcium, as when young trees from a nursery are planted in a soil deficient in this nutrient, they may show signs of wilting for a period of about a week after they have completed a month or more of growth in the spring or early summer. This period of wilting coincides with extensive dieback of the new roots. Mortality at this time may be high. Trees that survive, however, soon become extremely resistant to wilting. In fact, some will stand transplanting in mid-summer and show no signs of wilting.

Unlike calcium-deficient apple trees, the tops of peach trees reveal characteristic symptoms of inadequate calcium rather early. Two different manifestations of calcium deficiency in peach tops are common. The severity of the deficiency and the time during the growing season at which it begins appear to be determining factors. (1) If the deficiency starts in the spring or if it is severe at any time during which the trees are making rapid growth, it will be exhibited by necrosis of leaves and twigs. (2) If it develops late in the season when the trees are not growing rapidly, necrosis may not occur in the tops, but the roots may be injured.

When the supply of calcium in a peach tree fails to meet the requirements of rapidly growing tissues, the first pair of leaves near the bases of young growing twigs 4 to 8 inches long develop red or purplish-red discolorations along the margins and at the tips. This is followed by some loss of chlorophyll and by necrosis in the discolored areas and then by dropping of the affected leaves. These symptoms are illustrated in plate 11, D, page 237. Only immature basal leaves are affected; those on long twigs remain apparently normal.

Usually the deficiency then follows one of two different patterns. In both cases, the immature leaves develop reddish-brown or dark-brown necrotic areas along the midribs and at the blade tips, similar to those illustrated in plate 11, C. These areas expand in size, and in one type of manifestation the defoliation progresses toward the midportions of twigs both from the bases and from the tips (plate 11, B). The defoliated twigs die back for only a few inches. In the second type of manifestation, in which there is a greater deficiency of calcium, twig tips and young leaves are killed as by a blight, and the necrosis progresses rapidly down the twigs and affects all immature and some apparently mature leaves. An early stage of this is shown in plate 11, A. Many of the twigs die back to their bases, and some of the branches supporting them die. Below the outermost 2 or 3 inches on each twig, necrosis and discoloration of leaves are similar to those described for the first type of defoliation.

Previous to the development of foliage necrosis, calcium-deficient peach trees form an unusually large number of large leaves.

It is evident that a bad case of calcium deficiency developing early in the growing season may very seriously injure peach trees, especially those newly planted. Fortunately, however, a deficiency of such magnitude seldom, if ever, affects mature trees. They would necessarily exhibit symptoms of mild calcium deficiency for at least one or more seasons, and this could be corrected before becoming more acute.

Figure 10.—Longitudinal rolling of leaves on calcium-deficient peach tree.

When calcium deficiency develops rather late in the growing season, or when this nutrient becomes slightly deficient a month or two after the renewal of growth in the spring, linear extension of twigs is gradually restricted. Many twigs become abnormally thickened, especially near the tips. Foliage remains dark and somewhat tannish green rather than normal green. Although the leaves do not grow to a larger size than is normal for the variety, an unusual number of large leaves develop. Fruit-bud formation starts early in the season, and conspicuously large buds are present in abundance toward the end of summer. Lenticels (pores on the stems) enlarge and become unusually prominent, resembling those on girdled trees. On some trees, the leaf blades roll longitudinally, as shown in figure 10. The tendency for the leaves to roll in this manner is not peculiar to calcium-deficient trees but appears to be associated in some way with restricted translocation of foods.

MAGNESIUM DEFICIENCY

After heavy summer rains, magnesium deficiency occasionally develops in peach trees grown on light sandy soils. In New Jersey the deficiency has been found during wet seasons in trees grown on very acid loams and on sandy loams that had received heavy applications of oyster-shell lime—a high-calcium form of lime that contains no more than a trace of magnesium.

Although magnesium is readily translocated and reutilized in the peach, small and large 1-year-old trees may develop symptoms of the deficiency at about the same time. In all cases observed, both in greenhouse studies and in the field, mature leaves in the initial stages of the deficiency appear dark green—in some instances, blue green. Leaves near the tips of growing twigs sometimes become slightly but definitely chlorotic. All leaves formed thereafter are abnormally thin. Leaf size, however, may not be affected.

When the supply of available magnesium in the soil fails to meet the requirements for new growth, dark-green, water-soaked blotches appear on the lowermost leaves on large current-season branches, or on the main stems of 1-year-old trees. The pattern of this blotching and the purplish-red discolorations bordering the necrotic areas are shown in plate 8, B, page 234. Within a few hours the dark-green blotches may change to gray white or green white and then to a fawn color. The latter does not change unless exposed to rain, after which it becomes a medium brown. Within a few days the blotched leaves drop.

In the field, defoliation often continues until nearly half the current growth is bare. In greenhouse studies, however, it may continue until only immature, terminal leaves are left (figure 11). Twigs on such trees become abnormally flexible.

In New Jersey most peach trees that lose many leaves as a result of magnesium deficiency during their first season in the orchard fail to live through the winter.

In fruit-growing regions where magnesium deficiency has been found in mature peach trees, fruit-bud formation has been drastically reduced.

ZINC DEFICIENCY

In parts of Florida and California, zinc deficiency has caused serious losses in peach orchards. The ailment in those regions has been called "little leaf" because of the characteristic rosettes of small leaves that form on the terminals of badly affected trees.

When zinc deficiency develops in a peach tree for the first time, it is manifested as a chlorotic mottling in the foliage late in the summer. This chlorosis progresses upward from the lowermost leaves to those at the tips of twigs. Although 1-year-old trees may exhibit these symptoms, the trees are usually 2 years old or older before the deficiency develops.

Unless zinc is supplied to these trees, symptoms characteristic of the deficiency will be exhibited the following spring or early summer. Chlorotic leaves appear with yellow-green areas between veins. As the leaves mature, these areas become light yellow, and some develop purple-red pigmentation. Necrotic areas appear at the tips and in the blades of badly mottled foliage. This foliage drops prematurely and often leaves the twigs entirely bare.

Figure 11.—Normal and magnesium-deficient peach trees grown in sand culture. The magnesium-deficient tree on the right made nearly as much linear growth as the normal tree, but was practically defoliated by late August.

At the terminals of twigs, crinkled and chlorotic foliage such as that shown in figure 12 may develop. On the other hand, when the deficiency reaches the stage at which considerable defoliation occurs, rosettes of small leaves are formed at the terminals (figure 13). In severe cases, the leaves in these rosettes may be nearly sessile (without leafstalks), very small, and abnormally rigid. Figure 13 also shows the formation of new twigs below the stunted terminals. Such trees are usually late in renewing growth the following spring. Twigs that fail to develop foliage die back for more or less indefinite distances, as shown in figure 13. The trees usually die within 3 or 4 years after the onset of the deficiency.

Although fruit-bud formation on zinc-deficient peach trees may be drastically curtailed, some buds usually develop. Very few fruits are produced, however, and those that set on badly affected branches are misshapen and worthless.

Courtesy of R. D. Dickey and G. H. Blackmon, Florida Agricultural Experiment Station

Figure 12.—Crinkling, waving, and chlorosis of Jewel peach leaves as a result of zinc deficiency in a Florida orchard. Leaf at right is normal.

BORON DEFICIENCY

Boron deficiency rarely occurs in peach orchards. It has been found, however, in commercial orchards in the northwestern United States. The symptoms exhibited resemble those of other boron-deficient plants. The affected trees are characterized by their small, thick, misshapen, and brittle leaves.

Peach trees grown in boron-deficient treatments in sand cultures soon develop areas of dead tissue at the twig tips. This is followed by dieback of the injured twigs and considerable defoliation. As with the apple and many other plants, it is characteristic of boron-deficient branches to develop many side branches following this dieback.

Compound Deficiencies in Peach Trees

Although marked stunting of growth may occur when peach trees are grown on soils deficient in two or more basic (or metallic) nutrients, such as potassium, calcium, or magnesium, it is very rare indeed for a tree to exhibit diagnostic symptoms of more than one such deficiency at a time. In fact, trees planted on such soils,

Figure 13.—Characteristic symptoms of acute zinc deficiency in young Jewel peach tree in Florida: "Little leaf," crinkling, rosette, defoliation, and twig dieback.

Courtesy of R. D. Dickey and G. H. Blackmon,
Florida Agricultural Experiment Station

because of their abnormally slow growth, sometimes fail to exhibit specific deficiency symptoms until they are fertilized with one of the nutrients of which there is a shortage. When attempts have been made to create in sand cultures a deficiency of both potassium and calcium, peach trees have grown very slowly. It was not uncommon to find one tree exhibiting symptoms of calcium deficiency at the same time that a neighboring tree, receiving the same treatment, showed definite symptoms of potassium deficiency. From these studies and from orchard observations it has been concluded that when there is a shortage of two or more basic nutrients in a soil at the same time, deficiency symptoms are apt to be developed only for the nutrient that is most needed in the tree.

Experience with peach trees grown in soils and in sand cultures in which both nitrogen and phosphorus were deficient has shown that, because the former is needed in much greater amounts than is the latter, nitrogen deficiency usually limits growth before the reserves of phosphorus in the tissues are exhausted. An exception to this statement will be described presently.

A similar situation usually exists where nitrogen and some one of the basic nutrients are deficient in the soil. A lack of nitrogen is exhibited by the tree and limits growth before the reserves of other nutrients in the plant tissues are exhausted.

A deficiency of phosphorus, on the other hand, may coexist with that of one of the basic nutrients—potassium, calcium, or magnesium. This, in fact, is likely to occur in peach orchards in which either potassium or calcium is deficient. Growers who do not fertilize with potash seldom use phosphates on the trees. Moreover, in acid, calcium-deficient soils the amounts of available phosphorus present are apt to be very low indeed. It has been repeatedly observed and adequately substantiated that, when a compound deficiency of phosphorus and one of the basic nutrients develops in peach trees, the distinctive symptoms of one deficiency are superimposed upon those of the other. In most cases, however, the symptoms for one nutrient developed before those for the second. The symptoms exhibited are so distinct as to cause little confusion.

Compound Phosphorus-Potassium Deficiency

In New Jersey, a compound deficiency of phosphorus and potassium is second only to that of nitrogen in frequency of occurrence. In some orchards, the symptoms may be those of typical phosphorus hunger with occasional leaves 4 to 8 inches from twig tips showing a slight potassium-deficiency necrosis. In other orchards the trees may exhibit symptoms of severe potassium hunger, but at the same time they may show an abnormal amount of pigmentation in the necrotic leaves and typical phosphorus-deficiency mottling on old leaves.

One symptom that is particularly characteristic of this compound deficiency is an early cessation of terminal growth. This is typical of phosphorus deficiency but not of potassium deficiency in peaches.

It is not uncommon, however, for growth to be resumed again during the same season.

In plate 12, page 238, peach leaves show typical symptoms of potassium deficiency and at the same time have small, abnormally pigmented dots. The over-all color of the leaves is ochre green, a characteristic of phosphorus deficiency. Moreover, they exhibit a mottling between the veins that is common to phosphorus-deficient leaves but does not occur on leaves lacking only potassium.

Under orchard conditions, peach trees affected by compound phosphorus-potassium deficiency may at times exhibit symptoms of nitrogen deficiency. In fact, such trees usually respond to applications of nitrogen, although relatively large amounts are necessary. This nitrogen deficiency appears to be induced by the lack of potassium. It may be recalled that this was found to occur also when peach trees were deficient in potassium but adequately provided with other nutrients. When this condition develops, immature leaves remain small, and those on the upper halves of current-season twigs become somewhat crinkled, while the margins tend to roll toward the midribs. At the same time, leaves on the lower portion of the twigs may droop and show phosphorus-deficiency mottling. Red pigmentation is particularly abundant and increases in intensity from the bases to the tips of twigs. Fruit buds are very sparse or entirely lacking. Foliage and twig symptoms associated with this compound deficiency are illustrated in plate 13, page 239.

This type of growth has been observed on peach trees, particularly on 1- and 2-year-old trees, in New Jersey for many years. It was recognized as a physiological ailment and was called "false little peach" because the small size, discoloration, and drooping of foliage on the lower portions of twigs resembles that caused by the virus disease "little peach." Within recent years, however, work at the New Jersey Agricultural Experiment Station has demonstrated that false little peach is caused by a compound deficiency of phosphorus and potassium.

STRAWBERRIES

Nitrogen Deficiency

The beginning of nitrogen deficiency in strawberry plants is indicated by the yellow-green color of old leaves and by the small size of newly maturing ones. The plants thereafter form relatively few and weak runners. As the deficiency of nitrogen becomes acute, young leaves also acquire a yellow-green color, while mature foliage becomes yellower and at the same time becomes pigmented with red, especially toward the margins of blades. This stage is soon followed by the firing and withering of old leaves near the crowns.

PHOSPHORUS DEFICIENCY

A deficiency of phosphorus in strawberry plants is indicated first by abnormally dark green foliage resulting from the accumulation of purplish pigmentation in the leaf surface. This symptom is followed successively by (1) a reduction in leaf size or an intensification of the dark color, which changes to coppery purple, and (2) a mottling and dying of old leaves.

POTASSIUM DEFICIENCY

Strawberry plants exhibit definite symptoms of potassium deficiency by the development of marginal leaf scorch. This scorching may be distinguished from the firing, or marginal necrosis, caused by nitrogen deficiency in that the latter is produced first on old leaves and is always preceded by pronounced yellowing and reddening. Scorch due to potassium deficiency, on the other hand, usually develops first on mature leaves of intermediate age and may not be confined to margins. Moreover, the scorched leaves may have a fairly normal green color except for the areas of dead tissue, or they may show more or less purple-red pigmentation.

CALCIUM DEFICIENCY

Unlike those of the nutrients previously discussed, a deficiency of calcium affects the buds or growing points of the crown first. These tissues are killed, and subsequent growth must take place from lateral buds. Very young leaves, as well as those that are half grown, may also be affected. The entire leaf, or a leaflet, or a portion of a leaflet, may die. Red-brown discoloration may develop around the base of the leaflet, or it may be more or less general over the leaf surface.

Roots usually show considerable injury before the tops are seriously affected. The root injury becomes progressively worse as the deficiency continues. Roots die back from their tips after making relatively short growth. This is followed by the development of new rootlets behind the dead portion. The entire root system, therefore, consists of a small mass of short growths.

MAGNESIUM DEFICIENCY

Magnesium-deficient strawberry plants develop abnormally thin leaves, which exhibit a bright green color not found in healthy foliage. Blotching begins near the margins of old leaves and spreads until the whole surface is necrotic. The affected areas usually exhibit a slightly purple, gray-brown color. Withering of the injured leaves progresses from the bases upward toward the young leaves.

OTHER SMALL FRUITS

The characteristic symptoms of nutrient deficiencies in bush fruits and grapes closely resemble those in the strawberry and the apple. Thus, for example, nitrogen deficiency in the small fruits in general is characterized by a retardation of growth, yellowing of foliage, hardening of twigs, and the development of more or less reddish pigmentation.

PLANT-TISSUE TESTS FOR THE DETECTION OF NUTRIENT DEFICIENCIES

For those who are not familiar with nutrient-deficiency symptoms in fruit trees, plant-tissue tests for major nutrients usually offer a simple and reliable method for confirming a diagnosis. Also, where the identification of a deficiency is complicated by the presence of insect, disease, or spray injury, these tests may prove very useful. Moreover, in very light or in acid soils, growth may be inhibited to such an extent that positive symptoms of a nutrient deficiency may be lacking. For several years the writer has prepared extracts from apple and peach twigs as a means of comparing the composition of the plants with the growth characteristics.

Extracts are prepared in the following manner: Several twigs that are well exposed and representative of nearly the best growth on a tree are selected. A low content of nutrients in weak side branches or in insect- or spray-injured twigs is not in general an indication that a deficiency is limiting the growth of the tree. Five-gram samples of finely minced tissue comprising the terminal 5-inch portions of apple twigs or 6-inch portions of peach twigs are prepared. These are placed in small mortars to which are added ¼ gram of Darco brand, phosphorus-free, powdered charcoal, and 25 milliliters of the Hester soil-extracting solution (8). The latter contains 5 grams of sodium hydroxide and 10 milliliters of glacial acetic acid, made to a volume of 1 liter with distilled water. In order to facilitate grinding, only about 10 milliliters of the extracting solution are added at first. The tissue is ground for about 5 minutes, and then the remainder of the solution is added and the grinding is continued for another 5 minutes. The extract is filtered through a Whatman No. 1 paper. A clear extract is necessary. If a small amount of charcoal should come through, it may be removed by refiltering with the same paper. If much yellow or brown color is present, an additional ¼ gram of charcoal should be used. When the color persists, an additional 25-milliliter portion of extracting solution may be used. In general, no extra charcoal or extracting solution is necessary for peach-twig samples. The same is true of apple twigs collected during the spring and early summer. During the late summer and fall, however, most apple twigs contain sufficient tannin to impart yellow or brown discolorations to the extracts. Fortunately, it is often possible by working rapidly to complete estimations of phosphorus and of magnesium content before the color in the extract interferes too much.

Recently, Hester (9) proposed the use of a Waring blender for preparing plant-tissue extracts. This machine has four small, stainless-steel blades that rotate at a speed of 10,000 or 12,000 revolutions per minute and quickly reduce the tissue to a pulp. From 5 to 20 grams of tissue, $\frac{1}{2}$ gram of charcoal, and 200 milliliters of extracting solution are placed in the machine and ground for 5 minutes. The extract thus prepared is filtered as described.

The nutrients may be estimated by the methods described by Hester (8), or Carolus (3), or by other methods that may be suitable. The writer used for this purpose modifications of quantitative methods used for blood analysis. All values are expressed as parts per million of the nutrient elements in the green tissue.

The nutrient content of extracts from trees making poor growth may be compared with that of similar varieties of trees making good growth. In general, this procedure should be adopted in addition to the use of chemical standards until one has acquired experience with these tests.

Terminal portions of apple and peach twigs have not been found to be greatly different in nutrient content; a deficiency of phosphorus in either case may be suspected when 5- or 6-inch twig tips during the growing season contain less than 50 parts per million of this nutrient. The following table may be useful as a guide in interpreting the results of such tests on apple and peach twigs:

PARTS PER MILLION OF NUTRIENTS IN TERMINAL
PORTIONS OF GREEN APPLE AND PEACH TWIGS [1]

Nutrient element	Deficient trees P. p. m.	Good trees P. p. m.
Phosphorus	Less than 100	200– 700
Potassium	" " 1,000	2,000–7,000
Calcium	" " 100	300–1,000
Magnesium	" " 60	200– 500

[1] Terminal 5 inches of apple twigs or terminal 6 inches of peach twigs.

Inasmuch as apple and peach twigs do not normally contain more than traces of nitrate nitrogen, if any, testing for it seems useless.

Plant-tissue tests are particularly valuable in that they not only reveal a low content of a nutrient but also frequently confirm other evidence. Thus, when calcium or magnesium is deficient in peach twigs, potassium alone or both magnesium and potassium tend to be present in relatively large amounts. Likewise, when only potassium is deficient, calcium or magnesium or both may be found in relatively high concentrations.

KEY TO PLANT-NUTRIENT DEFICIENCY SYMPTOMS IN DECIDUOUS FRUIT TREES

ELEMENT
DEFICIENT

A. Symptoms which, in the early stages of the deficiency, are general on the whole tree or tend to be localized in the older leaves of the current season's growth.

 B. Symptoms rather generally distributed but usually most prominent on lower leaves of current season's growth. No areas of dead tissue developing on foliage except in advanced and severe cases.

  C. Leaves yellowish green; discoloration begins on old, mature leaves and progresses toward the tip. Accumulations of reddish and purplish-red pigments usually obvious. Under prolonged deficiency, twigs hard and slender and foliage small............... Nitrogen

  C. Young and nearly matured leaves dark green, while mature leaves are bronzed or ochre-dark green. Old leaves usually mottled with light-green areas developing between dark-green veins. Stems and leafstalks developing abnormal amounts of purplish pigment, especially during cool summer weather. As the deficiency continues, new twigs are slender and leaves small (apple) or strap-shaped (peach).. Phosphorus

 B. Symptoms appearing first on mature or lower portion of current season's growth and occurring as mottling or chlorosis, with or without spots, blotches, marginal scorching, or other necrotic (dead) areas in foliage.

  C. Foliage necrosis (death of tissues) varying in size from very small spots or dots to patches or extensive marginal areas. Foliage, especially of peach, usually crinkled. Necrotic areas developing first on mature leaves near the middle or lower half of the current season's growth. Twigs usually slender................... Potassium

  C. Foliage necrosis occurring as fawn-colored patches on most mature, large leaves. Affected leaves dropping progressively toward the tips of the current season's twigs. Severe defoliation common, leaving a tuft or rosette of thin, dark-green leaves at the terminals. Magnesium

  C. Foliage small, narrow, more or less crinkled, and chlorotic at tips of new growth; twigs slender, with very short internodes near tips, producing rosettes of leaves. Defoliation progressive from bases to tips of twigs... Zinc

A. Symptoms appearing first on young tissues and tending to be localized at the terminals of twigs.

 B. Twigs dying back from terminals. Newly developing or nearly mature leaves showing severe necrosis.

  C. Immature leaves, especially those at terminals, dying back from tips and margins or along the midribs. Following severe injury to foliage at terminals, twigs die back for an indefinite distance. These symptoms are always associated with injury to root tips... Calcium

  C. Leaves more or less chlorotic and wrinkled; sometimes abnormally thick and brittle. In severe cases, there is dieback of twigs and spurs. With bearing trees, deficiency is associated with necrotic areas in the flesh or on the surface of fruits even when no abnormal growth is apparent in vegetative parts.................... Boron

SELECTED REFERENCES

(1) BLAKE, M. A., NIGHTINGALE, G. T., and DAVIDSON, O. W.
 1937. NUTRITION OF APPLE TREES. N. J. Agr Expt. Sta. Bul. 626, 41 pp., illus.

(2) BURRELL, A. B.
 1940. THE BORON-DEFICIENCY DISEASE OF APPLE. N. Y. (Cornell) Agr. Expt. Sta. Bul.
 428, 28 pp., illus.

(3) CAROLUS, R. L.
 1938. THE USE OF RAPID CHEMICAL PLANT NUTRIENT TESTS IN FERTILIZER DEFICIENCY
 DIAGNOSES AND VEGETABLE CROP RESEARCH. Va. Truck Expt. Sta. Bul. 98,
 pp. [1527]-1556.

(4) CHANDLER, W. H.
 1937. ZINC AS A NUTRIENT FOR PLANTS. Bot. Gaz. 98: 625-646, illus.

(5) DAVIS, M. B., and HILL, H.
 1928. NITROGEN, PHOSPHORIC ACID AND POTASH STARVATION AT DIFFERENT STAGES OF
 THE GROWTH OF FRAGARIA. Canada Dept. Agr. Pam. (n.s.) 96, 8 pp., illus.

(6) DICKEY, R. D., and BLACKMON, G. H.
 1940. A PRELIMINARY REPORT ON LITTLE-LEAF OF THE PEACH IN FLORIDA—A ZINC DEFI-
 CIENCY. Fla. Agr. Expt. Sta. Bul. 344, 19 pp., illus.

(7) DUNBAR, CHARLES, and ANTHONY, R. D.
 1938. TWO CASES OF POTASSIUM DEFICIENCY IN PEACH ORCHARDS IN SOUTH CENTRAL
 PENNSYLVANIA. Amer. Soc. Hort. Sci. Proc. 35: 320-325, illus.

(8) HESTER, JACKSON B.
 1934. MICRO-CHEMICAL SOIL TESTS IN CONNECTION WITH VEGETABLE CROP PRODUCTION.
 Va. Truck Expt. Sta. Bul. 82, pp. [1119]-1135.

(9) ————
 1940. A SATISFACTORY GRINDER FOR PREPARING PLANT TISSUE FOR RAPID CHEMICAL TESTS.
 Amer. Soc. Agron. Jour. 32: 549.

(10) HILL, H., and DAVIS, M. B.
 1936. PHYSIOLOGICAL DISORDERS OF APPLES. Sci. Agr. 17: 199-208, illus.

(11) KIDSON, E. B., ASKEW, H. O., and CHITTENDEN, E.
 1940. MAGNESIUM DEFICIENCY OF APPLES IN THE NELSON DISTRICT OF NEW ZEALAND.
 New Zeal. Jour. Sci. and Technol. 21: 305A-318A, illus. Also pub. in Jour.
 Pomol. and Hort. Sci. 18: 119-134, illus., 1940.

(12) McLARTY, H. R.
 1940. BRITISH COLUMBIA USES BORON FOR FRUIT. Better Crops with Plant Food 24(4):
 8-11, 37-38, illus.

(13) MANN, C. E. T.
 1924. THE PHYSIOLOGY OF THE NUTRITION OF FRUIT TREES.—I. SOME EFFECTS OF CAL-
 CIUM AND POTASSIUM STARVATION. Bristol Univ. Agr. and Hort. Res. Sta.
 Ann. Rpt. 1924: [30]-45, illus.

(14) RIDGWAY, H. W.
 1938. A CASE OF ROSETTE ON APPLE IN VIRGINIA. Amer. Soc. Hort. Sci. Proc. 35: 227-
 229, illus.

(15) WALLACE, THOMAS.
 1928. LEAF SCORCH ON FRUIT TREES. Jour. Pomol. and Hort. Sci. 6: 243-281, illus.

Plate 1.—Nitrogen-deficiency symptoms in apple twig. Note the relatively small, yellowish-green leaves and the reddish leaf stalks, which form narrow angles with the stem.

Plate 2.—Symptoms of phosphorus deficiency in a growing tip of the apple. Leaves are abnormally small and dark green, with conspicuous purple pigmentation. Twig is slender and abnormally purplish.

Plate 3.—Successive stages of marginal scorching due to potassium deficiency in apple foliage. Upper leaf is normal. An early stage is shown by the dark-purplish discoloration of leaf on lower left. Well-developed scorch is shown in leaf on lower right. Leaves are typical of those found along midportions of current-season twigs. After exposure to rain the scorched areas turn dull brown.

[229]

Plate 4.—Symptoms of prolonged and severe potassium deficiency in the apple. In this stage, scorched leaves may be found near the tips of twigs. Dark areas in upper leaf are due to plasmolysis preceding scorching.

Plate 5.—Symptoms of calcium deficiency in young and nearly mature apple leaves. Top row, upper and lower surfaces of young leaf showing early stages of discoloration and death of tissues. Bottom row, upper and lower surfaces of nearly mature leaf showing extensive areas of dead tissue.

[231]

Plate 6.—Symptoms of calcium deficiency in mature apple leaves. Top row, upper and lower leaf surfaces showing a mottled type of discoloration and necrosis (death of tissues). Bottom row, upper and lower surfaces showing a marginal type of necrosis.

Plate 7.—Symptoms of magnesium deficiency in the apple. Three leaves showing successive
stages of blotching. This type of necrosis starts near the base of current-season growth and
progresses toward the tip. All stages of blotching may occur in leaves on the same twig.

Plate 8.—A, Early, intermediate, and advanced stages of nitrogen deficiency in peaches as revealed by leaf symptoms (left to right).

Plate 8.—B, Successive stages of magnesium deficiency in peach foliage. Large leaves are from Elberta trees grown in sand culture in a greenhouse. Small leaves are from seedling trees grown in the field.

Plate 9.—Symptoms of phosphorus deficiency in the peach. A, An early stage in which leaves, especially those on the lower half of current-season growth, are pigmented with a slight amount of purple and considerable bronze. B, Terminal twig showing mottling and curving of blades. C, Leaf discoloration characteristic of advanced phosphorus deficiency preceding dropping of leaves.

Plate 10.—Symptoms of potassium deficiency in the peach. A and B, Severe potassium deficiency in new spring growth. C and D, Crinkling and curling of leaves—an early symptom of the deficiency. E, Necrotic spots on small basal leaf from side branch. F, Necrotic spotting and marginal scorching following stage D.

Plate 11.—Symptoms of calcium deficiency in the peach. A, An early stage of the deficiency in a growing tip. B, An advanced stage of calcium deficiency in peach twig and foliage. C, Midrib necrosis in mature leaf. D, Discoloration and necrosis of blade of basal leaf from young side branch of current-season branch. E, Necrosis of blade tissue of nearly mature leaf.

Plate 12.—Foliage symptoms of compound phosphorus-potassium deficiency in the peach. Mottling and color resemble symptoms of phosphorus deficiency. Curling, spotting, and necrosis are caused by potassium deficiency. The symptoms of potassium deficiency appear to be superimposed upon those of phosphorus deficiency.

Plate 13.—Symptoms of compound phosphorus-potassium deficiency ("false little peach") in a twig from a field-grown nursery peach tree. Notice similarity in characteristics of basal leaves on this twig and those shown in plate 9, B. Leaf scorch is due to potassium deficiency.

CHAPTER VIII

Plant-Nutrient Deficiency Symptoms in Legumes

By E. E. DeTurk [1]

PROGRESS in the study of deficiencies of nutrient elements in the soil and the resulting symptoms in growing plants has brought out the fact that the physiological processes involved are interdependent—that is, the deficiency of a given element does not directly produce a given symptom. Rather, it usually throws the rate of occurrence of normal processes out of balance, with the result that there are accumulations of certain unused intermediate materials or shortages of others. This leads ultimately to the abnormal conditions recognized as symptoms, which thus bear an indirect but nonetheless definite relation to the unfavorable nutritional environment of the growing plants. The situation, of course, is the same in the case of animal or human nutrition. A symptom of vitamin B_1 deficiency is not the disease itself. It is a sign of an internal unbalance produced by the deficiency.

Botanically the legumes are characterized by the pods in which the seeds are borne, but to the farmer a more distinguishing characteristic is their ability to fix elemental nitrogen in assimilable forms through the agency of nodule bacteria. This at once suggests the possibility of eliminating nitrogen from the list of limiting elements merely by inoculation. Some years ago, when the soils of the Corn Belt States were not generally inoculated with soybean and alfalfa nodule bacteria, it was not uncommon to see small pale-green or yellowish-green areas of these crops growing in uninoculated check strips beside vigorous, darker green, inoculated plants in demonstration plots. Plate 1, A, page 259, illustrates a typical case.

The legumes, perhaps more than other crop plants, tend to show nutritional deficiencies not by specific abnormalities of form or color but by slow growth, producing undersized plants which are normal in appearance. The plants shown in figures 1, 2, 3, and 4 are typical. There may be several reasons for this.

In acid soils deficient in calcium, legumes that are particularly sensitive to acidity are for the most part small-seeded plants whose

[1] E. E. DeTurk is Professor of Soil Fertility, College of Agriculture, and Chief in Soil Fertility, Agricultural Experiment Station, University of Illinois.

Courtesy of Purdue University Agricultural Experiment Station

Figure 1.—Red clover and other small-leaved legumes make slow growth on a poor soil when phosphorus and potassium are omitted, as in the second and third pots from the left. Compare figures 2, 3, and 4.

early growth is slow; under such conditions the young plants usually succumb to winter-killing or summer drought when they are so small that symptoms of calcium shortage, should they develop, go unnoticed. Under the same conditions species that are tolerant of acid soils apparently secure sufficient calcium for their needs. Thus

Courtesy of Purdue University Agricultural Experiment Station

Figure 2.—Alsike clover shows results similar to those in red clover (fig. 1) when grown on the same soil. Apparently both the red clover and the alsike clover were able to obtain their nitrogen from the air.

Courtesy of Purdue University Agricultural Experiment Station

Figure 3.—Sweetclover responded to the application of phosphorus and potassium and also to nitrogen. The soil—the same as that used for red and alsike clovers (see figs. 1 and 2)—was apparently too acid for the best functioning of the nitrogen-fixing bacteria.

Courtesy of Purdue University Agricultural Experiment Station

Figure 4.—Alfalfa when grown on the same soil as the other legumes responded to phosphorus, potassium, and nitrogen in much the same manner as sweetclover.

calcium-deficiency symptoms are rarely seen under field conditions, although they can be produced in controlled cultures.

Nitrogen hunger in many plant species produces symptoms almost identical with those of drought—chlorosis followed by death and drying up of the leaves, proceeding from older to younger ones. The symptoms of water shortage and nitrogen hunger may be traceable to the same cause, since it has been shown that low moisture content, or tissue drought, accompanies nitrogen starvation, though it cannot be said with certainty whether the destruction of chlorophyll is a direct result of the lack of water or of the translocation of nitrogen or other essential substances from the older leaves to younger tissues.

As for phosphorus, most of the legumes have the ability to obtain this element from sources too slowly available to supply the grasses and other groups of crop plants, and some species of legumes require only small amounts.

Potassium is the one common element a deficiency of which is shown by easily recognized symptoms that are well known because of their common occurrence in a wide variety of legume crops. An excellent review of the functions of potassium in plant nutrition has been prepared by Hoffer (4).[2]

No key is provided for aid in identifying the causes of deficiency symptoms in legumes, mainly because the information obtainable at this time is too sketchy and incomplete to permit the construction of a useful key. Another reason is that the number of variable factors—different essential elements, several different plant species, and variation in symptoms in different climatic and soil regions—would result in a key so complex as to be of doubtful utility.

COLOR SYMPTOMS

The early symptoms of plantfood hunger usually take the form of changes in color. The most common color symptom results from chlorosis, or loss of the green chlorophyll pigment. This may be followed sooner or later by necrosis (death) of the chlorotic areas. Chlorosis may consist of a paling of the green color or the appearance of various shades of yellow, or even white, dots or patches, depending presumably on the relative abundance of the yellow pigments, carotin, xanthophyll, and sometimes flavones (parent substances of a large number of yellow dyestuffs), the presence of which is normally masked by the green chlorophyll; or possibly on whether

[2] Italic numbers in parentheses refer to Literature Cited, p. 258.

the yellow pigments are destroyed along with the chlorophyll.

Chlorosis occurs in various patterns which differ in different species and also with different deficiencies. For example, it may occur as mottling around the edge of the leaf, merging into a yellow border, as in potassium deficiency in the soybean. It may quickly spread over the whole leaf, including the veins, with no mottling, as in severe iron deficiency in the same species. It may appear as white dots, as in calcium hunger in red clover. It may be permanent in one case and reversible to the normal green in another. It may affect the oldest leaves first, owing to translocation of mobile ions, such as those of potassium, or appear first in the youngest leaves or throughout the plant. The last occurs in the case of a deficiency of some element, such as boron, that does not readily move from one part of the plant to another.

Next to chlorosis, perhaps the most frequent color aberrations are those due to the anthocyanins and closely related compounds. These are water-soluble pigments found usually in the thin outermost layers of cells (the epidermis) in solution or as crystals. The colors observed—usually purple to red—depend partly on the presence of other pigments (green and yellow) and their relative amounts. The symptoms are more frequent in members of the grass family and other nonlegumes than among legumes. Like chlorosis, these symptoms are indirectly related to the cause through a series of intermediate processes. Anthocyanins contain a sugar as part of the molecule, and their presence usually, but not always, indicates sugar accumulation. In some cases removal of sugar from the leaf may be prevented by blocking of the conducting channels; in others its utilization in forming other substances, such as proteins, may be retarded by shortage of a necessary element or by unfavorable temperatures.

Because of the indirect relation of observable symptoms to their ultimate causes, their use for diagnosis depends mainly on an understanding of the physiological processes linking cause and symptom.

NITROGEN DEFICIENCY

Nitrogen deficiencies in legumes are largely ruled out for species native to a region, because the soil ordinarily contains the appropriate nodule bacteria which supply adequate amounts of nitrogen to the plants as a result of fixation. This is not generally true of introduced species until after they have been grown with artificial inoculation in the areas concerned. Plate 1, A, page 259, shows an uninoculated strip of soybeans in a field the rest of which had been inoculated. The picture was taken on the University of Illinois farm 15 years ago. Few such demonstrations can now be carried out in the Illinois corn belt because of the prevalence of soybean nodule bacteria in farm soils as a result of many years of growing soybeans. A similar change has occurred in the case of alfalfa.

The nitrogen nutrition of many species of legumes is related to soil reaction and liming. Not only do many legumes fail to grow satisfactorily on highly acid soils, but the nodule bacteria also thrive only within certain ranges of soil reaction. In general, the vigor and effectiveness of the nodule bacteria decrease with increasing soil acidity, and the length of time they persist in the soil in the absence of the legume host also tends to decrease as the soil becomes more acid. Thus problems of soil acidity are definitely related to the nitrogen nutrition of legume crops.

A deficiency of nitrogen results in slow growth, a decrease in branching of the plants, and smaller plants at maturity. These may occur without the appearance of specific symptoms and have little or no diagnostic value. Severe deficiency often causes mild chlorosis in which the leaves become pale green with a yellowish tinge rather than distinctly yellow. The chlorosis usually spreads evenly over the entire leaf surface (see the soybean leaves in plate 1, B, page 259). The affected foliage usually appears first at the base of the plant, as in nitrogen starvation in corn and small grains, but it shows up almost simultaneously in various other parts of the plant, usually toward the tips of branches or that of the main stem. Nitrogen-starved leaves remain chlorotic for a week or more, showing little change, while the plant as a whole makes no apparent growth. The normal green color is promptly restored on addition of available nitrogen in fertilizers. In this respect the symptom differs from that in potassium hunger, in which the tissues die shortly after the onset of chlorosis.

The chlorotic condition of the leaves is a frequent result of nitrogen hunger. To diagnose the condition as nitrogen deficiency, however, requires a careful check of soil conditions and the elimination of other possible causes of the chlorosis.

In extreme nitrogen starvation of soybeans in controlled gravel cultures, the appearance of bronze-colored patches on the leaves has been observed along with or preceding chlorosis, but this symptom has not been seen under field conditions.

PHOSPHORUS DEFICIENCY

None of the common legume crops tends to exhibit symptoms of phosphorus deficiency other than slow growth, the plants remaining small and undeveloped. Flowering and seed production tend to be delayed and a bluish-green tinge tends to develop in the leaves, but there are no symptoms that can be used with assurance for diagnostic purposes.

The dwarfed size of the plants is illustrated for red clover, alsike clover, sweetclover, and alfalfa in figures 1, 2, 3, and 4, which show plants that were grown in a poor soil in pot cultures. The slow growth when phosphate was omitted may be seen in the second jar from the left in each case.

POTASSIUM DEFICIENCY

Of all the symptoms observable in legumes, those of potassium hunger are probably the most outstanding and easily recognized. All of the common legume species require relatively large amounts of potassium, in spite of the fact that it does not enter into organic combination in plant tissues but occurs in solution (as potassium ions) in the sap in the vacuoles (small cavities in the protoplasm of the cells) and in the intercellular spaces.

The broad-leaved legumes, such as the soybean, quickly show evidence of insufficient potassium by irregular yellow mottling around the edges of the leaflets (plate 2, A, page 260). The chlorotic areas soon merge, forming a continuous yellow border around the tip and along the sides, but rarely around the base. Death of the chlorotic area that first became mottled follows promptly, along with a downward cupping of the leaf edges. Then the dead tissue falls out, giving the leaflet a ragged appearance. The marginal firing often spreads to include half or more of the area of the leaflet while the center and base are still green (plate 2, B).

The functions of potassium associated with photosynthesis and subsequent transformation of carbohydrates may be related to the early chlorotic symptoms. The fact that potassium is concerned with regulation of the water content of the cytoplasm (the part of the cell outside the nucleus), swelling, and resistance to drought injury suggests that the impairing of these properties of the tissues is the cause of the rapid drying out and necrosis of the chlorotic areas very soon after chlorosis appears.

In the other common legumes the symptoms are similar to those in the soybean, especially in the later stages of potassium starvation (plate 3, A, page 261).

In the earlier stages in red clover, alsike, sweetclover, and alfalfa, the yellowing is preceded by the appearance of numerous very small white or yellowish dots arranged more or less in a crescent around the tips of the leaflets (plate 3, B, and plate 4, A, pages 261, 262). Progress from this point on resembles that in the soybean, except that there is less tendency for the symptoms to start at the base of the plant and move upward; rather, all parts of the plant are affected almost simultaneously (plate 4, B, page 262). Also, the appearance of symptoms is delayed until the plants are too far advanced to profit greatly by additions of potash fertilizers. In fact, the deficiency is already very severe before symptoms appear (plate 5, A, page 263). In the case of soybeans and possibly of cowpeas, however, the symptoms may develop early enough so that there is greater possibility of benefit from potash fertilization provided the application is made immediately on observing the first symptoms.

The early chlorosis due to potassium shortage is distinguishable from that due to nitrogen hunger by the definite localization of the former around the tip of the leaf and the distinct yellow color. Nitrogen deficiency results in a gradual paling of the green color over the whole leaf blade with only a slight yellowish tinge.

CALCIUM DEFICIENCY

The calcium requirements of different species of crop plants vary greatly. They have usually been associated in the technical literature with soil reaction, or the acid-alkaline balance. This is probably due to the fact that soil acidity is corrected almost exclusively by the application of calcium compounds, including high-calcium limestone, dolomitic limestone, burned lime, slaked lime, etc.

Among common farm crops the legumes in general are less tolerant of excessive soil acidity than the nonlegumes, and they also have relatively high calcium requirements. But this does not mean that calcium requirements vary directly with "lime requirements" or intolerance of acidity. For example, Albrecht (1) has found for the soybean, which is relatively tolerant of acid soils, that at pH values below 5.0, acidity is the dominant factor controlling growth and nodulation, while above pH 5.0 the supply of calcium rather than the acidity is the important factor. The availability of calcium is also influenced by the degree of saturation of the soil colloids (minute clay particles) with this element.[3]

With crops that are more sensitive to acid soils, high acidity interferes with the ability of the plant to take up and retain soluble calcium present in the soil. This has been shown by Crane (3) with red clover in sand cultures. High acidity (low pH), even in the presence of adequate amounts of soluble calcium, produced the symptoms of calcium starvation, and analyses of the plants showed that calcium absorption or retention had been inhibited (table 1).

TABLE 1.—EFFECT OF ACIDITY ON CALCIUM ABSORPTION BY RED CLOVER AND ON ITS DRY WEIGHT

(Equal number of plants per jar)

Calcium in solution, acidity (pH), and condition of plants	Dry weight of plants		Calcium in plants			
	Tops	Roots	Tops	Roots	Tops	Roots
	Gms. per jar	Gms. per jar	Mgs. per jar	Mgs. per jar	Percent	Percent
High calcium (as calcium chloride), pH 7, plants normal...................	33	18	351	80	1.02	0.44
No calcium, pH 7, plants stunted...................	9	3	38	13	.44	.42
High calcium (as calcium chloride), pH 5, plants stunted...................	3	1	13	7	.43	.56

High acidity may not only retard the absorption of calcium by plants; it tends to increase the plant concentration of certain other elements that occur in solution in the soil in sufficiently active forms to be obtained by the plants. This is particularly true of manganese, aluminum, and iron, which may be absorbed in toxic quantities from acid soils.

These examples indicate the difficulty of recognizing the signs of calcium starvation with certainty in the presence of so many other conflicting and interacting factors.

Although calcium deficiency may be rather clearly identified in some species, it is not always easily recognized in the legumes under

[3] That is, soybeans obtain more calcium from a soil whose base-exchange capacity is three-fourths saturated with calcium than from a soil at only one-fourth saturation, even though the total amount of replaceable calcium is the same in both cases.

field conditions. In fact, well-defined symptoms do not often appear. As already pointed out, the acid-sensitive common legumes, among which are sweetclover, alfalfa, and perhaps red clover, have such small seeds that the seedlings are small and grow slowly at first. If weakened by soil acidity, they usually succumb to summer drought or winter-killing during the first year, while the plants are still small, without developing symptoms; and any symptoms that might develop are not usually noticed. This is particularly the case on soils of low fertility.

Courtesy of Illinois Agricultural Experiment Station

Figure 5.—This calcium-starved red clover grown in sand culture not only has made very little growth, but exhibits certain other well-defined symptoms. The pattern of chlorosis in the leaves consists of many small white dots distributed over the entire surface. The leafstalks collapse, allowing the leaves to fall over. The leaf blades remain turgid for some time before wilting occurs. Many new leaves start at the crown, none of which entirely unfolds.

Crane (*3*) has shown that red clover grown in sand cultures exhibits pronounced symptoms when calcium is not supplied to the roots but the supply of other essential elements is adequate. The plants grow normally at first, even with no calcium except that contained in the seeds. Then they stop growing and the symptoms appear a few days later. The symptoms are mainly of three kinds: (1) Chlorosis appears in the form of small white dots distributed irregularly over the entire surface of the full-grown older leaves (fig. 5). After 6 to 8 days the dots have become gray and the rest of the leaf appears grayish green and devitalized, though it does not die. (2) Many of the stalks (petioles) of the older leaves suddenly collapse (fig. 6), allowing the leaf to hang down, but without immediate wilting of the leaf blades. After several days these leaves wither and die. (3) The emerging young leaves remain small, undeveloped, and unfolded, and the petioles do not lengthen. More new leaves emerge similarly in rapid succession, forming a clump at the crown. With a larger but still inadequate supply of calcium the plants grow normally for a longer period, attain larger size, and then develop the symptoms described.

Where an adequate amount of calcium is supplied, but under conditions of high acidity, symptoms similar to those described

Figure 6.—Close-up of collapsing leaf-stalks of red clover plants affected by calcium starvation.

Courtesy of Illinois Agricultural Experiment Station

for calcium starvation appear, especially those under (1) and (2), and the calcium content of the plant tissues is low (table 1) as in calcium-starved plants (fig. 7).

Though the functions of calcium are not fully understood, the symptoms observed would indicate that they have to do with cell-wall formation and maintenance of healthy protoplasm. Weakening of cell walls and degradation of protoplasm cause the sudden collapse of the cells, without the dehydration that occurs in nitrogen and potassium hunger. It will be noted also that the youngest as well as the more mature parts of the plant are affected. These symptoms resemble those in other plants, notably corn, to the extent that sudden death of the cells occurs previous to water loss, in contrast to the early drying of the tissues that occurs in nitrogen and potassium hunger.

Courtesy of Illinois Agricultural Experiment Station

Figure 7.—Increasing the acidity of the growth medium (left to right) produces symptoms in red clover quite similar to those of calcium starvation. The collapsing of leafstalks and drooping of leaves is obvious here. Chemical analysis also shows that these plants, grown with an abundance of soluble calcium but under acid conditions, are as deficient in calcium in the tissues as those grown without a calcium supply. High acidity interferes with the absorption and retention of calcium by the plant roots.

MAGNESIUM DEFICIENCY

The presence of magnesium as a part of the chlorophyll molecule explains the chlorosis which is the most characteristic symptom to be observed in magnesium deficiency. The occurrence of chlorosis as an early symptom of many deficiencies lessens its value as a diagnostic aid, except insofar as the pattern of the chlorotic areas and the nature of the subsequent symptoms may be a guide. The pattern in legumes with magnesium deficiency varies with the species. In the soybean (plate 6, A, page 264) and the cowpea the areas between the main veins become pale green and then yellow, the areas along the veins remaining green.

The effects of magnesium deficiency in crotalaria plants grown in controlled sand cultures are described by A. L. Sommer [4] as follows:

[4] In private correspondence, 1940.

The magnesium deficiency symptoms of crotalaria varied from the yellowing of the older leaves with the veins remaining green to an almost complete yellowing of all leaves in the most severe cases (fig. 8). In a number of cases magnesium deficiency was evidenced only by a difference in the size of the plants when compared with those receiving this element (fig. 9). A decrease in growth appeared to be all that characterized crimson clover growing in the absence of a sufficient amount of magnesium.

In peanut plants grown with inadequate magnesium the leaves drooped (fig. 10). This and a yellow tinge were characteristic of severe magnesium deficiency. The dry weight in such cases, however, was often greater than for plants which received magnesium. The greatest difference was in the yield of peanuts (fig. 11). There was often a marked difference in the yield when no magnesium deficiency symptoms of the tops were apparent.

Courtesy of Anna L. Sommer, Alabama Agricultural Experiment Station

Figure 8.—Extreme inhibition of growth and yellowing of the leaves, particularly the older ones at the base of the plant, may result from severe deficiency of magnesium in crotalaria. Where chlorosis occurs, the first development is a yellowing between the veins followed in more severe starvation by complete yellowing of the entire leaf surface.

No record of magnesium-deficiency symptoms on other legume crops has been obtained.

DEFICIENCIES OF TRACE ELEMENTS

A number of chemical elements essential for plant growth are required in extremely small quantities; hence they are sometimes called trace elements. They have also been commonly known as minor elements, but from the standpoint of their importance in the nutrition of growing plants they may as properly be considered major

Courtesy of Anna L. Sommer, Alabama Agricultural Experiment Station

Figure 9.—Mild magnesium deficiency in crotalaria may result only in moderate reduction in growth.

Figure 10.—The principal result of magnesium deficiency in peanuts grown in controlled sand cultures was a reduction in yield. There is sometimes, but not always, a decrease in the amount of top growth, and occasionally there is drooping of the leaves.

elements as those utilized in larger quantities. The necessary trace elements are usually considered to include iron, manganese, copper, zinc, and boron, because it has been shown that these are essential for some species, though their indispensability for a wide range of crop plants has not been proved by experiment.

IRON

The importance of iron in chlorophyll production has long been known. Its exact role, however, has not been determined. Some research has indicated that it may be necessary in the synthesis of a part of the chlorophyll molecule (the pyrrole ring). Aside from its con-

nection with chlorophyll, there is evidence of its functioning in respiration, and it probably has still other roles in plant growth.

The quantity of iron required by plants is small and it is obtained in the form of both ferric and ferrous ions, though with varying facility among different species. A deficiency is associated with alkaline soil conditions, and because of this it has been generally thought that the solubility of iron in the soil under alkaline conditions is too low to permit an adequate intake by plants. Analyses of plant tissues suggest another basis for deficiency—that under alkaline conditions iron already in the plant is thrown out of solution, principally in or near the nodes (joints) so that it fails to reach the leaves where

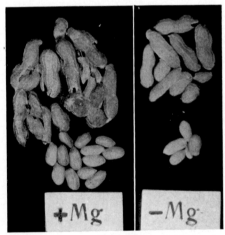

Figure 11.—The yield of peanuts is often reduced by magnesium deficiency even though no symptom or decrease in weight of top is observed.

it is needed. Both conditions help to explain the chlorosis that results from overliming.

Iron is comparatively immobile in growing plants, that is, it is not moved from older leaves to younger tissues when a deficiency sets in. Thus leaves once green remain so, while the younger leaves become chlorotic.

Chlorosis due to iron hunger is not a frequently observed symptom in the legumes. Plate 6, B, page 264, illustrates iron chlorosis of soybeans as found in the field in alkaline soil.

Varietal differences in susceptibility to iron chlorosis have been observed in soybeans. In a rod-row comparison of several varieties on alkaline soil in Illinois, Williams and Earley [5] found that one variety exhibited extreme iron-deficiency symptoms, while plants of other varieties growing beside it remained normal. Normal green color was restored by supplying iron. Whether the difference lay in ability to absorb iron or in its physiological utilization is not known. This instance illustrates the profound effects of genetic characteristics upon the relation of plants to their nutrient environment.

Chlorosis caused by iron deficiency consists of disappearance of chlorophyll, large areas between the veins first becoming yellowish green and then yellow. As the severity increases the entire leaf becomes involved, including the veins and midrib, but without immediate death of the tissues. For several days the leaves retain the ability to recover normal green color on receiving adequate amounts of iron.

BORON

Symptoms traceable to boron deficiency have been observed on a number of legume species. In the Central States, the most pronounced symptom observed is red coloration, sometimes with a purplish tint, affecting first the margins of the leaves or the distal (tip) half. The abnormal color spreads to take in the entire leaf surface, including the veins, while the leaf tips first affected die, becoming dark brown, presumably because of the red pigment, and later lighter brown when the red pigment has disintegrated. The leaves affected are distributed over the entire plant, the condition being most marked in the younger portions, as is typical where immobile elements are concerned. The symptoms are similar in red clover, alsike, Korean lespedeza, and, to a lesser extent, alfalfa (plates 5, B, page 263, and 7, A and B, page 265). In alfalfa

[5] Private correspondence with L. W. Williams and E. B. Earley, United States Regional Soybean Industrial Products Laboratory, 1940.

the red to purple coloration is associated with yellow, and the symptoms are more definitely centered at the top of the plant. The identification of these symptoms as due to boron deficiency has been established by Cook (2) in Michigan.

In western United States and Canada boron deficiency in alfalfa is found to exhibit a yellow chlorosis affecting first the upper portions of the plant, and the red color is not present to a marked extent (6). The condition is commonly known as yellowtop. These variations of symptoms of the same deficiency in different regions indicate the importance of external factors and emphasize the necessity of caution in connecting the symptom and the cause.

Another symptom found in field-grown alsike plants is associated with those described. This is a malformation of the plants at the blossoming stage in which the petals are replaced by small leaves, some with leafstalks, others without. In addition to these aberrations, other clumps of small leaves appear in the leaf axils, resulting in the appearance shown in plate 5, B, page 263, in which some of the leaves show the usual color symptoms of boron deficiency. The association of the malformations with the color symptoms is suggestive of boron hunger as the cause of the former, but this is not supported by conclusive evidence. Similar aberrations of corn plants have been observed, likewise without definite knowledge as to the cause. That the cause is nutritional is indicated by the presence of similarly affected foxtail plants alongside the corn.

OTHER TRACE ELEMENTS

Much has been written of the probable functions and the symptoms of deficiencies of other trace elements, including copper, zinc, and manganese. It has not been possible, however, to obtain conclusive illustrations of these symptoms for plants in the legume family.

TOXICITY SYMPTOMS

Excessively high concentrations of any of the essential elements interfere with normal growth processes and result in some cases in symptoms that serve diagnostic purposes. Higher concentrations are required to produce toxicity where the nutrient environment is otherwise well balanced and adequate than where the plants are generally underfed or the other elements are not present in suitable proportions.

Not only are the trace elements required in very small amounts for normal growth, but their nontoxic range is also very narrow.

That is, relatively small increases in concentration above the optimum have toxic effects, especially with poorly nourished plants. Two types of such toxicity are likely enough to occur under field conditions to justify mention.

In many of the cool humid sections of the United States in soils of high acidity, relatively high concentrations of available forms of manganese are found. No cases of proved toxicity from this cause have come to the writer's attention. It has been suggested, however, that certain symptoms of field-grown nonlegume crops observed in the Central States may be due to manganese toxicity. Manganese toxicity has been brought about in germinating soybeans in greenhouse cultures in soil. Under these conditions, following excessive applications of manganese carbonate, seed germination is retarded and irregular. The stems fail to elongate so that the seedlings are short and stocky. The leaves are dark green and thick, and in severe cases do not completely unfold. Additions of manganese carbonate equal to the lime requirement of rather highly acid soils prevented germination.

After the seedling stages, in gravel culture, excess manganese (300 parts per million) causes necrosis of small, irregular patches scattered over the entire leaf surface between the main veins, the color being at first dark brown. This is quickly followed by a merging of the dead areas and a change in color to light brown or nearly white. The light-colored patches become somewhat translucent, and the tissue then falls out, leaving the leaves ragged in appearance but not crumpled or ruffled. Soybeans grown in gravel culture with a smaller but toxic concentration of manganese (30 parts per million) made fairly tall but poor growth (3 feet as compared with 6 feet in normal plants). The symptoms of toxicity (plate 8, A, page 266) included mild chlorosis and much crinkling of the leaves, with marginal cupping. Evidently the marginal growth rate was less than that of the rest of the leaf. The severity of symptoms decreased from the top downward.

Another possibility of toxicity under field conditions is from zinc accumulations in the soil in areas near smelters. Although much of the destruction of vegetation in such regions is brought about by other causes (chiefly atmospheric gases), it has been shown that surface soils, especially to the leeward of smelters, become highly acid, lose by leaching significant amounts of the strong bases—calcium, potassium, and magnesium—and accumulate determinable amounts of zinc (up to 150 parts per million of the dry surface soil). In pot cultures with acid soils the addition of neutral zinc salts to soybeans causes the plants to be dwarfed and unbranched. The stalks of the simple leaves and of the leaflets of the older trifoliate leaves bend down so that the blades hang vertically, without wilting. The midribs and main veins of the older leaves become increasingly deep red and finally almost black, while the younger leaves become pale green and the terminal bud is damaged or killed (plate 8, B, page 266).

Liming the soil to a pH above 6.5 prevents the intake of zinc in harmful amounts (5). In the field this makes the rebuilding of soil productivity possible. Toxic concentrations of gases in the atmosphere sufficient to injure the foliage would of course nullify the effects of restored soil productivity.

LITERATURE CITED

(1) ALBRECHT, WILLIAM A.
    1941. PLANT NUTRITION BY COLLOIDALLY ABSORBED IONS. Soil Sci. Soc. Amer. Proc. 5. (In press.)

(2) COOK, R. L.
    1937. BORON DEFICIENCY IN MICHIGAN SOILS. Soil Sci. Soc. Amer. Proc. 2: 375-382.

(3) CRANE, F. H.
    1926. INTERRELATION OF CALCIUM, PHOSPHORUS AND H-ION CONCENTRATION IN RELATION TO THE GROWTH OF PLANTS. Master's Thesis, University of Illinois.

(4) HOFFER, G. N.
    1938. POTASH IN PLANT METABOLISM. Indus. and Engin. Chem. 30: 885-889.

(5) LOTT, W. L.
    1938. THE RELATION OF H-ION CONCENTRATION TO THE AVAILABILITY OF ZINC IN SOIL. Soil Sci. Soc. Amer. Proc. 3: 115-121.

(6) POWERS, W. L.
    1939. BORON AS A FERTILIZER FOR WESTERN OREGON SOILS. Science 90: 36-37.

Courtesy of O. H. Sears, University of Illinois

Plate 1.—A, Symptoms of nitrogen hunger in uninoculated soybeans growing in soil which does not contain the appropriate nitrogen-fixing nodule bacteria. Note the pale-green to yellowish color and the lower height of the plants in the check strip, which was uninoculated.

Courtesy of U. S. Regional Soybean Industrial Products Laboratory

Plate 1.—B, Soybean leaves showing progressive stages of nitrogen hunger. (Plants grown with controlled nutrients in gravel culture.)

[259]

Plate 2.—A, Potassium-starvation symptoms in soybean leaves, early stages. Chlorosis begins with yellow mottling, then forms a continuous band along the sides and tip end of the leaf. The chlorotic area enlarges toward the center of the leaf, and death of tissues in some areas may occur.

Courtesy of Agronomy Department, University of Illinois

Plate 2.—B, Advanced stages of potassium-deficiency symptoms in soybean leaves. Note that as the chlorosis proceeds inward, the margins of the leaves fire to a medium-brown color. The center of the leaf may still be green after the margin is completely dead.

Courtesy of American Potash Institute, Inc.

Plate 3.—A, Potassium-starvation symptoms in cowpeas resemble those in soybeans. The chlorosis around the leaf margins may be more or less mottled, a condition which also occurs in soybeans, and the edges become ragged when the deficiency is severe.

Courtesy of Agronomy Department, University of Illinois

Plate 3.—B. Potassium hunger in this field-grown red clover plant (potted for transportation and photographing) is first observed as a series of yellowish to white dots around the tip and sides of the leaf. The entire margin of the leaf soon becomes yellowish and then dies as the condition spreads toward the center.

Plate 4.—A, Alfalfa plants exhibit symptoms of potassium starvation very similar to those observed in red clover. Chlorosis appears first as small dots; then it involves the entire leaf margin and is followed by death of the tissues, which turn brown. The edges of the leaves become broken and ragged in the more advanced stages.

Courtesy of American Potash Institute, Inc.

Plate 4.—B, Potassium-hunger symptoms are easily seen in the field, as they are not confined to the oldest leaves at the base of the plant, which are usually the first to be affected. Symptoms are distributed over the plant from the base to the top.

Plate 5.—A, Alsike plants do not differ appreciably from red clover or alfalfa in the general appearance or detailed pattern of potassium-hunger symptoms. In alsike and red clover, symptoms are not often seen until shortly before the blossoming stage; like alfalfa, the plants are in desperate straits when symptoms appear.

Plate 5.—B, Close-up of boron deficiency in alsike. It will be noticed that the reddening is followed by death of the tissues. The dead tissue is at first dark brown, owing to the red pigment; later the red disappears, leaving a lighter brown color. The ends of the dying leaves frequently split or are broken off.

[263]

Plate 6.—A, Magnesium-starvation symptoms in soybeans. Left, normal leaf; right, leaf affected by chlorosis due to magnesium deficiency. Chlorosis from this cause may continue for some time after it has spread throughout the plant without actual firing or death of the leaf tissues.

Courtesy of American Potash Institute, Inc.

Plate 6.—B, Iron chlorosis in soybeans occurs in the areas between the main veins of the leaf, leaving the veins green at first. It differs from magnesium chlorosis in that the leaves suffering the most severe deficiency become entirely yellow, even including the veins and the midrib.

Plate 7.—A, Leaves of Korean lespedeza affected by boron deficiency, showing red discoloration followed by firing around the tip end and splitting of leaf tips.

Plate 7.—B, Accumulation of red pigments accompanied by mild chlorosis in alfalfa resulting from boron deficiency. These symptoms are typical of those found to result from boron deficiency in Michigan and are probably characteristic of this deficiency for the Middle West. With the exception of alfalfa yellowtop, symptoms of boron deficiency observed in the small-seeded legumes are very similar.

Plate 8.—A, Soybean leaves showing, left, manganese-deficiency symptoms with no manganese supplied; center, normal, with 0.5 parts of manganese per million; and right, toxicity with 30 parts per million. Slight toxicity symptoms were observed with 15 parts of manganese per million, but none with 10 parts.

Plate 8.—B, Older leaves of soybeans poisoned by an excess of zinc. The leaves turn sharply down but are not wilted, and a dark-red color appears along the veins, both on the upper and the under sides. There is also a mild chlorosis of the youngest leaves at the top of the plant, and frequently the terminal bud dies.

CHAPTER IX

Symptoms of Citrus Malnutrition

By A. F. Camp, H. D. Chapman, George M. Bahrt, and E. R. Parker [1]

THE use of specific symptoms as guides to the nutritional needs of citrus trees, which has been common for many years, probably had its inception in the use of copper compounds to correct the symptoms of dieback or exanthema. In fact the use of the symptoms involved in dieback as a guide to copper applications preceded any very clear understanding of the role of copper. As knowledge of the field has developed, the symptoms of zinc, manganese, iron, boron, and magnesium deficiencies have been described and used as general diagnostic characters with notable success. The symptoms of these deficiencies fortunately have been quite definite and easily recognizable, so that in the hands of the citrus grower the information has been of great value as a guide to the nutritional needs of the trees.

Mineral deficiencies have been much more widely distributed in Florida than in California or other citrus-growing areas because of the very light and acid soil and heavy leaching rains. Because of these and other factors, deficiencies developed soon after extensive areas of these light sandy soils were planted to citrus, and the use of copper, zinc, manganese, magnesium, and, to a lesser extent, iron became an integral part of commercial practice. Although mineral deficiencies are less common in other citrus areas, zinc deficiency is widespread in California and elsewhere and copper deficiency, though somewhat rarer, is likewise well known. Manganese deficiency, also, has recently been recognized in California. It seems probable that the contributing factor in many areas outside of Florida is the alkalinity of the soil, which results in the formation of insoluble compounds of many of the elements needed by the citrus tree.

In the succeeding discussion particular attention is given to deficiencies that occur commonly in the field and the symptoms of which are used as a guide in fertilizing practices. Symptoms known only from water and sand culture studies are discussed in less detail, first because less is known concerning them and second because

---

[1] A. F. Camp is Horticulturist in Charge, Citrus Experiment Station of the University of Florida; H. D. Chapman is Associate Professor of Agricultural Chemistry, Citrus Experiment Station of the University of California; George M. Bahrt is Associate Soil Technologist, Soil Fertility Investigations, Bureau of Plant Industry, United States Department of Agriculture; and E. R. Parker is Associate Horticulturist, Citrus Experiment Station of the University of California.

their practical value has not been demonstrated at the present time.

A key at the end of the chapter summarizes deficiency symptoms for ready identification and reference.

BORON DEFICIENCY

Boron deficiency of citrus has been definitely proved in the field only in Rhodesia, South Africa, where it was described in detail by Morris (27),[2] although similar symptoms have been found in Florida by Camp (7) and Camp and Fudge (8). Though its occurrence in the field is limited boron deficiency has been studied in water culture. Such studies were first reported in California by Haas, and later the anatomical and physiological features of the deficiency were described by Haas and Klotz (25). Morris, however, did not find in the field all of the symptoms reported from water culture, and he described some hitherto unreported additional symptoms. Boron deficiency is known in Rhodesia as "hard fruit."

Symptoms

Morris reported that boron deficiency in the field was characterized by small water-soaked spots or flecks in the leaves, the spots becoming translucent as the leaves matured. There was a premature shedding of leaves resulting in severe defoliation. The chief leaf symptom reported by Haas and Klotz (25) as characteristic of boron deficiency in cultures was an enlargement of the veins accompanied by a splitting and corking of the upper surface of the veins. Morris reported, however, that corking of the veins was not characteristic of boron deficiency in the field in Rhodesia. Accompanying the leaf symptoms is a dying back of the trees and a bushy upright growth similar to that described for zinc-deficiency symptoms.

The chief fruit symptoms in the field reported by Morris include premature shedding of young fruits. Such fruits had brownish discolorations in the white portion of the rind (the albedo), described commonly as gum pockets but more accurately as impregnations of the tissue with gum, an unusually thick albedo, and a peculiar "feel" on cutting, as though cheesy instead of normally crisp. Older fruits were misshapen, with an unusually thick albedo containing gum deposits; seed failed to develop, and gum deposits were common around the axis of the fruit (plate 1, page 301). Affected fruits were unusually hard and dry, and the small amount of juice obtainable by

[2] Italic numbers in parentheses refer to Literature Cited, page 297.

hand squeezing was low in sugars. Subsequent to Morris's report, Haas reported the finding of similar fruit symptoms on trees growing in cultures.

Symptoms similar to those reported by Morris in Rhodesia found in a few groves in Florida by Camp have not been consistent over a period of time in the same grove, and boron treatments have commonly resulted in toxicity or poisoning of the trees. It is believed, however, that the symptoms are probably those of boron deficiency due to unusual drought, since a resumption of rains causes them to disappear rather quickly.

Boron deficiency has not been found in California, but some irrigation waters there contain sufficient boron to cause symptoms of excess on citrus trees.

Cause and Treatment

No cause for boron deficiency is given by Morris, but he reports excellent results from soil applications of boron followed by irrigation. Similar treatments in Florida resulted in toxicity.

CALCIUM DEFICIENCY

Calcium deficiency has never been reported from the field, and it appears rather doubtful that it will develop on the soils commonly used for citrus. On very acid sands in Florida available calcium may be so low as to result in an unusually large intake of potassium, but results from applications of calcium have not been obtained except as they were associated with the correction of acidity and with base saturation of the colloidal complex in the soil. On such soils lime has given a response by producing more favorable soil-fertility conditions, but the use of other calcium sources which did not materially affect the reaction of the soil failed to produce any result that would indicate a condition of calcium deficiency as far as the trees were concerned. This was true even though the level of calcium in the soil was so low as theoretically to affect soil fertility adversely. The alkaline soils of California are well supplied with calcium, and irrigation waters in that State also provide this element. Symptoms of calcium deficiency have been reported from sand cultures by Reed and Haas (*36, 37, 38*) in California, and further information has been developed by Chapman in work now in progress.

Symptoms

Some of the early culture work is difficult to evaluate, since the so-called vein chlorosis, in which the veins fade to a much lighter

Figure 1.—Calcium-deficiency symptoms on leaves of lemon (top row), grapefruit (middle row), and sweet orange (bottom row). Note the yellowing of areas of internal tissue (mesophyll) and the peppering of small necrotic(dead) spots. The symptoms are from trees in sand cultures, since calcium deficiency has never been reported in the field.

Courtesy of California Agricultural Experiment Station

color than the surrounding tissue, is reported as a symptom, whereas it may be due to rotting of the roots and a consequent reduction in mineral intake. This symptom, which will be discussed in more detail under nitrogen deficiency, is the common result of girdling, damaged root systems, or other conditions which disrupt the transfer of nutrients. Omitting this as a definite diagnostic symptom, it was found that leaves on calcium-deficient trees in sand culture developed a fading of the chlorophyll along the margins and between the main veins (fig. 1). Small necrotic (dead) spots developed in the faded areas, and in the case of lemon leaves these developed into larger burned areas (plate 2, A, page 302). There was a premature shedding of these leaves, followed by the development of additional leaves which also fell prematurely. The twigs died back from the tip and weak shoots developed from the lateral buds, but these soon died. Reed and Haas (38) reported some rotting of roots, but Chapman did not find this in his cultures (results unpublished). No effects on fruit have been reported, as the trees presumably did not live long enough to produce fruit. These symptoms are probably far more acute than any that might be developed in the field, since under field conditions calcium would always be present in fair amounts.

COPPER DEFICIENCY

Copper deficiency is widespread in Florida and occurs frequently in California. "Dieback," the name by which it is commonly known in Florida, has been reported from other citrus-growing areas, but the use of the term makes the accurate interpretation of some of the reports difficult, and in many cases the dieback reported is not caused by copper deficiency. Apparently it is neither so common nor so serious in other areas as it is in Florida. Copper deficiency is also known to growers as "ammoniation," "red rust," or "exanthema." The symptoms were first described from Florida in 1875 by Fowler (18), who considered the deficiency a fungus disease. In 1917 Floyd (17) in Florida described the symptoms in detail very much as they are recognized today. The origin of the use of copper as a corrective is obscure, but Floyd (16) reported successful results from the use of bordeaux sprays in 1913, and Grossenbacher (20) reported successful results from soil applications of copper sulfate in 1916. The origin of the practice of inserting bluestone crystals under the bark is unknown. Although the use of copper as a corrective was common in both Florida and California, the trouble was not recognized as a copper deficiency until after successful work on zinc deficiency, which tended to clarify the situation.

Symptoms

The first evidence of incipient copper deficiency is the occurrence of unusually large dark-green leaves on long, soft, angular shoots, the leaves commonly of irregular contour, usually with a "bowing up" of the midrib. The soft twigs sag at the tips or become S-shaped. In this stage the tree appears to the casual observer as unusually vigorous, although in California this excessive growth is not so prominent. When the deficiency is more acute, very small leaves may develop and quickly shed on twigs that are going to die back, but on the older wood the leaves will be large, dark green, and somewhat twisted or malformed. This peculiar twisting and mal-formation of foliage is particularly common on copper-deficient grapefruit trees. In very acute cases the leaves may be greatly distorted, the margins irregular, and the color light green with a fine network of darker green veins. In such cases the growth of the twigs is restricted, fine, and very angular.

Following the appearance of the initial symptoms the affected twigs usually show a development of multiple buds. These produce a dense, somewhat bushy growth, particularly in lemon trees of moderate vigor. Occasionally gum pockets develop between the bark and the wood. These may break through to the surface and the gum may exude, though it is readily soluble in rain water and frequently is overlooked for that reason. As the deficiency be-comes more acute, new growth develops and then dies back for sev-eral inches (plate 3, page 303). In the very acute cases heavy twigs having multiple buds put out a profusion of young soft shoots with small leaves which quickly die back from the tips. In this stage the twigs have a reddish excrescence over a large portion of the bark. Neither the dying back nor the reddish excrescence is so pronounced in grapefruit as it is in oranges, and it is still less obvious in tangerines. As the acute stage is reached there is a pronounced loss of growth due to dying back, and in very serious cases the tree may be almost killed (fig. 2). The dying starts on the outer shoots of the tree; soon the characteristic large soft shoots appear as water sprouts on large branches in the center of the tree, and these in turn develop the characteristic symptoms. In acute stages gumming has been found in the roots also, and con-siderable loss of roots takes place.

In cases of mild copper deficiency the fruit is marked irregularly with reddish-brown excrescences, which are light-colored on young fruit but progressively darken until they may be black on mature fruit (plate 4, page 304). When copper deficiency is acute young fruits are sometimes bumpy and generally have an unusually light green color and a very smooth skin with or without the light reddish-

brown excrescences.   By June some of the fruits will be almost covered with these excrescences and drop from the tree.   Such fruits
as are left usually have juice low in acid and very insipid, and the
pulp dries out early in the season.   In such acute cases there are
gum pockets in the rind and gum at the axes of the segments; splitting of young fruits is common and includes both the ordinary
longitudinal splitting which starts at the stylar end and transverse

Courtesy of Florida Agricultural Experiment Station

Figure 2.—Pineapple orange tree (left) affected with acute copper deficiency showing dying
back of new growth and very large foliage on water shoots; tree (right) of same age and
with same fertilizer treatment except that it has received applications of copper sulfate.

splitting which starts in an excrescence and extends part way
around the fruit.

The symptoms described are typical of oranges; in grapefruit
the excrescences on the peel are less common, and though gum
pockets are numerous in the rind, gum is seldom found around the
seeds.   Fruits from copper-deficient grapefruit trees are commonly
yellower than normal and are frequently lopsided, and as they mature pits develop on the rind that are similar to storage pits but
smaller.   Acute copper deficiency is uncommon in grapefruit and
seldom observed in tangerines.   An acute deficiency of copper can,
however, put trees entirely out of production, but in the inter-

mediate stage there is a less noticeable but nevertheless heavy loss due to lowered grade and reduced crops.

Zinc deficiency is commonly associated with copper deficiency in Florida (see the later section on zinc deficiency). This results in some modification of the growth symptoms owing to the growth-restraining characteristics of zinc deficiency. There is also considerable evidence to indicate that copper deficiency restrains absorption of zinc by the roots, so that in acute cases of copper deficiency symptoms of zinc deficiency almost always develop even though the amount of available zinc in the soil is adequate for healthy trees.

Copper deficiency frequently occurs on acid sands associated with magnesium deficiency, without the exaggerated growth symptoms characteristic of copper deficiency, although very short dead twigs occur which are a miniature reproduction of the uncomplicated symptoms.

CAUSE AND TREATMENT

Insufficient copper in the soil is believed to be the primary cause of the symptoms described. In past years in Florida the symptoms were believed to have been due to too much nitrogen (then designated as ammonia in fertilizer mixtures), and this gave rise to the term "ammoniation." On the basis of available information the cause might be termed an unbalanced nitrogen-copper ratio, but the term "copper deficiency" is preferred for the practical reason that copper applications constitute a specific remedy. The relation of copper deficiency to nitrogen utilization is not so evident in California.

It has recently been shown by Peech (unpublished) that the formation of insoluble copper compounds is the probable cause of copper deficiency on light, acid, sandy soils in Florida. Early treatments consisted of withholding nitrogenous fertilizers and inserting crystals of copper sulfate under the bark. Treatments in Florida now consist of copper sprays (bordeaux or so-called neutral copper compounds) or applications of copper sulfate to the soil. Both methods are in common use. In California sprays appear to be the only satisfactory treatment. Recovery is extremely rapid, applications of the proper kind before growth starts in the spring resulting in a good setting of normal fruit on severely affected trees.

IRON DEFICIENCY

Iron deficiency has been recognized in California for many years, Lipman and Gordon (26) in 1925 and Thomas and Haas (45) in

1928 having reported on experiments for its control; and it is still a considerable problem under certain soil conditions. It has also been of importance in Arizona, and Finch, Albert, and Kinnison (*14, 15*) have reported on experiments to control it in the case of both citrus and eucalyptus. In Florida it occurs in an acute form in limited areas where the soil is closely underlain by limerock. Such soils are alkaline in reaction and subject to severe drought conditions, both of which may contribute to iron deficiency. Recently Bahrt and Hughes (*3*) have reported on responses from ferrous sulfate applications to trees on acid sands in Florida. So far treatment of iron deficiency has been less satisfactory than that of other deficiencies.

In Florida, iron deficiency is commonly associated with zinc, manganese, and magnesium deficiencies, and applications of all these elements frequently result in material improvement of the trees and crop.

SYMPTOMS

In iron deficiency citrus leaves are unusually thin with a very fine network of green veins on a much lighter background (plate 5, A, page 305). In acute cases in Florida the entire leaf will be yellowish, often almost orange-colored, this being particularly noticeable on leaves of orange trees. Leaves of iron-deficient grapefruit trees are small and very fragile when young and show a brown impregnation when older. Leaves shed freely, but in many cases the lower parts of the tree have a fair amount of good foliage while the top may show only sparse foliage and defoliated twigs. No particular twig symptoms have been noted, but there is considerable dying of twigs, particularly in the tops of trees, the entire tree eventually becoming involved. No particular fruit symptoms have been noted, but severely affected trees bear very little fruit.

In California, the reddish or brownish coloration of leaves is not common. The disorder is characterized primarily by light-colored foliage, particularly on the terminal twigs; the younger leaves are light green with a network of darker green veins. In more severe cases the leaves become very pale, even whitish, and the color of the smaller veins fades out until only a very pale green midrib remains. At this stage necrotic spots often appear in the leaves, which begin to drop at the terminals. New growth is sparse, with the result that the trees die back. Acute leaf symptoms are most common on the south side of affected trees. In this extreme form of the deficiency the fruit is small, hard, coarse, and light in color.

CAUSE AND TREATMENT

Iron deficiency is usually associated with too much alkalinity in the soil, but there also appears to be a definite relationship to extreme fluctuations in moisture supply. Treatments are generally unsatisfactory in both California and Florida, although some recent experimental work is promising; sprays produce a spotted greening (fig. 3), and while injections of iron citrates and iron tartrates into trunks of trees of other species have given fairly satisfactory results, the results on citrus have not been satisfactory owing to lack of penetration and killing of the wood. Applications of iron salts to alkaline soils on which citrus trees showed typical iron deficiency have failed to give uniformly satisfactory results. Bahrt and Hughes (*3*), working on acid sands in Florida, report a marked improvement following soil applications of iron, manganese, and magnesium where trees showed a leaf pattern very similar to that described here. This is probably a combination of these deficiencies, but it is described and illustrated by Bahrt and Hughes (*3*) as type E of bronzing. Fortunately, iron deficiency is not so widespread as some of the other deficiencies and presents a much less important commercial problem. The literature with regard to the effects of iron treatments is complicated by the fact that in many cases reported response to treatment was found later to be due to impurities in the iron salt used.

Courtesy of Florida Agricultural Experiment Station
Figure 3.—Leaves from tree deficient in iron showing green spots which developed following an application of iron spray.

MAGNESIUM DEFICIENCY

Magnesium deficiency is a major problem on practically all citrus soils in Florida, but it has not been reported as a commercial problem elsewhere. The first report of favorable response to magnesium applications in the field was by Averna-Sacca in Brazil in 1912, but this report apparently led to no commercial application. Bahrt (*1*) reported favorable response to magnesium applications in Florida in 1934, and further reports of a similar nature were made by Tait (*43*) and by Bryan and DeBusk (*4*) in 1936.

Reed and Haas (*38*) in California described symptoms of magnesium deficiency from sand cultures, and further information was secured by Chapman. Magnesium deficiency in Florida is commonly termed "bronzing," but the term is too broadly applied and includes symptoms other than those of magnesium deficiency. While Camp and Fudge (*8*) in Florida recognize a general complex of symptoms induced by low magnesium and varying somewhat with other nutritional factors, Bahrt includes magnesium deficiency under the general classification of bronzing. He splits this into several subclasses, of which types A, B, and C represent derangement in the ratios between magnesium and other elements such as calcium and potassium. Different symptoms are given for each class. The general classification followed by Camp and Fudge corresponds closely with the symptoms described by Reed and Haas, and more recently by Chapman, and to type B of bronzing as described by Bahrt.

Symptoms

Symptoms of magnesium deficiency occur on mature leaves at any season of the year. Irregular yellow blotches start along the midrib of leaves near the fruit and eventually coalesce to form an irregular yellow band on each side of the midrib (plate 6, page 306). This area rapidly enlarges until only the tip and the base of the leaf are green, the base showing a more or less inverted V-shaped area pointed on the midrib. In more advanced stages the entire leaf may become yellow. According to Bahrt and Hughes (*3*) this pattern occurs where the calcium-magnesium and potassium-magnesium ratios are unbalanced, and they refer to it as type B of bronzing (plate 7, page 307). The fading from green to yellow may follow several patterns depending upon other nutritional conditions and the variety of fruit. Two patterns slightly different from that described are recognized by Bahrt. Of these, type A is considered due to an unbalanced calcium-magnesium relationship. He describes it as starting with the break-down of chlorophyll in small patches along the midrib which fade to yellow and spread outward to the edge of the leaf until the entire leaf eventually becomes yellow. Type C, also considered to be due to an unbalanced calcium-magnesium ratio, is definitely different from type A and differs from type B in that the fading from green to yellow starts in the tip (apical) portion of the leaf; a small green area, extending more than halfway up the midrib, remains at the base. The green area is irregular in shape with points on the lateral veins giving roughly the outline of an American holly leaf, but it gradually fades and diminishes in size until in the last stage only a small area at the tip of the leaf and a small triangular area at the base remain very light green. This classification into types A, B, and C is based by Bahrt on chemical analysis of the leaves as well as on studies of each type through all stages in the field. All forms may appear on the same tree, but types A and C are predominant when potassium fertilization is maintained at a normal level, while type B predominates when potassium fertilization is unusually high. One type of yellowing associated with nitrogen deficiency, which starts as a mottling over the entire leaf, is frequently confused with the symptoms of magnesium deficiency (see under nitrogen deficiency, p. 285).

Fudge (*19*) of Florida has shown that magnesium deficiency is due primarily to the movement of magnesium from the leaves to the developing fruit, although there may also be such translocation from older leaves to developing leaves. As soon as any considerable portion of the leaf is involved it may shed, the loss of leaves being accentuated by such other conditions as cold weather or toxic sprays. Severely affected orange trees are frequently completely defoliated by the end of November. In grapefruit defoliation is slower and may be delayed until late winter if no cold weather or other shock to the trees occurs (fig. 4). Bahrt reported from actual counts made of the leaves on trees in the field that the development of leaf symptoms was associated with the seediness of fruit. Seedy grapefruit and seedy oranges such as the Pineapple are very severely affected, whereas seedless varieties such as Marsh Seedless grapefruit and Hamlin and Jaffa oranges are only slightly affected under the same soil conditions. This was verified by Fudge (*19*), who also associated the leaf symptoms with the development of the fruit. In seedy varieties, heavily fruited limbs will be almost devoid of green leaves while unfruited portions of the tree may be bearing only green leaves. Trees bearing heavy crops of fruit will also be very yellow or almost defoliated while adjoining trees without a crop are very green. This relationship to fruit production is particularly noticeable in the case of seedy grapefruit, the fruit of which is more irregularly distributed, both on the individual tree and in the grove as a whole, than is that of nearly seedless strains of either grapefruit or oranges. Alternation of bearing is common in seedy varieties of grapefruit affected by magnesium deficiency, and during the year when they are producing little or no fruit the leaves remain green and the trees recover in considerable measure from the defoliation accompanying the heavy fruit crop of the previous year.

No pronounced twig or growth symptoms have been described,

Figure 4.—Grapefruit tree acutely deficient in magnesium showing extreme defoliation in the fall of the year, with fruit left unprotected by foliage.

Courtesy of Florida Agricultural Experiment Station

but the defoliated twigs are weakened and subject to invasion by fungi and may die after or even before the fruit is picked. This makes excessive pruning necessary in magnesium-deficient groves, and severely affected trees are consequently reduced in size.

Though definite fruit symptoms such as those characteristic of copper and zinc deficiencies have not been described, magnesium deficiency causes a reduction in total crop and in size of fruit, and in addition there is a tendency for the fruit to be weak and to give trouble in transit. Unpublished work of the Citrus Experiment Station in Florida has shown that when all other deficiencies are eliminated in oranges except acute magnesium deficiency, there is a great reduction in color, both externally and internally, and a coarser rind. Under the same conditions the sugar, acid, and vitamin C content of the juice were also greatly reduced as compared with similar trees to which magnesium had been applied. Magnesium-deficient trees also showed much more natural droppage of fruit and it dried out (crystallized) much faster when mature.

CAUSE AND TREATMENT

Magnesium deficiency in citrus groves on light sandy soils in Florida is primarily due to the low natural level of available magnesium in such soils combined with the use of fertilizer low in magnesium. Such soils leach magnesium very readily, so that the amount of this element that might be added incidentally in the ordinary fertilizer program is quickly lost. Leaching is frequently intensified by very acid fertilizers. As a result of the combined effects of these factors magnesium deficiency is almost universal when sandy soils have a degree of acidity below 5.0 on the pH scale, but it may occur at any degree of acidity or alkalinity if the magnesium level in the soil is too low. The commonly used treatment consists of applying dolomitic limestone to reduce the acidity and furnish magnesium, in addition using some soluble or quickly available form such as magnesium sulfate to supplement the more slowly available dolomite. When the degree of soil acidity is above pH 6.0 magnesium sulfate is usually used alone. Under some conditions it is more satisfactory to use high-calcium limestone plus a soluble magnesium material instead of dolomite. Since the magnesium requirements of citrus are comparatively large the treatments must be correspondingly large. Magnesium cannot be satisfactorily applied in a spray, probably because the requirement is larger than the amount the leaves are able to absorb.

MANGANESE DEFICIENCY

Manganese deficiency occurs commonly in Florida, responses to manganese applications having been first reported by Skinner and Bahrt (41) and by Skinner, Bahrt, and Hughes (42). More recently this deficiency has been reported from New Zealand by Taylor and Burns (44) and from California by Parker, Chapman, and Southwick (34). It probably occurs in other citrus areas but may be confused with zinc deficiency, or its symptoms may be masked by those of the latter. The symptoms of manganese deficiency were described by Haas (21) in California in 1932, but his descriptions do not correspond exactly with that given here, which is compiled from work done in the field in Florida and California. No common name is applied specifically to manganese deficiency, but in Florida a combination of zinc- and manganese-deficiency symptoms is known as "marl chlorosis" and acute symptoms on older leaves are sometimes classified as "bronzing," while in New Zealand, Taylor and Burns (44) refer to it as "mottle-leaf."

Symptoms

Young leaves show a network of green veins on a lighter green background, but the pattern is not so distinct as that in zinc and iron

Figure 5.—Manganese-deficiency patterns in naval-orange leaves from trees grown in cultures. A, Pattern of mild deficiency in which midrib and main veins are green with a green band of varying width on either side—contrast between areas not so marked as in zinc deficiency; B and C, patterns similar to that in A, accompanied by spots distributed at random in interveinal areas; D, same as C, but with some brown resinous spots; E, more advanced stage of chlorosis.

Courtesy of California Agricultural Experiment Station

deficiencies and the leaf is greener (plate 2, B, page 302). As the leaf matures the pattern resolves itself into dark irregular bands along the midrib and main lateral veins with lighter green between the veins. All gradations occur from light-green splotches between the main lateral veins to a more pronounced pattern nearly approaching that of zinc deficiency but never showing the extreme contrast in color that characterizes the latter. In severe cases almost the entire leaf gradually assumes a dull yellowish-green color. Leaves are not noticeably reduced in size or changed in form but may show a little reflex puckering. Young leaves do not have the normal bright color, and as they reach maturity they become very dull in appearance. Such leaves appear to become senescent (aged) prematurely and fall from the tree, which gives it an open appearance. A pronounced development of pattern is reported from culture experiments (fig. 5) by Chapman, Liebig, and Parker (10). They also noted the brown specks distributed over the leaf which had been noted earlier by Haas (21), who believes them to be due to cell disintegration and exudation of gum. A stippling of lighter colored spots in the light-green areas was also reported. Nearly all of the leaf patterns produced on lemons and oranges (plate 8, page 308) in controlled cultures have been seen on bearing trees in the field in California, but in the field the range of symptoms is wider. In Florida severely affected trees are short of foliage and have an open appearance, while trees that are only slightly deficient in manganese may show a mild pattern on young leaves which disappears after the flush of growth is completed. This is also true in California, where manganese deficiency may be associated with a form of decline in lemon trees (34, 35).

No particular twig symptoms have been reported, but in acute cases there is considerable loss of small wood. This is more noticeable in tangerines and Temple oranges than in other varieties. Dying of twigs is more noticeable in trees affected with combinations of zinc and manganese deficiencies than in trees deficient only in manganese.

No striking fruit symptoms have been noted such as those characteristic of zinc and copper deficiencies. Skinner and Bahrt (41), Skinner, Bahrt, and Hughes (42), and Bahrt and Hughes (2) have reported an intensification in skin color and juice color as well as increased firmness following applications of manganese, and Roy (40) has reported an increase in sugar in the juice. Manganese deficiency also results in a reduction in yield.

Cause and Treatment

In Florida manganese deficiency occurs on both acid and alkaline soils; it is probably due to leaching in the acid soils and to insolubility in the alkaline soils. On very acid sands it is commonly associated with deficiencies of zinc, copper, and magnesium, as evidenced by both tree response and soil analysis. Soil factors are not discussed in New Zealand reports and the finding of manganese deficiency in California is too recent for this phase to have been studied there. Culture work by Chapman, Liebig, and Parker (10) showed that manganese deficiency occurred in a neutral or alkaline medium (pH maintained at 7.0 or above) even though manganese was regularly supplied. Treatment by sprays of manganese sulfate neutralized with lime and soil treatments with manganese sulfate are used in Florida, and preliminary reports indicating corrective effects from sprays are available from New Zealand. In California, sprays of manganese sulfate neutralized with lime or soda ash have given experimentally satisfactory results.

NITROGEN DEFICIENCY

Identification of nitrogen-deficiency symptoms is somewhat involved because a peculiar type of leaf pattern, in which the tissue along the midrib and the larger veins is distinctly lighter in color than the remainder of the leaf, has been classified by Haas (in Fawcett (13)) as a symptom of nitrogen deficiency. His descriptions, however, would fit fairly well the pattern associated in the field primarily with girdling of the twig, limb, or tree in such a way as to destroy or severely injure the food-conducting tissues without destroying the water-conducting tissues. When such girdling occurs the leaves become yellow along the midrib and larger veins, the remainder of the leaf usually remaining a dark dull-green color for a time and then fading slowly to yellow (plate 5, B, page 305). Tissues along the midrib and veins may become extremely light in color, giving rise to the terms "inverted frenching" and "vein chlorosis." The pattern can be produced artificially by girdling a twig or branch, but it is associated in the field in Florida with root-rot and gum diseases due to species of *Diplodia* and *Phomopsis,* which destroy the bark or roots, and with lightning injury which has girdled the tree; in California rodent injury and injury due to a fluctuating water table are common causes. The affected portion of the tree can be healed only by supplying the missing conducting tissue, as by inarching.

Though leaves affected as described are likely to have an abnormal chemical composition and to show deficiencies of a number of elements, this pattern can hardly be considered a deficiency in the sense in which the term is here used. Applications of specific elements are not indicated for correction but rather the supplying of a new conducting tissue where this is easily possible. A very similar pattern appears on older leaves in some groves following a heavy flush of new growth. The leaves become more deeply colored, however, and then shed.

Deficiency symptoms that respond to applications of nitrogen are almost too well known to need description, but since they may be confused in some instances, attention is called to some of the outstanding characteristics involved. Nitrogen-deficiency symptoms fall into two classes—symptoms on trees that are continuously starved for nitrogen and symptoms brought on by a sharp decline in nitrogen supply. The second type of deficiency is not extremely common in Florida but does occur occasionally in an acute form when the nitrogen supply falls during the period of maximum fruit development. The following descriptions apply strictly to what may be accurately termed nitrogen-deficiency symptoms.

Symptoms

If nitrogen is deficient when growth begins, the young leaves are light yellowish green in color; the veins frequently are very slightly, but not markedly, lighter in color than the tissues between. The young leaves are undersized, thin, and fragile and develop a very light green color which may ultimately become yellow if any fruit is produced. Shedding of leaves is heavy on such trees, and consequently the foliage is sparse. This type of symptom is common in unfertilized trees. The second type of pattern may develop when the trees have sufficient nitrogen during the spring, put on a heavy normal growth and bear a normal crop, and then become acutely deficient in nitrogen during the summer and fall when the fruit is maturing and there is a heavy drain on the trees. Under such conditions the green leaves slowly bleach to a mottled, irregular, green and yellow pattern and may ultimately become entirely yellow and shed. This pattern slightly resembles the symptoms of magnesium deficiency. The condition has been observed frequently in ridged groves that are not sufficiently fertilized in summer to take care of the crop of fruit. Trees growing on ridged soils are limited in root space, and this is further accentuated by the waterlogging of part of the ridge during the rainy season.

Though no specific twig or growth symptoms have been identified, trees that are constantly short of nitrogen are stunted and unsymmetrical in shape and the growth is very short and irregular. The lack of foliage results in an open appearance. Considerable twig dieback occurs and the tree looks brushy. Such trees seldom die, but they remain in a permanently stunted condition until nitrogen is supplied in adequate amounts. Orange and grapefruit trees deficient in nitrogen frequently produce fruit of a good quality as far as texture and flavor are concerned, but the crop is very small and the fruit is usually somewhat pale in color. In California, lemon trees growing under conditions of deficient nitrogen show less change in color of leaves than do orange trees. There is, however, a great decrease in vigor and the trees mature their fruit prematurely before it reaches picking size.

Modifications of nitrogen-deficiency symptoms are not particularly important, but the ability to distinguish between true nitrogen deficiency and deficiency of other elements is important. As mentioned under magnesium deficiency, the symptoms of a deficiency of the latter were commonly ascribed to nitrogen deficiency until the importance of magnesium was established. There may still be confusion between the two. It must always be remembered that yellow leaves are not necessarily, or in fact commonly in Florida, an indication of nitrogen deficiency.

Cause and Treatment

While the cause of the first type of nitrogen deficiency is simply a lack of nitrogen, there is some evidence that the second may be produced in regions of heavy summer rainfall and very porous soil by a failure either to time the summer application properly or to judge accurately the amount of nitrogen necessary to mature the crop. There is some indication that improper nitrification due to waterlogging of the soil during the summer rainy season may result in a temporary deficiency of nitrogen which is relieved by dry weather.

In California temporary nitrogen starvation is sometimes the result of excessive applications of organic matter or excessive competition by cover crops. Parker (unpublished) reports that such competition may result in decreased crops when it occurs at critical seasons, but the leaf symptoms may exist only temporarily. In pot cultures using soil the second type of symptoms has been produced by overdoses of phosphate.

In ordinary cases of nitrogen deficiency the obvious treatment is to supply nitrogen in the required amounts. In the case of acute deficiency due to fruit production, consideration should be given to the form of nitrogen and method of application, particularly in relation to irrigation. The use of nitrates usually would be indicated, owing to their immediate availability. The subject of nitrogen fertilization is too complex, however, for complete discussion here.

PHOSPHORUS DEFICIENCY

Phosphorus-deficiency symptoms have never been definitely identified in groves, although phosphate has been extensively used in the fertilization of citrus in many areas. In Florida it has been so generally used that a deficiency would hardly be expected, and in California no response has been reported to phosphate applications in the field even on soils on which other crops show such a response.

Courtesy of California Agricultural Experiment Station

Figure 6.—Phosphorus-deficient navel-orange tree (left) in comparison with tree of comparable age receiving phosphate (right). Note the restricted growth and fruiting on the phosphorus-deficient tree. These symptoms were produced in cultures. No phosphorus-deficiency symptoms in the field have been reported.

Symptoms of the deficiency on cuttings have been produced in sand and solution cultures by Haas (22) of California, and Chapman in an unpublished report has described phosphorus-deficiency symptoms on citrus trees grown in 55-gallon oil drums in a calcareous soil of low phosphate availability. The symptoms described below are summarized from the latter report.

SYMPTOMS

Young citrus trees deprived of phosphorus showed a reduced growth rate (fig. 6), with the older leaves losing their deep green color and luster and becoming faded green to bronze. Some of these leaves later developed burned areas (fig. 7) which had no definite pattern or position on the leaf. However, this burning was neither a general nor a consistent symptom; it was most prominent in the spring following bloom and a new cycle of growth. The affected leaves shed somewhat prematurely but the young growth continued, probably utilizing phosphorus translocated from older

Courtesy of California Agricultural Experiment Station

Figure 7.—Navel-orange leaves from phosphorus-deficient trees showing burned areas. This symptom does not occur on all leaves.

leaves, since the latter showed a reduced content and the young tissues a nearly normal content of both total and inorganic phosphorus. Young trees showed a sparse foliage owing to the restricted growth and shedding of leaves. Some twigs died back, but this condition was not pronounced. There was a very limited flower development and no fruit was produced.

POTASSIUM DEFICIENCY

Potassium deficiency has been produced in the field by Bahrt (unpublished) in Florida by withholding potassium fertilizers from orange trees on light sandy soil. Symptoms appeared about the third year. Reed and Haas (*36*) in California and later Haas (*24*) reported on symptoms produced on trees in culture. Chapman and Brown of California have carried out further culture work (unpublished) which tends to show that, although the symptoms varied somewhat with the variety, they are constant for a given variety through wide variations in the culture solution. Eckstein, Bruno, and Turrentine (*12*) reported leaf and fruit symptoms, but the con-

Figure 8.—Potassium deficiency in oranges causes "tucking" in the leaf blades. The leaf at the right is normal.

Courtesy of United States Department of Agriculture

ditions under which they were developed are not clear. The widespread use of potassium fertilizers and of organic materials such as manure, hay, and straw on citrus has possibly prevented the common development of the symptoms even on light sandy soils.

Symptoms

The leaf symptom of potassium deficiency reported on oranges by all workers is a "fluting" or "tucking," as though the midrib were too short for the leaf (figs. 8 and 9). This distortion should not be confused with injury produced by aphids and other insects. Another symptom reported by Bahrt in his field experiments is the occurrence of tiny light gum spots which gradually enlarge and become rough and finally darken to brown or black (plate 9, page

309).   This probably corresponds to the gum spots on affected leaves reported by the California workers, who also report the extensive development of necrotic areas on older lemon leaves (fig. 10).   In acute potassium deficiency in cultures the development of weak lateral shoots with small leaves is also reported, the shoots often being S-shaped as in copper deficiency.   In orange and grapefruit trees there was some splitting of the bark and the development

Courtesy of California Agricultural Experiment Station

Figure 9.—Potassium-deficiency symptoms on sweet-orange seedling shoot (left), and lemon-cutting shoot (right).   Note multiple branches bearing small leaves.   Crinkled and twisted leaves are prominent on both shoots.

of gum.   No fruit symptoms have been reported from cultures, but potassium deficiency has generally been supposed to produce thick-skinned, coarse fruit of poor color as described by Eckstein, Bruno, and Turrentine.   Specific information on this point is not clear, however.   Bahrt (unpublished) reports from field experiments in Florida that potassium-deficient trees produced a small yield of fruit and that the individual fruits were small with a thin rind of a less intense color than that of fruit from trees receiving potash. The juice was low in acid but higher than normal in total solids.

SULFUR DEFICIENCY

Sulfur deficiency has not been identified in the field, but a brief description of leaf symptoms on Valencia orange cuttings grown in sand cultures lacking sulfate has been given by Haas (23). Further information derived from both sand and soil cultures with young bearing orange trees and lemon, grapefruit, and sweet-orange

Figure 10. — Potassium-deficiency effects on lemon leaves from trees grown in cultures: A, Brown, almost dead area at base, with gum spots following main veins; B and C, necrotic burn; D, gum spots on edge of leaves, unevenly faded chlorophyll; E and F, necrotic spotting, with midrib and some veins lighter colored than rest of leaf.

Courtesy of California Agricultural Experiment Station

seedlings has been obtained by Chapman (results unpublished). The following brief description is from the latter work.

Symptoms

The leaf symptoms in general consisted of a chlorosis quite similar to that produced by nitrogen deficiency. Sulfur deficiency, however, was characterized at its onset by a very much yellower new growth, the older leaves remaining green (plate 10, page 310). This contrast in coloration was marked and gave the trees a striking appearance. No abnormal twig characteristics developed, but some dying back occurred as the deficiency progressed. The immature fruit from sulfur-deficient trees was of a lighter green color than normal fruit and the mature fruit of a lighter orange color. Some of the fruits were dwarfed and misshapen and others had an abnormally thick peel. The interior was pulpy and juiceless, with some of the juice sacs gelatinized as in granulation.

ZINC DEFICIENCY

Zinc deficiency is probably more widespread in citrus than any other except that of nitrogen, and its characteristic symptoms have been reported from practically every citrus-growing area. In California, work leading to the use of zinc as a corrective started about 1930, growing out of work by Chandler, Hoagland, and Hibbard (*9*) on little leaf of deciduous trees and by Parker (*29, 30*) on mottle-leaf of citrus. In Florida, the use of zinc on citrus trees was an outgrowth of work by Mowry and Camp (*28, p. 27*) on zinc deficiency of tung trees and Satsuma oranges. As a result of successful individual efforts by Johnston, Parker, and Thomason in California, and work by Camp, Reuther, and Bahrt in Florida, zinc was in widespread commercial use in both States by 1934. Similarly favorable results have been reported from most of the citrus-growing areas. The characteristic deficiency symptoms were produced and corrected in cultures by Chapman, Vanselow, and Liebig (*11*) in 1937. In Florida the symptoms are termed "frenching" and in California and many other areas "mottle-leaf."

SYMPTOMS

The symptoms on mature leaves are striking. There are irregular green bands along the midrib and lateral veins, and the remaining tissue is light green, greenish yellow, or even a very pale yellow. The relative amounts of green and yellow tissue vary; in some leaves only the basal portion of the midrib is green, while others may show only splotches of white, yellow, or pale green between the lateral veins.

Narrow leaves on twigs with short internodes are characteristic; in acute cases leaves may be very small with a tendency to stand erect (plate 11, page 311). Where the condition is mild the characteristic leaf pattern often starts as a network of green veins on a light-green background. As the leaf matures the green veinal areas tend to broaden and deepen in color and the interveinal areas to become lighter. Lemon leaves are not so distinctly mottled but are dull green in color and frequently have wavy margins. Mature green leaves have only occasionally been observed to develop the characteristic pattern. After treatment with a zinc spray affected leaves become green, although they do not increase in size. The new leaves, however, are normal in both size and color (*39*).

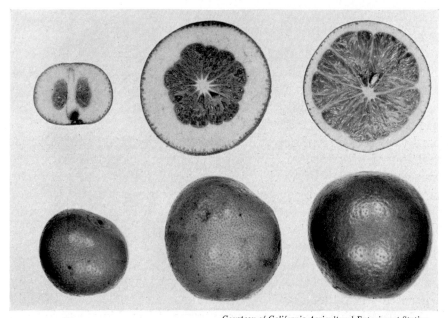

Courtesy of California Agricultural Experiment Station

Figure 11.—Grapefruit showing, on the left, the effects of acute zinc deficiency; center, fruit from similar tree two months after treatment showing discolored tough areas impregnated with gum in the thick rind; and, on the right, fruit from a similar tree treated 15 months previously.

When zinc deficiency is mild only a few weak twigs show the characteristic symptoms. In California these twigs are usually on the south side of the tree, but this has not been observed in Florida. When the deficiency is more acute, growth is usually slow, the entire outside of the tree bearing very fine, short twigs carrying the pointed and often small leaves that have a tendency to stand upright. These growth characteristics give the tree an upright, bushy appearance, and as time goes on the twigs die back over the outside of the tree, considerably reducing its size. As the outside of the tree dies back, water sprouts bearing nearly normal or slightly affected foliage develop on the main branches and trunk. Thus leaves showing symptoms which vary greatly in intensity are present on the tree at the same time. The very small twigs produce growth of quite normal appearance after zinc treatment, provided no other deficiencies are present. When this normal growth occurs in the spring the increase in crop resulting from treatment is very rapid (*32, 33*).

The fruits borne on the affected twigs vary in quality and quantity in proportion to the severity of the zinc-deficiency symptoms

Courtesy of Florida Agricultural Experiment Station

Figure 12.—Acute zinc-deficiency symptoms on Pineapple orange (left), showing very small, smooth fruit and pointed leaves with striking contrasts in the leaf pattern, and (right) fruit and foliage from a similar tree one year after treatment showing immediate resumption of normal growth.

exhibited by the respective twigs. Severely affected orange and grapefruit twigs in California are reported by Parker (*32*) as bearing small thick-skinned fruits (fig. 11) whereas fruits from such twigs in Florida commonly have an unusually smooth, light-colored, thin skin (fig. 12); but in both States the pulp is woody, dry, and insipid. Parker also reports firm gum pockets occurring in the albedo of such fruits, but this has not been observed in Florida unless other deficiencies are present.

Fruit on severely affected twigs of lemons in California is small, thin-skinned, juicy, elongated, and pointed (figs. 13 and 14). In any of these lemon varieties, acute zinc deficiency results in very

small fruits of no commercial value. The symptoms of zinc deficiency are thus so severe that they mask or alter very markedly the
symptoms of other deficiencies or disorders, and they should be
corrected before an attempt is made to determine deficiencies of
other elements (31).

Oranges exhibit the symptoms more often than do grapefruit or
tangerines, although all types of citrus may be affected. Deep till-

Courtesy of California Agricultural Experiment Station

Figure 13.—Normal lemons (left) in comparison with lemons from trees severely affected by
zinc deficiency.

age, lack of organic matter, or rootstocks unsuited to the soil may
result in an increase of the symptoms. It appears that many other
factors which reduce the vigor of the tree have the same effect.
Work in Florida apparently indicates that deficiencies of magnesium and copper reduce zinc intake through root injury, thereby
giving rise to characteristic symptoms of zinc deficiency even though
the soil is not depleted of zinc. As a result of this tendency of copper deficiency to intensify zinc deficiency, frenching was frequently
classed as a symptom of dieback by earlier workers. Because of
this relationship, zinc-deficiency symptoms are very often reduced
when a coincidental copper deficiency is corrected—a response that is
frequently misleading to casual observers. In such cases there is
sufficient available zinc in the soil for the ordinary needs of the trees,
but they are unable to absorb it. When symptoms of zinc deficiency

are brought on by a lack of available zinc in the soil, however, the trees respond only to zinc treatment.

CAUSE AND TREATMENT

A deficiency of zinc in the soil commonly occurs in Florida, California, and other citrus soils with a low acidity (above pH 6.0) and is probably due to the formation of insoluble compounds. In California it is not entirely dependent on soil reaction and is more preva-

Figure 14.—Eureka lemon tree severely affected with zinc deficiency showing bunchy growth.

Courtesy of California Agricultural Experiment Station

lent on some soil types than on others. In Florida zinc deficiency also occurs on sandy soils of high acidity (pH 4.5 to 5.25); here it is probably due to the formation of acid-insoluble compounds (Peech, unpublished). Zinc deficiency also occurs on other soils in Florida in which availability is not a factor, apparently because of exhaustion by cropping.

The treatment commonly recommended is the use of a spray of zinc sulfate neutralized with hydrated lime or lime-sulfur in Florida, while a spray of zinc sulfate with lime or soda ash or a zinc oxide spray is usually used in California and other areas. Soil treatments on alkaline soils have been generally unsatisfactory, but on some soils in Florida with a pH between 5.5 and 6.0 excellent response has been obtained from small applications of zinc sulfate (Camp (5) and Bahrt, unpublished). In these latter cases the deficiency is believed to be due to exhaustion of the soil rather than to the formation of insoluble compounds.

KEY TO PLANT-NUTRIENT DEFICIENCY SYMPTOMS OF CITRUS FRUITS

ELEMENT
DEFICIENT

A. Symptoms originating with new growth.
　B. Leaves uniform in color over entire area.
　　C. Growth reduced, frequently resulting in bushy appearance.
　　　D. New leaves light green to yellow green, growth short .... Nitrogen
　　　D. New leaves very light yellow green to yellow, markedly yellower than above.. Sulfur [3]
　　　D. New leaves with water-soaked flecks becoming translucent, fruit with hard gummy lumps in the rind........................... Boron
　　　D. Leaves green with fluting or tucking along midrib................ Potassium
　　C. Growth greater than normal to excessive (not evident in California).
　　　D. Leaves usually large and very dark green, gummy excrescences on fruit and in axes of fruit segments .... Copper
　B. Leaves showing a pattern in which veins and midrib are darker than tissues between the veins.
　　C. Leaves reduced in size, pointed, with sharply contrasting pattern of green along midrib and main laterals; tissue between the veins very light green or yellow.. Zinc
　　C. Leaves approximately normal in shape and size.
　　　D. Dark green along midrib and main lateral veins with tissues between the veins lighter green, pattern not distinct and leaf dull......... Manganese
　　　D. Fine network of green veins on very light green to yellow or whitish background, growth greatly reduced, and dying of twigs common.. Iron
　　　D. Fine network of green veins on light-green background with leaves malformed, fruit with gummy excrescences and gum in axes of segments.. Copper
A. Symptoms originating on mature leaves and frequently associated with fruit production.
　B. Fading of chlorophyll starting in localized areas and gradually spreading.
　　C. Fading of chlorophyll starting in blade of leaf parallel to midrib and spreading from there, but with base of leaf usually remaining green to very advanced stages.................................... Magnesium
　　C. Fading of chlorophyll starting along edges of leaf and gradually involving areas between veins.. Calcium [3]
　B. Fading of chlorophyll not localized at start.
　　C. Fading starting as mottled yellow green and yellow over entire leaf, which eventually becomes yellow............................... Nitrogen
　　C. Fading of leaf to dull green and eventually to orange yellow; in extreme cases, burned areas on leaves................................. Phosphorus [3]

[3] Described only from cultures; data not complete enough to make place in key absolutely definite.

LITERATURE CITED

(1) BAHRT, G. M.
1934. PROGRESS REPORT OF SOIL FERTILITY AND FERTILIZER EXPERIMENTS ON BRONZING OF CITRUS. Fla. State Hort. Soc. Proc. 47:18-20.

(2) ——— and HUGHES, A. E.
1935. RECENT DEVELOPMENT IN CITRUS SOIL FERTILITY INVESTIGATIONS. Fla. State Hort. Soc. Proc. 48:31-39.

(3) ——— and HUGHES, A. E.
1937. SOIL FERTILITY AND EXPERIMENTS ON BRONZING OF CITRUS. Fla. State Hort. Soc. Proc. 50:23-28, illus.

(4) BRYAN, O. C., and DeBUSK, E. F.
1936. CITRUS BRONZING—A MAGNESIUM DEFICIENCY. Fla. Grower 44(2):6, 24.

(5) CAMP, A. F.
1934. ZINC SULPHATE AS A SOIL AMENDMENT IN CITRUS GROVES. Fla. State Hort. Soc. Proc. 47:33-39.

(6) ———
1938. PHYSIOLOGY OF FRUIT PRODUCTION. Fla. Agr. Expt. Sta. Ann. Rpt. 1938:142-145.

(7) ———
1939. BORON IN CITRUS NUTRITION IN FLORIDA. Citrus Indus. 20(2):6-7, 18.

(8) ——— and FUDGE, B. R.
1939. SOME SYMPTOMS OF CITRUS MALNUTRITION IN FLORIDA. Fla. Agr. Expt. Sta. Bul. 335:1-55.

(9) CHANDLER, W. H., HOAGLAND, D. R., and HIBBARD, P. L.
1932. LITTLE-LEAF OR ROSETTE OF FRUIT TREES, II: EFFECT OF ZINC AND OTHER TREATMENTS. Amer. Soc. Hort. Sci. Proc. 29:255-263.

(10) CHAPMAN, H. D., LIEBIG, GEORGE F., JR., and PARKER, E. R.
1939. MANGANESE STUDIES CALIF. SOILS AND CITRUS LEAF SYMPTOMS OF DEFICIENCY. Calif. Citrograph 24:427-454; 25:11, 15.

(11) ——— VANSELOW, A. P., and LIEBIG, G. F., JR.
1937. THE PRODUCTION OF CITRUS MOTTLE-LEAF IN CONTROLLED NUTRIENT CULTURES. Jour. Agr. Res. 55:365-379.

(12) ECKSTEIN, OSKAR; BRUNO, ALBERT; and TURRENTINE, J. W.
1937. POTASH DEFICIENCY SYMPTOMS. 235 pp., illus. Berlin.

(13) FAWCETT, H. S.
1936. CITRUS DISEASES AND THEIR CONTROL. Ed. 2, 656 pp., illus. New York. McGraw-Hill Book Co., Inc.

(14) FINCH, A. H., ALBERT, D. W., and KINNISON, A. F.
1933. A CHLOROTIC CONDITION OF PLANTS IN ARIZONA RELATED TO IRON DEFICIENCY. Amer. Soc. Hort. Sci. Proc. 30:431-434.

(15) ——— ALBERT, D. W., and KINNISON, A. F.
1934. PROGRESS ON THE CONTROL OF CITRUS CHLOROSIS OR DECLINE. Amer. Soc. Hort. Sci. Proc. 32:20-23.

(16) FLOYD, B. F.
1913. BORDEAUX MIXTURE FOR THE CONTROL OF DIE-BACK. Fla. Agr. Expt. Sta. Ann. Rpt. 1913:27-29.

(17) ———
1917. DIEBACK, OR EXANTHEMA OF CITRUS TREES. Fla. Agr. Expt. Sta. Bul. 140:1-31.

(18) FOWLER, J. H.
1875. ON THE DIE-BACK IN ORANGE TREES. Fla. Fruit Growers' Assoc. Proc. 1875:62-67.

(19) FUDGE, B. R.
1938. MAGNESIUM DEFICIENCY IN RELATION TO YIELD AND CHEMICAL COMPOSITION OF SEEDY AND COMMERCIALLY SEEDLESS VARIETIES OF GRAPEFRUIT. Fla. State Hort. Soc. Proc. 51:34-43.

(20) GROSSENBACHER, J. G.
  1916. SOME BARK DISEASES OF CITRUS TREES IN FLORIDA. Phytopathology 6:29-50.

(21) HAAS, A. R. C.
  1932. INJURIOUS EFFECTS OF MANGANESE AND IRON DEFICIENCIES ON THE GROWTH OF
    CITRUS. Hilgardia 7:181-206.

(22) ———
  1936. PHOSPHORUS DEFICIENCY IN CITRUS. Soil Sci. 42:93-117.

(23) ———
  1936. DEFICIENCY CHLOROSES IN CITRUS. Soil Sci. 42: 435-443.

(24) ———
  1936. THE GROWTH OF CITRUS IN RELATION TO POTASSIUM. Calif. Citrograph 22:6,
    17, 54, 62.

(25) ——— and KLOTZ, L. J.
  1931. SOME ANATOMICAL AND PHYSIOLOGICAL CHANGES IN CITRUS PRODUCED BY BORON
    DEFICIENCY. Hilgardia 5:175-196.

(26) LIPMAN, C. B., and GORDON, A.
  1925. FURTHER STUDIES ON NEW METHODS IN THE PHYSIOLOGY AND PATHOLOGY OF
    PLANTS. Jour. Gen. Physiol. 7:615-623.

(27) MORRIS, A. A.
  1938. SOME OBSERVATIONS ON THE EFFECTS OF BORON TREATMENT IN THE CONTROL OF
    "HARD FRUIT" IN CITRUS. Jour. Pomol. and Hort. Sci. 16(2):167-181.

(28) MOWRY, HAROLD, and CAMP, A. F.
  1934. A PRELIMINARY REPORT ON ZINC SULPHATE AS A CORRECTIVE FOR BRONZING OF
    TUNG TREES. Fla. Agr. Expt. Sta. Bul. 273:1-34.

(29) PARKER, E. R.
  1934. EXPERIMENTS ON THE TREATMENT OF MOTTLE-LEAF OF CITRUS TREES. Amer.
    Soc. Hort. Sci. Proc. 31:98-107.

(30) ———
  1935. EXPERIMENTS ON THE TREATMENT OF MOTTLE-LEAF OF CITRUS TREES. II. Amer.
    Soc. Hort. Sci. Proc. 33:82-86.

(31) ———
  1936. EXPERIMENTS ON THE TREATMENT OF MOTTLE-LEAF OF CITRUS TREES. III. Amer.
    Soc. Hort. Sci. Proc. 34:213-215.

(32) ———
  1937. EFFECT OF ZINC APPLICATIONS ON THE CROP OF GRAPEFRUIT TREES AFFECTED WITH
    MOTTLE-LEAF. Hilgardia 11:35-53.

(33) ———
  1938. EXPERIMENTS ON THE TREATMENT OF MOTTLE-LEAF OF CITRUS TREES. IV. Amer.
    Soc. Hort. Sci. Proc. 35:217-226.

(34) ——— CHAPMAN, H. D., and SOUTHWICK, R. W.
  1940. MANGANESE DEFICIENCY FOR CITRUS IN CALIFORNIA. Science 91:169-170.

(35) ——— SOUTHWICK, R. W., and CHAPMAN, H. D.
  1940. RESPONSES OF CITRUS TREES TO MANGANESE APPLICATIONS. Calif. Citrograph
    25:74, 86, 87.

(36) REED, H. S., and HAAS, A. R. C.
  1923. STUDIES ON THE EFFECTS OF SODIUM, POTASSIUM, AND CALCIUM ON YOUNG ORANGE
    TREES. Calif. Agr. Expt. Sta. Tech. Paper 11:1-33.

(37) ——— and HAAS, A. R. C.
  1923. GROWTH AND COMPOSITION OF ORANGE TREES IN SAND AND SOIL CULTURES. Jour.
    Agr. Res. 24:801-814.

(38) ——— and HAAS, A. R. C.
  1924. NUTRIENT AND TOXIC EFFECTS OF CERTAIN IONS ON CITRUS AND WALNUT TREES WITH
    ESPECIAL REFERENCE TO THE CONCENTRATION AND pH OF THE MEDIUM. Calif.
    Agr. Expt. Sta. Tech. Paper 17:1-75.

(39) REED, H. S., and PARKER, E. R.
   1936. SPECIFIC EFFECTS OF ZINC APPLICATIONS ON LEAVES AND TWIGS OF ORANGE TREES AFFECTED WITH MOTTLE-LEAF. Jour. Agr. Res. 53:395-398.

(40) ROY, W. R.
   1937. THE EFFECT OF SOIL APPLICATIONS OF MANGANESE ON THE MINERAL COMPOSITION OF FOLIAGE AND MATURITY OF FRUIT IN CITRUS. Fla. State Hort. Soc. Proc. 50:29-37.

(41) SKINNER, J. J., and BAHRT, G. M.
   1931. TREND OF FERTILIZER PRACTICE WITH REFERENCE TO CITRUS CULTURE IN FLORIDA. Fla. State Hort. Soc. Proc. 44:4-7.

(42) ——— BAHRT, G. M., and HUGHES, A. E.
   1934. INFLUENCE OF FERTILIZERS AND SOIL AMENDMENTS ON CITRUS TREES, FRUIT PRODUCTION AND QUALITY OF FRUIT. Fla. State Hort. Soc. Proc. 47:9-17.

(43) TAIT, W. L.
   1936. SOME FIELD TESTS WITH MAGNESIUM SOURCES. Fla. State Hort. Soc. Proc. 49:9-14.

(44) TAYLOR, G. G., and BURNS, M. M.
   1938. "MOTTLE LEAF" OF CITRUS IN NEW ZEALAND. New Zealand Jour. Sci. and Technol. 20:115A-119A.

(45) THOMAS, E. E., and HAAS, A. R. C.
   1928. INJECTION METHOD AS A MEANS OF IMPROVING CHLOROTIC ORANGE TREES. Bot. Gaz. 86:355-362.

Courtesy of Florida Agricultural Experiment Station

Plate 1.—Grapefruit showing symptoms of boron deficiency as described by Morris in Rhodesia. Upper fruit shows aborted seed and gum pockets near the axis. Lower fruit shows part of the seed aborted without gum formation. The hard impregnations in the rind are not shown in either of these fruits.

Plate 2.—A, Advanced stage of calcium deficiency on lemon leaves showing dead areas developed in the mesophyll regions.

Plate 2.—B, Symptoms of manganese deficiency in lemon leaves. The leaf at the left shows very mild symptoms which become progressively more acute in those to the right. The symptoms shown by the leaf at the left are commonly seen in the field, but those on the other three leaves occur occasionally.

Courtesy of Florida Agricultural Experiment Station

Plate 3.—Copper deficiency in citrus, showing large leaves with weak twigs growing from multiple buds, which die back before they are fully developed.

Plate 4.—Copper deficiency in Pineapple orange, showing brown excrescences on the surface of the fruit. Such fruits are also likely to have gum pockets in the rind and gum in the axes of the segments.

Plate 5.—A, Iron deficiency in orange leaves, showing fine green veins on a yellow-green to yellow background and fine twig growth.

Plate 5.—B, Leaves showing so-called vein chlorosis which is a result of girdling, rotting of the root, or any other injury that disrupts transfer of plantfood.

[305]

Plate 6.—Magnesium deficiency in grapefruit foliage showing yellowing of leaves adjacent to fruit. The yellowing starts near the midrib and gradually spreads outward until it takes in the entire leaf, after which the leaf sheds, frequently leaving the fruit on a long twig devoid of leaves.

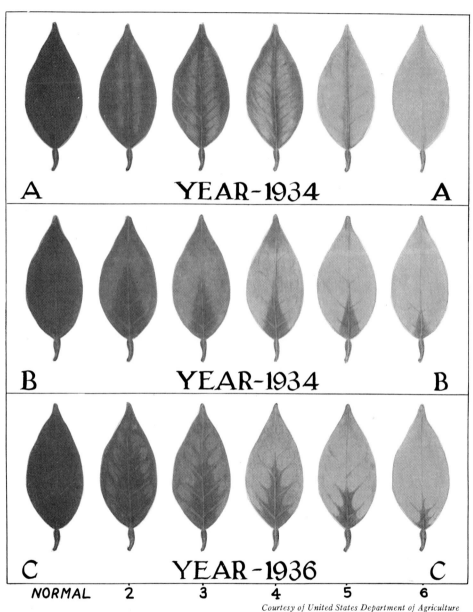

A   YEAR-1934   A

B   YEAR-1934   B

C   YEAR-1936   C

NORMAL   2   3   4   5   6

Courtesy of United States Department of Agriculture

Plate 7.—Types of bronzing related to magnesium metabolism as described by Bahrt. In all cases the fading starts on mature green leaves and is related to fruit development.

Plate 8.—Manganese deficiency on newly matured orange leaves, showing dark-green areas along the midrib and main lateral veins and light-green areas between the veins. Note that the leaves are normal in size and shape. These leaves become very dull green at full maturity.

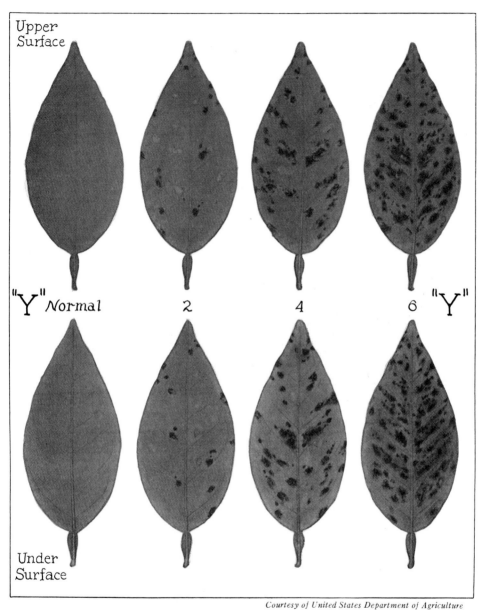

Upper
Surface

"Y" Normal   2   4   6 "Y"

Under
Surface

Plate 9.—Potassium-deficiency symptoms on orange leaves, showing brown areas in the mesophyll regions.

Plate 10.—Shoot from navel-orange tree in early stages of sulfur deficiency. New growth is very yellow as compared with older growth. Yellow leaves are similar in appearance to nitrogen-starved leaves. In a more acute stage of deficiency, the older leaves are less green than those shown here and many of them have a yellowish midrib. These symptoms are from trees grown in large containers of soil. Sulfur deficiency has not been identified in the field.

Plate 11.—Zinc-deficiency symptoms showing dark-green coloration along the midrib and main lateral veins with tissue between the veins a light yellow. Note that the leaves are narrow and pointed and growth is very fine and upright in character. This gives the tree a bushy appearance.

[311]

INDEX